ASCENT®
CENTER FOR TECHNICAL KNOWLEDGE

Autodesk® Revit® 2021
Fundamentals for Residential Design

Learning Guide
Imperial Units - 1st Edition

AUTODESK.
Authorized Publisher

ASCENT - Center for Technical Knowledge®
Autodesk® Revit® 2021
Fundamentals for Residential Design
Imperial Units - 1st Edition

Prepared and produced by:

ASCENT Center for Technical Knowledge
630 Peter Jefferson Parkway, Suite 175
Charlottesville, VA 22911

866-527-2368
www.ASCENTed.com

Lead Contributor: Cherisse Biddulph

ASCENT - Center for Technical Knowledge (a division of Rand Worldwide Inc.) is a leading developer of professional learning materials and knowledge products for engineering software applications. ASCENT specializes in designing targeted content that facilitates application-based learning with hands-on software experience. For over 25 years, ASCENT has helped users become more productive through tailored custom learning solutions.

We welcome any comments you may have regarding this guide, or any of our products. To contact us please email: feedback@ASCENTed.com.

Contents

Preface

The Autodesk® Revit® software is a powerful Building Information Modeling (BIM) program that works the way residential architects think. The program streamlines the design process through the use of a central 3D model, where changes made in one view update across all views and on the printable sheets.

The objective of the *Autodesk® Revit® 2021: Fundamentals for Residential Design* guide is to enable you to create a full 3D architectural project model, including walls, doors, windows, components, floors, ceilings, roofs, and stairs, using the basic tools that the majority of architectural users need. This includes how to navigate the user interface and use the basic drawing, editing, and viewing tools. The final part of the course focuses on creating construction documents.

Topics Covered

- Understanding the purpose of BIM and how it is applied in the Autodesk Revit software.

- Navigating the Autodesk Revit workspace and interface.

- Working with the basic sketching and modifying tools.

- Setting up a project.

- Creating a 3D building model with walls, floors, windows, and doors.

- Adding component features, such as furniture and casework.

- Adding floors, ceilings, and simple and complex roofs to the building model.

- Modeling stairs and railings.

- Setting up sheets for plotting with text, dimensions, details, tags, and schedules.

- Creating details.

Prerequisites

- Access to the 2021.0 version of the software, to ensure compatibility with this guide. Future software updates that are released by Autodesk may include changes that are not reflected in this guide. The practices and files included with this guide might not be compatible with prior versions (e.g., 2020).

- An understanding of architectural terminology is an asset.

Note on Software Setup

This guide assumes a standard installation of the software using the default preferences during installation. Lectures and practices use the standard software templates and default options for the Content Libraries.

Students and Educators Can Access Free Autodesk Software and Resources

Autodesk challenges you to get started with free educational licenses for professional software and creativity apps used by millions of architects, engineers, designers, and hobbyists today. Bring Autodesk software into your classroom, studio, or workshop to learn, teach, and explore real-world design challenges the way professionals do.

Get started today - register at the Autodesk Education Community and download one of the many Autodesk software applications available.

Visit www.autodesk.com/education/home/

Note: Free products are subject to the terms and conditions of the end-user license and services agreement that accompanies the software. The software is for personal use for education purposes and is not intended for classroom or lab use.

Lead Contributor: Cherisse Biddulph

Cherisse is an Autodesk Certified Professional for Revit as well as an Autodesk Certified Instructor. She brings over 17 years of industry, teaching, and technical support experience to her role as a Learning Content Developer with ASCENT. With a passion for design and architecture, she received her Associates of Applied Science in Drafting and Design and has worked in the industry assisting firms with their CAD management and software implementation needs as they modernize to a Building Information Modeling (BIM) design environment. Although her main passion is the Revit design product, she is also proficient in AutoCAD, Autodesk BIM 360, and Autodesk Navisworks. Today, Cherisse continues to expand her knowledge in the ever-evolving AEC industry and the software used to support it.

Cherisse Biddulph is the Lead Contributor for this first release of *Autodesk Revit 2021: Fundamentals for Residential Design*.

Co-Contributors

Kenniston Crane has more than 20 years of experience working in the building industry and has spent time doing custom residential architecture and electrical designs. He created the main model used in the practices for this guide.

Jamie Owens is an Autodesk Certified Professional for Revit, as well as an Autodesk Certified Instructor. He brings 14 years of experience to his role as a Building Solutions expert. He has a graduate degree in Architecture and has spent a decade working in various architectural firms.

Tom Tobin is an Autodesk Certified Professional for AutoCAD and Revit Architecture, as well as an Autodesk Certified Instructor. He brings over 27 years of experience as a BIM/CAD/project manager in the architecture and building systems field, and has worked for production and custom home builders.

Kenniston Crane, Jamie Owens, and Tom Tobin are co-contributors for this first release of *Autodesk Revit 2021: Fundamentals for Residential Design*.

In This Guide

The following highlights the key features of this guide.

Feature	Description
Practice Files	The Practice Files page includes a link to the practice files and instructions on how to download and install them. The practice files are required to complete the practices in this guide.
Chapters	A chapter consists of the following - Learning Objectives, Instructional Content, Practices, Chapter Review Questions, and Command Summary.
	• **Learning Objectives** define the skills you can acquire by learning the content provided in the chapter.
	• **Instructional Content**, which begins right after Learning Objectives, refers to the descriptive and procedural information related to various topics. Each main topic introduces a product feature, discusses various aspects of that feature, and provides step-by-step procedures on how to use that feature. Where relevant, examples, figures, helpful hints, and notes are provided.
	• **Practice** for a topic follows the instructional content. Practices enable you to use the software to perform a hands-on review of a topic. It is required that you download the practice files (using the link found on the Practice Files page) prior to starting the first practice.
	• **Chapter Review Questions**, located close to the end of a chapter, enable you to test your knowledge of the key concepts discussed in the chapter.
	• **Command Summary** concludes a chapter. It contains a list of the software commands that are used throughout the chapter and provides information on where the command can be found in the software.
Appendices	Appendices provide additional information to the main course content. It could be in the form of instructional content, practices, tables, projects, or skills assessment.

Practice Files

To download the practice files for this guide, use the following steps:

1. Type the URL **exactly as shown below** into the address bar of your Internet browser, to access the Course File Download page.

   Note: If you are using the ebook, you do not have to type the URL. Instead, you can access the page simply by clicking the URL below.

https://www.ascented.com/getfile/id/eugeneiatus

2. On the Course File Download page, click the **DOWNLOAD NOW** button, as shown below, to download the .ZIP file that contains the practice files.

3. Once the download is complete, unzip the file and extract its contents.

   The recommended practice files folder location is:
   C:\Revit 2021 for Residential Design Practice Files

   Note: It is recommended that you do not change the location of the practice files folder. Doing so may cause errors when completing the practices.

Stay Informed!

To receive information about upcoming events, promotional offers, and complimentary webcasts, visit:

www.ASCENTed.com/updates

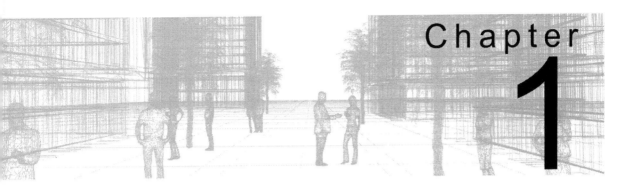

Chapter 1

Introduction to BIM and Autodesk Revit

Building Information Modeling (BIM) and the Autodesk® Revit® software work hand in hand to help you create smart, 3D models that are useful at all stages in the building process. Understanding the software interface and terminology enhances your ability to create powerful models and move around in the various views of the model.

Learning Objectives in This Chapter

- Describe the concept and workflow of Building Information Modeling in relation to the Autodesk Revit software.
- Navigate the graphic user interface, including the ribbon (where most of the tools are found), the Properties palette (where you make modifications to element information), and the Project Browser (where you can open various views of the model).
- Open existing projects and start new projects using templates.
- Use viewing commands to move around the model in 2D and 3D views.

1.1 BIM and Autodesk Revit

Building Information Modeling (BIM) is an approach to the entire building life cycle, including design, construction, and facilities management. The BIM process supports the ability to coordinate, update, and share design data with team members across disciplines.

The Autodesk Revit software is a true BIM product. It enables you to create complete 3D building models (as shown on the left in Figure 1–1) that provide considerable information reported through construction documents, and enables you to share these models with other programs for more extensive analysis.

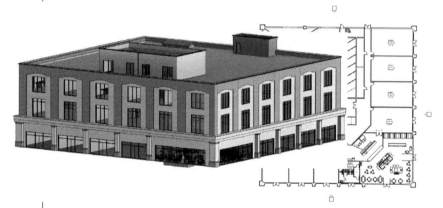

Figure 1–1

The Autodesk Revit software is considered a Parametric Building Modeler:

- *Parametric:* A relationship is established between building elements: when one element changes, other related elements change as well. For example, if you add an element in a plan view, it also displays in all of the other views.

- *Building:* The software is designed for working with buildings and the surrounding landscape, as opposed to gears or highways.

- *Modeler:* A project is built in a single file based on the 3D building model, as shown on the left in Figure 1–1. All views, such as plans (as shown on the right in Figure 1–1), elevations, sections, details, construction documents, and reports are generated based on the model.

- It is important that everyone who is collaborating on a project works in the same version and build of the software.

Workflow and BIM

BIM has changed the process of how a building is planned, budgeted, designed, constructed, and presented to the homeowner.

In the traditional design process, construction documents are created independently, typically including plans, sections, elevations, details, and notes. Sometimes, a separate 3D model for marketing is created in addition to these documents. Changes made in one document, such as the addition of a light fixture in a plan, have to be coordinated with the rest of the documents and schedules in the set, as shown in Figure 1–2.

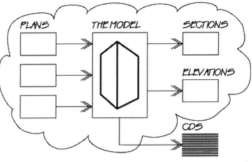

Figure 1–2

In BIM, the design process revolves around the model, as shown in Figure 1–3. Plans, elevations, and sections are simply 2D versions of the 3D model, while schedules are a report of the information stored in the model. Changes made in one view automatically update in all views and related schedules. Even construction documents update automatically with callout tags in sync with the sheet numbers. This is called bidirectional associativity. By creating complete models and associated views of those models, the Autodesk Revit software takes much of the tediousness out of producing a building design.

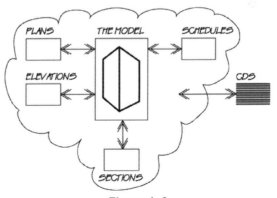

Figure 1–3

Revit Terms

When working in the Autodesk Revit software, it is important to know the typical terms used to describe items. Views and reports display information about the elements that form a project. There are three types of elements: model, datum, and view-specific, as shown in Figure 1–4 and described below.

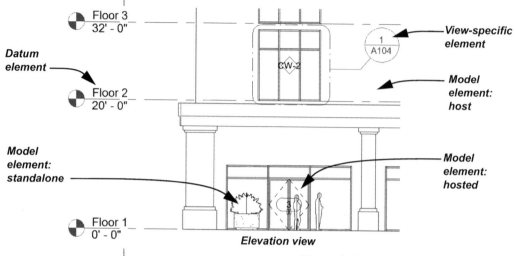

Elevation view

Figure 1–4

Views	Views enable you to display and manipulate the model. For example, you can view and work in floor plans, ceiling plans, elevations, sections, schedules, and 3D views. You can change a design from any view. All views are stored in the project.
Reports	Reports, including schedules, gather information from the building model element that can be presented in the construction documents or used for analysis.
Model Elements	Model elements include all parts of a building, such as walls, floors, roofs, ceilings, doors, windows, plumbing fixtures, lighting fixtures, columns, beams, furniture, casework, appliances, plants, and many more. • Host elements support other categories of elements. • Hosted elements must be attached to a host element. • Standalone elements do not require hosts.
Datum Elements	Datum elements define the project context, such as the levels for the floors and other vertical distances, grids, and reference planes.
View-specific Elements	View-specific elements only display in the view in which they are placed. The view scale controls their size. These include annotation elements such as dimensions, text, tags, and symbols, as well as detail elements such as detail lines, filled regions, and 2D detail components.

- Autodesk Revit elements are "smart": the software recognizes them as walls, columns, plants, ducts, lighting fixtures, etc. This means that the information stored in their properties automatically updates in schedules, which ensures that views and reports are coordinated across an entire project and are generated from a single model.

Revit and Construction Documents

In the traditional workflow, the most time-consuming part of the project is the construction documents. With BIM, the base views of those documents (i.e., plans, elevations, sections, and schedules) are produced automatically and update as the model is updated, saving hours of work. The views are then placed on sheets that form the construction document set.

For example, a floor plan is duplicated. Then, in the new view, all but the required categories of elements are hidden or set to halftone and annotations are added. The plan is then placed on a sheet, as shown in Figure 1–5.

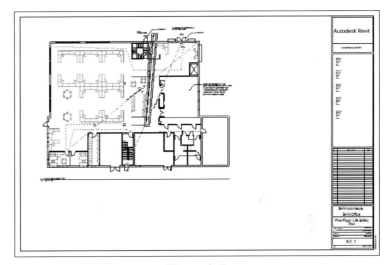

Figure 1–5

- Work can continue on a view and is automatically updated on the sheet.

- Annotating views in the preliminary design phase is often not required. You might be able to wait until you are further along in the project.

1.2 Overview of the Interface

The Autodesk Revit interface is designed for intuitive and efficient access to commands and views. It includes the ribbon, Quick Access Toolbar, Navigation Bar, and Status Bar, which are common to most of the Autodesk® software. It also includes tools that are specific to the Autodesk Revit software, including the Properties palette, Project Browser, and View Control Bar. Revit includes access to tools for architectural, HVAC, electrical, plumbing, and structural design but can be altered by utilizing a customized workspace. Setting up a customized workspace tailors your Revit environment to your specific discipline. A breakdown of the Revit interface is shown in Figure 1–6.

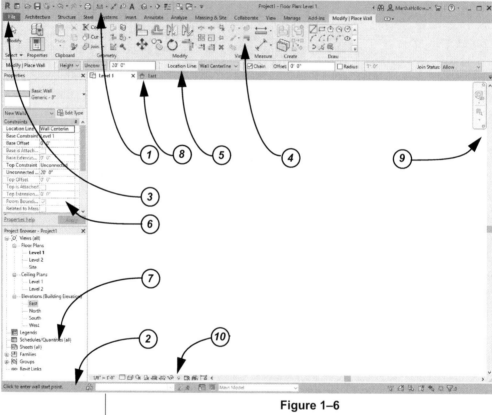

Figure 1–6

1. Quick Access Toolbar	6. Properties palette
2. Status Bar	7. Project Browser
3. *File* tab	8. View tabs
4. Ribbon	9. Navigation Bar
5. Options Bar	10. View Control Bar

For more information on how to use BIM 360 inside Revit, refer to the ASCENT guide Autodesk BIM 360: Fundamentals.

The Home Screen

When you first open the Autodesk Revit software, the Home screen displays, showing recently used projects and families, as well as links to BIM 360 files (as shown in Figure 1–7).

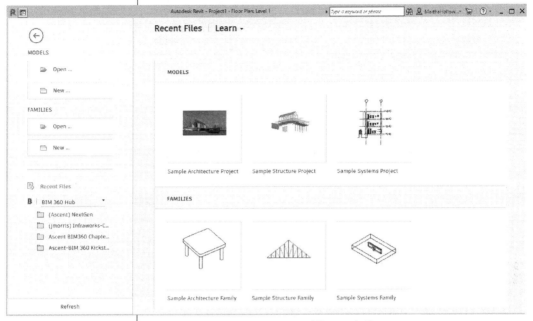

Figure 1–7

- Click on the picture to open a recent project. Hover over the name of the file to display additional information.

- In the Quick Access Toolbar, click (Home) to return to the screen.

- In the Home screen, click (Back) to return to the active model.

- Press <Ctrl>+<D> to toggle between the Home screen and the active model.

1. Quick Access Toolbar

The Quick Access Toolbar (shown in Figure 1–8) includes commonly used commands, such as **Home, Open, Save, Undo, Redo,** and **Print**. It also includes frequently used annotation tools, including Measuring tools, **Aligned Dimension**, **Tag by Category**, and **Text**. Viewing tools, including several different 3D views and **Sections**, are also easily accessed here.

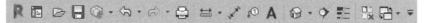

Figure 1–8

> **Hint: Customizing the Quick Access Toolbar**
>
> Right-click on the Quick Access Toolbar to change the docked location of the toolbar to be above or below the ribbon, or to add, relocate, or remove tools on the toolbar. You can also right-click on a tool in the ribbon and select **Add to Quick Access Toolbar**, as shown in Figure 1–9.
>
>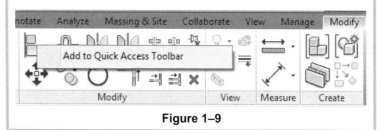
>
> Figure 1–9

The top toolbar also hosts the InfoCenter (as shown in Figure 1–10) which includes the Autodesk sign-in, access to the Autodesk App Store, and Help options. A search field, as shown in Figure 1–11, is also available to find help on the web

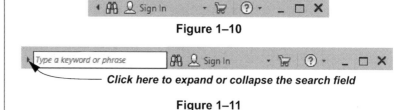

Figure 1–10

Figure 1–11

2. Status Bar

The Status Bar provides information about the current process, such as the next step for a command, as shown in Figure 1–12.

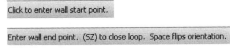

Figure 1–12

- Other options in the Status Bar are related to worksets (Advanced Tools) and design options, as well as selection methods and filters.

Hint: Shortcut Menus

Shortcut menus help you to work smoothly and efficiently by enabling you to quickly access required commands. These menus provide access to basic viewing commands, recently used commands, and the available browsers, as shown in Figure 1–13. Additional options vary depending on the element or command that you are using.

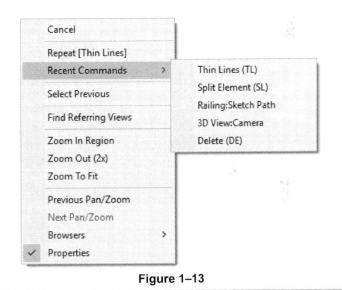

Figure 1–13

3. File Tab

For more information on how to use Cloud Model inside Revit, refer to the ASCENT guide Autodesk BIM 360: Fundamentals.

If you click the primary icon, rather than the arrow, it starts the default command.

The *File* tab of the ribbon provides access to file commands, settings, and documents, as shown in Figure 1–14. Hover the cursor over a command to display a list of additional tools.

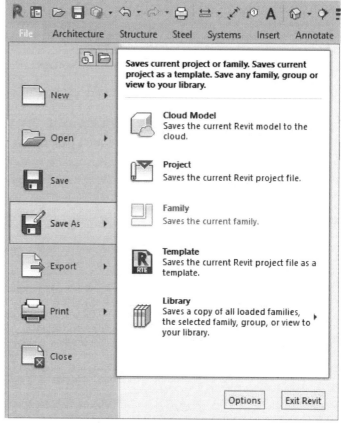

Figure 1–14

- To display a list of recently used documents, click
  (Recent Documents). The documents can be reordered, as shown in Figure 1–15.

Click (Pin) next to a document name to keep it available.

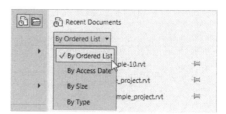

Figure 1–15

- To display a list of open documents and views, click

  📂 (Open Documents). The list displays the documents and views that are open, as shown in Figure 1–16.

You can use the Open Documents list to change between views.

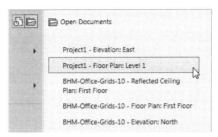

Figure 1–16

- Click 📄 (Close) to close the current project.

- At the bottom of the menu, click **Options** to open the Options dialog box or click **Exit Revit** to exit the software.

4. Ribbon

The ribbon contains tools in a series of tabs and panels as shown in Figure 1–17. Selecting a tab displays a group of related panels. The panels contain a variety of tools, grouped by task.

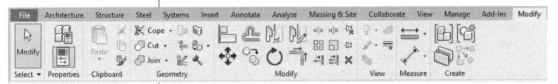

Figure 1–17

When you start a command that creates new elements or you select an element, the ribbon displays the *Modify | <contextual>* tab. This contains general editing commands and command specific tools, as shown in Figure 1–18.

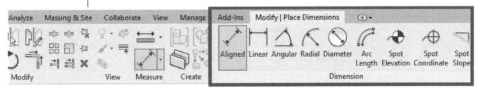

Contextual tab

Figure 1–18

- When you hover over a tool on the ribbon, tooltips display the tool's name and a short description. If you continue hovering over the tool, a graphic displays (and sometimes a video), as shown in Figure 1–19.

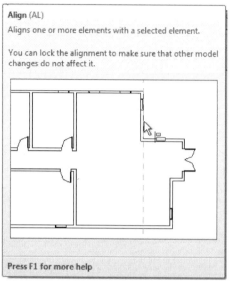

Align (AL)

Aligns one or more elements with a selected element.

You can lock the alignment to make sure that other model changes do not affect it.

Press F1 for more help

Figure 1–19

- Many commands have shortcut keys. For example, type **AL** for **Align** or **MV** for **Move**. They are listed next to the name of the command in the tooltips. Do not press <Enter> when typing shortcuts.

- To arrange the order in which the ribbon tabs are displayed, select the tab, hold <Ctrl>, and drag it to a new location. The location is remembered when you restart the software.

- Any panel can be dragged by its title into the view window to become a floating panel. Click the **Return Panels to Ribbon** button (as shown in Figure 1–20) to reposition the panel in the ribbon.

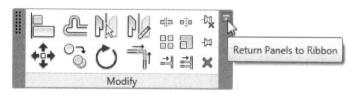

Return Panels to Ribbon

Modify

Figure 1–20

> **Hint: You are always in a command when using the Autodesk Revit software.**
>
> When you are finished working with a tool, you typically default back to the **Modify** command. To end a command, use one of the following methods:
>
> - In any tab on the ribbon, click ⌕ (Modify).
> - Press <Esc> once or twice to revert to **Modify**.
> - Right-click and select **Cancel...** once or twice.
> - Start another command.

5. Options Bar

The Options Bar displays options that are related to the selected command or element. For example, when the **Rotate** command is active, it displays options for rotating the selected elements, as shown at the top in Figure 1–21. When the **Place Dimensions** command is active, it displays dimension-related options, as shown at the bottom in Figure 1–21.

Options Bar for Rotate command

Options Bar for Dimension command

Figure 1–21

6. Properties Palette

The Properties palette contains several parts, as shown in Figure 1–22. The Type Selector can be found at the top, which enables you to choose the size or style of the element you are adding or modifying. The options available on the palette enable you to make changes to information (parameters). There are two types of properties:

- **Instance Properties** are set for the individual element(s) you are creating or modifying.

- **Type Properties** control options for all elements of the same type. If you modify these parameter values, all elements of the selected type change.

The Properties palette is usually kept open while working on a project to easily permit changes at any time. If it does not display, in the *Modify* tab>Properties panel, click ⊞ (Properties) or type **PP**.

Some parameters are only available when you are editing an element. They are grayed out when unavailable.

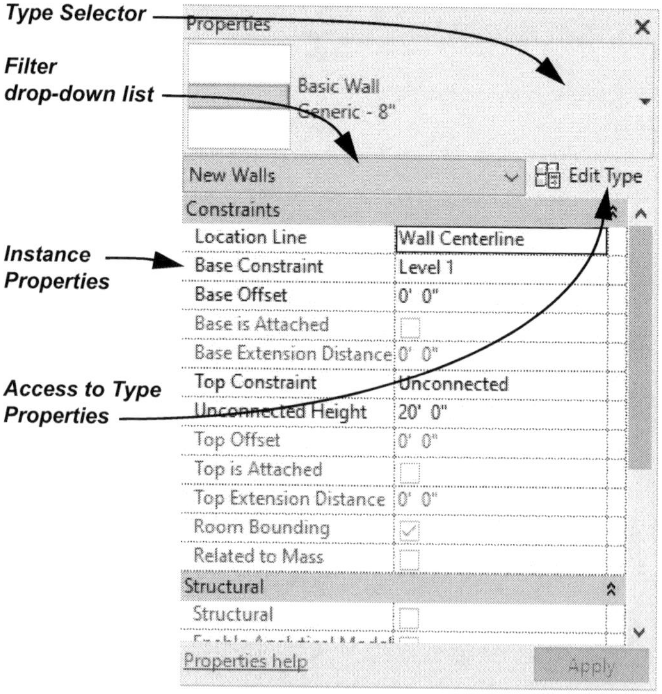

Figure 1–22

- Options for the current view display if the **Modify** command is active, but you have not selected an element.

- If a command or element is selected, the options for the associated element display.

- You can save the changes either by moving the cursor off of the palette, by pressing <Enter>, or by clicking **Apply**.

- When you start a command or select an element, you can set the element type in the Type Selector, as shown in Figure 1–23.

You can limit what shows in the drop-down list by typing in the search box.

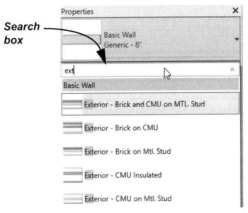

Figure 1–23

- When multiple elements are selected, you can filter the type of elements that display using the drop-down list, as shown in Figure 1–24.

The Properties palette can be placed on a second monitor, or floated, resized, and docked on top of the Project Browser or other dockable palettes, as shown in Figure 1–25. Click the tab to display its associated panel.

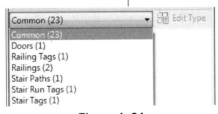

Figure 1–24

Figure 1–25

7. Project Browser

The Project Browser lists all views of the model in which you can work (as shown in Figure 1–26) and any additional views that you create, such as floor plans, ceiling plans, 3D views, elevations, sections, etc. It also includes schedules, legends, sheets (for plotting), lists of families by category, groups, and Autodesk Revit Links.

The Project Browser displays the name of the active project.

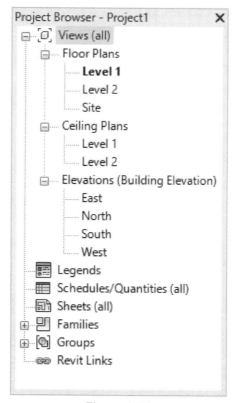

Figure 1–26

- To open a view, double-click on the view name or right-click and select **Open**.

- To rename a view, slowly click twice on the view name and the text highlights, as shown in Figure 1–27. You can also right-click on a view name and select **Rename...** or press <F2>.

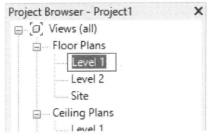

Figure 1–27

To display the views associated with a view type, click

⊞ (Expand) next to the section name. To hide the views in the

section, click ⊟ (Collapse). You can also expand and collapse
sets using the shortcut menu, as shown in Figure 1–28.

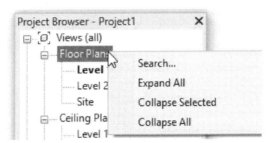

Figure 1–28

- If you no longer require a view, you can delete it. Right-click
  on its name in the Project Browser and select **Delete**.

- The Project Browser can be customized by changing the
  Browser Organization or its location within the application.
  The Project Browser can be floated, resized, or docked on
  top of the Properties palette.

How To: Search the Project Browser

1. In the Project Browser, right-click on a view and select
   Search....
2. In the Search in Project Browser dialog box, type the words
   that you want to find (as shown in Figure 1–29), and
   click **Next**.

3. In the Project Browser, the first instance of that search displays, as shown in Figure 1–30.

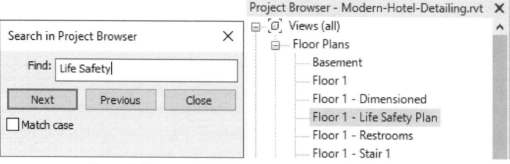

Figure 1–29   **Figure 1–30**

4. Continue using **Next** and **Previous** to move through the list.
5. Click **Close** when you are done.

8. View Tabs

Each view of a project opens in its own tab and can be pulled out of the application window and moved to another monitor. Each view displays a Navigation Bar (for quick access to viewing tools) and the View Control Bar, as shown in Figure 1–31.

In 3D views, you can also use the ViewCube to rotate the view.

Figure 1–31

- Click on the tab to switch between views. You can also:
  - Press <Ctrl>+<Tab>.
  - Select the view in the Project Browser.
  - In the Quick Access Toolbar or *View* tab>Windows panel, expand 🔁 (Switch Windows) and select the view from the list.
  - Expand the drop-down list at the far end of the view tabs, as shown in Figure 1–32.

Figure 1–32

- To close a tab, press the **X** that displays when you hover over the tab or the name in the list.

- To close all open views except the current view, in the Quick Access Toolbar or *View* tab>Windows panel, click 🗙 (Close Inactive Views). If you have multiple projects open, one view of each project remains open. If you have dragged a view to another monitor, that view will need to be manually closed by clicking the **X** in the upper-right corner.

- You can switch between tabbed and tiled views from the *View* tab>Windows panel by clicking ▢ (Tab Views) or ▤ (Tile Views).

- Drag the edge of tiled views to resize them. The other views resize to match.

9. Navigation Bar

The Navigation Bar enables you to access the 2D and Full Navigation (3D views) Wheel to navigate the view, as well as the Zoom in Region viewing commands, as shown in Figure 1–33.

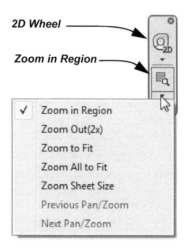

2D Wheel

Zoom in Region

Figure 1–33

10. View Control Bar

The View Control Bar (shown in Figure 1–34) displays at the bottom of each view window. It controls aspects of that view, such as the scale and detail level. It also includes tools that display parts of the view and hide or isolate elements in the view.

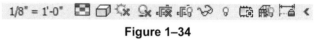

Figure 1–34

- The number of options in the View Control Bar change when you are in a 3D view, as shown in Figure 1–35.

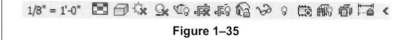

Figure 1–35

1/8" = 1'-0"	**View Scale**	Sets the scale of individual views.
	Detail Level	Sets the detail level of a view.
	Visual Style	Controls which graphic style representation is used for the view.
	Sun Path On/Off	Controls the visibility of the sun's path.
	Shadows On/Off	Controls elements' shadow visibility in a view.
	Show/Hide Rendering Dialog	Available in 3D only. Shows or hides the rendering dialog box.
	Crop View	Defines the crop boundaries for a view.
	Show/Hide Crop Region	Displays the crop region in a view.
	Unlocked/Locked 3D Views	Locks a 3D view's orientation.
	Temporary Hide/Isolate	Temporarily isolates/hides by category or element.
	Reveal Hidden Elements	Shows hidden elements or unhides them in the active view.
	Worksharing Display	Available when worksharing is enabled. Controls display settings.
	Temporary View Properties	Enables, applies, or restores view properties, and displays recent templates and applies them.
	Show or Hide the Analytical Model	Only used for structural and MEP to display the analytical information.
	Highlight Displacement Sets	Used to highlight displacement sets (also known as exploded views).
	Reveal Constraints	Used to temporarily view the dimension and alignment constraints in the active view.
	Preview Visibility	Available in the Family Editor only. Controls the visibility of the preview.

1.3 Starting Projects

File operations to open existing files, create new files from a template, and save files in the Autodesk Revit software are found in the *File* tab, as shown in Figure 1–36.

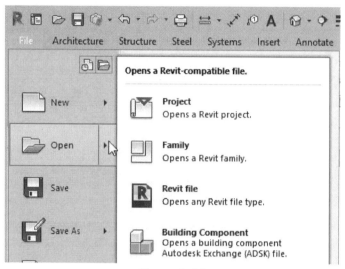

Figure 1–36

There are three main file formats:

- **Project files (.rvt):** These are where you do the majority of your work in the building model by adding elements, creating views, annotating views, and setting up printable sheets. They are initially based on template files.

- **Family files (.rfa):** These are separate components that can be inserted in a project. They include elements that can stand alone (e.g., a table or light fixture) or are items that are hosted in other elements (e.g., a door in a wall or a lighting fixture in a ceiling). Title block and annotation symbol files are special types of family files.

- **Template files (.rte and .rft):** These are the base files for any new project or family. Project templates hold standard information and settings for creating new project files. The software includes several templates for various types of projects. You can also create custom templates. Family templates include base information for creating families. Template files are usually saved as a new file.

Opening Projects

To open an existing project, in the Quick Access Toolbar or *File* tab, click 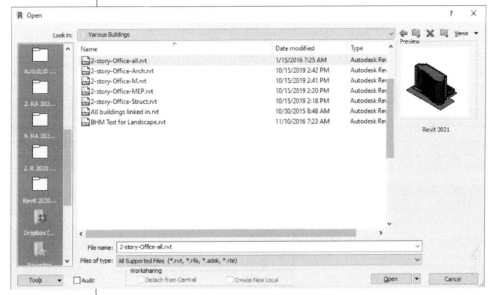 (Open), or press <Ctrl>+<O>. The Open dialog box opens, and you can navigate to the required folder and select a project file. An example of the Open dialog box is shown in Figure 1–37.

Figure 1–37

- The software release version of the currently selected project displays below the preview. Do not open a drawing that should remain in an earlier version, as you cannot save back to previous versions.

  Note: It is important that everyone working on a project uses the same software version (e.g., 2021) and is on the same updated version (e.g., 2021.1). While your software may be able to open files created in its earlier versions, it will not be able to open files created in versions newer than the one you are using currently. For example, if you are working in Revit 2020, you cannot open a model created in Revit 2021.

- When you open a file created in an earlier version, the Model Upgrade dialog box (shown in Figure 1–38) indicates the release of a file and the release to which it will be upgraded. If needed, you can cancel the upgrade before it completes.

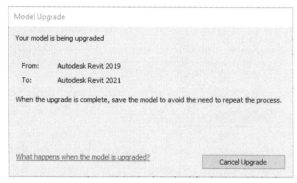

Figure 1–38

Hint: Opening Workset-Related Files

Worksets are used when the project becomes large enough for multiple people to work on it at the same time. At this point, a central model with multiple worksets (such as element interiors, building shell, and site) that are used by the project team members is created.

When you open a workset-related file, it creates a new local file on your computer, as shown in Figure 1–39. Do not work in the main central model.

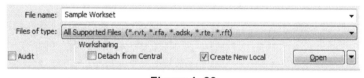

Figure 1–39

- For more information about opening and saving workset-related files, see *Appendix B: Introduction to Worksets*.

- When you click on a central model showing in the Home screen, a local copy of the file is created.

- For more information on establishing and using worksets, refer to the ASCENT guide *Autodesk Revit: Collaboration Tools*.

Starting New Projects

New projects are based on a template file. The template file includes preset levels, views, and some families, such as wall styles and text styles. Check with your BIM Manager about which template you need to use for your projects. Your company might have more than one based on the types of homes that you are designing.

How To: Start a New Project

1. In the *File* tab, expand (New) and click (Project) (as shown in Figure 1–40), or press <Ctrl>+<N>.

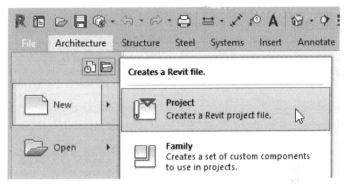

Figure 1–40

2. In the New Project dialog box (shown in Figure 1–41), select the template that you want to use and click **OK**.

The list of template files is set in the Options dialog box in the File Locations pane. It might vary depending on the installed product and company standards.

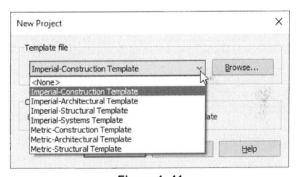

Figure 1–41

- You can select from a list of templates if they have been set up by your BIM manager.

- You can add 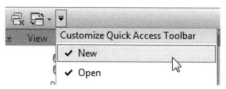 (New) to the Quick Access Toolbar. At the end of the Quick Access Toolbar, click ▼ (Customize Quick Access Toolbar) and select **New**, as shown in Figure 1–42.

Figure 1–42

Saving Projects

It is important to save your projects frequently. In the Quick Access Toolbar or *File* tab, click 💾 (Save), or press <Ctrl>+<S> to save your project. If the project has not yet been saved, the Save As dialog box opens, where you can specify a file location and name.

- To save an existing project with a new name, in the *File* tab, expand 💾 (Save As) and click 🗎 (Project).

- If you have not saved in a certain amount of time, the software will notify you with the Project Not Saved Recently alert box, as shown in Figure 1–43. Select **Save the project**. If you want to set reminder intervals or not save at this time, select the other options.

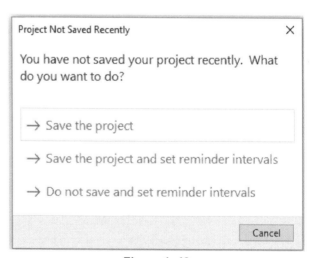

Figure 1–43

- You can set the *Save reminder interval* to **15** or **30 minutes**, **One**, **Two**, or **Four hours**, or to have **No reminders** display. In the *File* tab, click **Options** to open the Options dialog box. In the left pane, select **General** and set the interval, as shown in Figure 1–44.

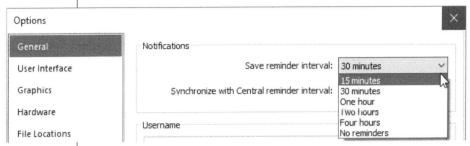

Figure 1–44

Saving Backup Copies

By default, the software saves a backup copy of a project file when you save the project. Backup copies are numbered incrementally (e.g., **My Project.0001.rvt**, **My Project.0002.rvt**, etc.) and are saved in the same folder as the original file. In the Save As dialog box, click **Options...** to control how many backup copies are saved. The default number is three backups. If you exceed this number, the software deletes the oldest backup file.

> ### Hint: Saving Workset-Related Projects
>
> If you use worksets in your project, you need to save the project locally and to the central model. It is recommended to save the local file frequently, just like any other file, and save to the central model every hour or so by synchronizing with the central model.
>
> To synchronize your changes with the main file, in the Quick Access Toolbar, expand 🔷 (Synchronize and Modify Settings) and click 🔷 (Synchronize Now). After you save to the central model, save the file locally again.
>
> At the end of the day, or when you are finished with the current session, in the Quick Access Toolbar, expand 🔷 (Synchronize and Modify Settings) and click 🔷 (Synchronize and Modify Settings) to relinquish the files you have been working on to the central model.
>
> - The maximum number of backups for workset-enabled files is set to 20 by default.
>
> - Workshared files do not have the same backup files as non-workshared files.

1.4 Viewing Commands

Viewing commands are crucial to working efficiently in most drawing and modeling programs and the Autodesk Revit software is no exception. Once in a view, you can use the Zoom controls to navigate in it. You can zoom in and out and pan in any view. There are also special tools for viewing in 3D.

Zooming and Panning

Using the Mouse to Zoom and Pan

Use the mouse wheel (shown in Figure 1–45) as the main method of moving around the models.

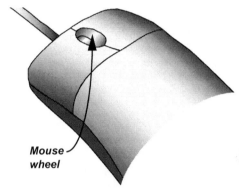

Mouse wheel

Figure 1–45

- Scroll the wheel on the mouse up to zoom in and down to zoom out.
- Hold the wheel and move the mouse to pan.
- Double-click on the wheel to zoom to the extents of the view.
- In a 3D view, hold <Shift> and the mouse wheel and move the mouse to rotate around the model.
- When you save a model and exit the software, the pan and zoom location of each view is remembered. This is especially important for complex models.

Zoom Controls

A number of additional zoom methods enable you to control the screen display. **Zoom** and **Pan** can be performed at any time while using other commands.

- You can access the **Zoom** commands in the Navigation Bar in the upper-right corner of the view (as shown in Figure 1–46). You can also access them from most shortcut menus and by typing the shortcut commands.

(2D Wheel) provides cursor-specific access to ***Zoom*** *and* ***Pan***.

Figure 1–46

Zoom Commands

	Zoom in Region (ZR)	Zooms in to a region that you define. Drag the cursor or select two points to define the rectangular area you want to zoom in to. This is the default command.
	Zoom Out(2x) (ZO)	Zooms out to half the current magnification around the center of the elements.
	Zoom to Fit (ZF or ZE)	Zooms out so that the entire contents of the project only display on the screen in the current view.
	Zoom All to Fit (ZA)	Zooms out so that the entire contents of the project display on the screen in all open views.
	Zoom Sheet Size (ZS)	Zooms in or out in relation to the sheet size.
N/A	**Previous Pan/Zoom (ZP)**	Steps back one **Zoom** command.
N/A	**Next Pan/Zoom**	Steps forward one **Zoom** command if you have done a **Previous Pan/Zoom**.

Viewing in 3D

Even if you started a project entirely in plan views, you can quickly create 3D views of the model, as shown in Figure 1–47. There are two types of 3D views: isometric views created by the **Default 3D View** command and perspective views created by the **Camera** command.

Figure 1–47

Working in 3D views helps you visualize the project and position some of the elements correctly. You can create and modify elements in both isometric and perspective 3D views, just as you can in plan views.

- Once you have created a 3D view, you can save it and easily return to it.

How To: Create and Save a 3D Isometric View

1. In the Quick Access Toolbar or *View* tab>Create panel, click
   (Default 3D View). The default 3D Southeast isometric view opens, as shown in Figure 1–48.

You can spin the view to a different angle using the mouse wheel or the middle button of a three-button mouse. Hold <Shift> as you press the wheel or middle button and drag the cursor.

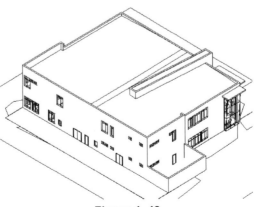

Figure 1–48

2. Modify the view to display the building from other directions.

3. In the Project Browser, double-click slowly or right-click on the {3D} view and select **Rename...**.
4. The name is placed in a text box with the original name highlighted, as shown in Figure 1–49. Type a new name in the Rename View dialog box, as shown in Figure 1–50.

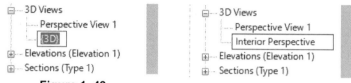

| Figure 1–49 | Figure 1–50 |

All types of views can be renamed.

• When changes to the default 3D view are saved and you start another default 3D view, it displays the Southeast isometric view once again. If you modified the default 3D view but did not save it to a new name, the **Default 3D View** command opens the view in the last orientation you specified.

How To: Create a Perspective View

1. Switch to a Floor Plan view.
2. In the Quick Access Toolbar or *View* tab>Create panel, expand ⬡ (Default 3D View) and click ▣ (Camera).
3. Place the camera on the view.
4. Point the camera in the direction in which you want it to shoot by placing the target on the view, as shown in Figure 1–51.

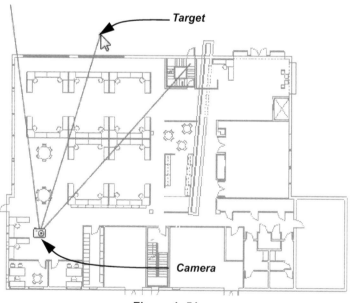

Figure 1–51

Use the round controls to modify the display size of the view and press <Shift> + the mouse wheel to change the view.

A new view is displayed, as shown in Figure 1–52.

Figure 1–52

5. In the Properties palette, scroll down and adjust the *Eye Elevation* and *Target Elevation* as needed.

• If the view becomes distorted, reset the target so that it is centered in the boundary of the view (called the crop region).

In the *Modify | Cameras* tab>Camera panel, click (Reset Target).

• You can further modify a view by adding shadows, as shown in Figure 1–53. In the View Control Bar, toggle (Shadows Off) and (Shadows On). Shadows display in any model view, not just in the 3D views. To set up the sun location, expand (Sun Path Off) and select **Sun Settings...** Select (Sun Path On) to see the visual location of the sun.

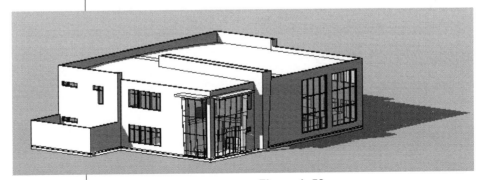

Figure 1–53

Hint: Using the ViewCube

The ViewCube provides visual clues as to where you are in a 3D view. It helps you move around the model with quick access to specific views (such as top, front, and right), as well as corner and directional views, as shown in Figure 1–54.

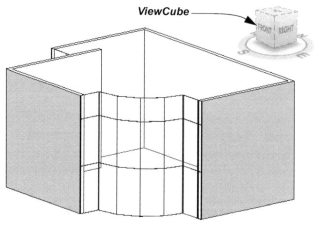

Figure 1–54

Move the cursor over any face of the ViewCube to highlight it. Once a face is highlighted, you can select it to reorient the model. You can also click and drag on the ViewCube to rotate the box, which rotates the model.

- 🏠 (Home) displays when you roll the cursor over the ViewCube. Click it to return to the view defined as **Home**. To change the Home view, set the view as you want it, right-click on the ViewCube, and select **Set Current View as Home**.

- The ViewCube is available in isometric and perspective views.

- You can switch between Perspective and Isometric mode by right-clicking on the View Cube and selecting **Perspective** or **Orthographic**.

Visual Styles

Any view can have a visual style applied. The **Visual Style** options found in the View Control Bar (as shown in Figure 1–55) specify the shading of the building model. These options apply to plan, elevation, section, and 3D views.

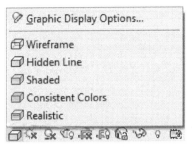

Figure 1–55

- (Wireframe) displays the lines and edges that make up elements, but hides the surfaces. This can be useful when you are dealing with complex intersections.

- (Hidden Line) displays the lines, edges, and surfaces of the elements, but it does not display any colors. This is the most common visual style to use while working on a design.

- (Shaded) and (Consistent Colors) give you a sense of the materials, including transparent glass. An example that uses Consistent Colors is shown in Figure 1–56.

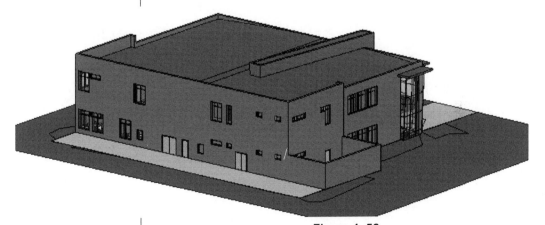

Figure 1–56

- (Realistic) displays what is shown when you render the view, including RPC (Rich Photorealistic Content) components and artificial lights. It takes a lot of computer power to execute this visual style. Therefore, it is better to use the other visual styles most of the time as you are working.

Rendering

Rendering is a powerful tool which enables you to display a photorealistic view of the model you are working on, such as the example shown in Figure 1–57. This can be used to help clients and designers understand a building's design in better detail.

Figure 1–57

- In the View Control Bar, click (Show Rendering Dialog) to set up the options. **Show Rendering Dialog** is only available in 3D views.

Practice 1a | Open and Review a Project

Practice Objectives

- Navigate the graphic user interface.
- Manipulate 2D and 3D views by zooming and panning.
- Create 3D isometric and perspective views.
- Set the visual style of a view.

In this practice, you will open a project file and view each of the various areas in the interface. You will investigate elements, commands, and their options. You will also open views through the Project Browser and view the model in 3D, as shown in Figure 1–58.

Figure 1–58

- This is a version of the main project you will work on throughout this guide.

Task 1 - Explore the interface.

1. In the *File* tab, expand ⬛ (Open) and click ⬛ (Project).

2. In the Open dialog box, navigate to the practice files folder and select **Residential-Final.rvt**.

If the Project Browser and Properties palette are docked over each other, use the Project Browser tab at the bottom to display it.

3. Click **Open**. The 3D view of the house opens in the view window.

4. In the Project Browser, expand the *Floor Plans* node. Double-click on **First Floor-Dimension Plan** to open it. This view is referred to as **Floor Plans: First Floor-Dimension Plan**.

5. Take time to review the floor plan to get acquainted with it.

6. Review the various parts of the screen.

7. In the view, hover the cursor over one of the doors. A tooltip displays describing the element, as shown in Figure 1–59.

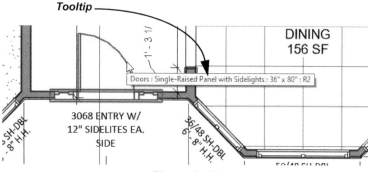

Figure 1–59

8. Hover the cursor over another element to display its description.

9. Select a door. The ribbon changes to the *Modify | Doors* tab.

10. Click in an empty space in the view to release the selection.

11. Hold <Ctrl> and select several elements of different types. The ribbon changes to the *Modify | Multi-Select* tab.

12. Press <Esc> to clear the selection.

13. In the *Architecture* tab>Build panel, click ⬚ (Wall). The ribbon changes to the *Modify | Place Wall* tab and at the end of the ribbon, the Draw panel is displayed. It contains tools that enable you to create walls. The rest of the ribbon displays the same tools that are found on the *Modify* tab.

14. In the Select panel, click (Modify) to return to the main ribbon.

15. In the *Architecture* tab>Build panel, click (Door). The ribbon changes to the *Modify | Place Door* tab and displays the options and tools you can use to create doors.

16. In the Select panel, click (Modify) to return to the main ribbon.

Task 2 - Look at views.

1. In the Project Browser, verify that the *Floor Plans* node is open. Double-click on the **First Floor** view.

2. The basic floor plan displays, but without the annotations that were displayed in the **First Floor-Dimension Plan** view.

3. Open the **First Floor-Furniture Plan** view by double-clicking on it.

4. Everything but the furniture is grayed out.

5. At the top of the views, click each tab to switch between the open views.

6. In the *View* tab>Windows panel, click (Tile Views) or type **WT**. All of the open views are tiled. Type **ZA** (for Zoom All) to zoom out to the extents of each view, as shown in Figure 1–60.

You might need to widen the Project Browser to display the full names of the views.

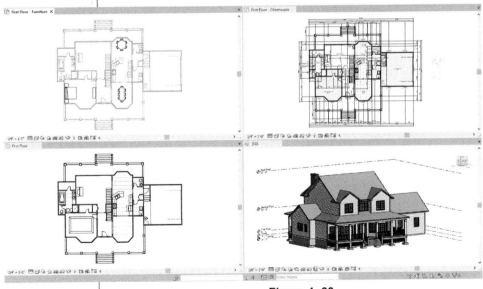

Figure 1–60

7. Click inside the 3D view to make it active.

8. In the *View* tab>Windows panel, click 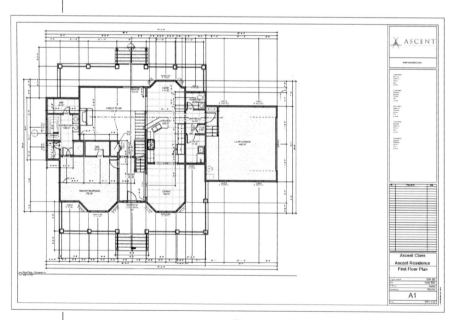 (Tab Views) or type **TW**. The views return to the tabs and the 3D view is first in the group.

*This view is referred to as the **Elevations (Building Elevation): East** view.*

9. In the Project Browser, scroll down and expand *Elevations (Building Elevation)*. Double-click on the **East** elevation to open the view.

10. Expand *Sections (Building Section)* and double-click on **Section 1** to open it.

11. At the bottom of the view window, in the View Control Bar, click (Visual Style) and select (Shaded). The elements in the view are now easier to read.

12. In the Project Browser, scroll down to the *Sheets (all)* node and expand the node.

13. View several of the sheets. Some have views already applied (e.g., **A1 - First Floor Plan** as shown in Figure 1–61).

Figure 1–61

Task 3 - Practice viewing tools.

Your options might look different depending on which views and how many views are open.

1. At the far right of the view tabs, expand **Switch Windows** and select **Residential-Final.rvt - Floor Plan: First Floor**, as shown in Figure 1–62.

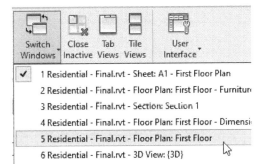

Figure 1–62

2. In the Navigation Bar, click and select **Zoom In Region** or type **ZR**. Zoom in on the stairs.

3. Pan to another part of the house by holding and dragging the middle mouse button or wheel. Alternatively, you can use the 2D Wheel in the Navigation Bar.

4. Double-click on the mouse wheel to zoom out to fit the extents of the view.

5. In the Quick Access Toolbar, click (Default 3D View) to open the default 3D view, as shown in Figure 1–63.

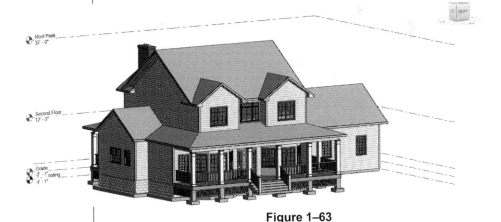

Figure 1–63

6. Hold <Shift> and use the middle mouse button or wheel to rotate the model in the 3D view.

7. In the View Control Bar, change the *Visual Style* to ⬜ (Shaded). Then try ⬜ (Consistent Colors). Which one works best when you view the back of the house?

8. Use the ViewCube to find a view that you want to use.

9. In the Project Browser, expand *3D Views*, right-click on the **{3D}** view, and select **Rename...**. Type in a new name for the view.

10. Review the other 3D views that have already been created.

11. Press <Ctrl>+<Tab> to cycle through the open views.

12. In the Quick Access Toolbar, expand 🗗 (Switch Windows) and select the **Residential-Final.rvt - Floor Plan: First Floor** view.

13. In the Quick Access Toolbar, click 🗗 (Close Inactive Views). This closes all of the other windows except the one in which you are working.

14. In the Quick Access Toolbar, expand 🏠 (Default 3D View) and click 📷 (Camera), as shown in Figure 1–64.

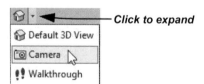

Figure 1–64

15. Click the first point inside the master bedroom and click the second point (target) outside the house, as shown in Figure 1–65.

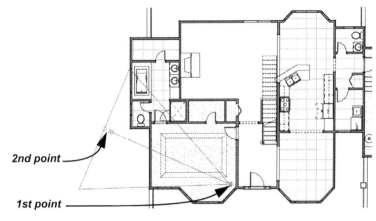

2nd point

1st point

Figure 1–65

16. The furniture displays even though it did not display in the floor plan view.

17. In the View Control Bar, set the *Visual Style* to ⬛ (Realistic).

18. In the Project Browser, right-click on the new camera view called **3D View 1** and select **Rename...**. Type **Master Bedroom View**.

19. In the Quick Access Toolbar, click 💾 (Save) to save the project.

20. In the *File* tab, click 🗔 (Close). This closes the entire project.

Chapter Review Questions

1. When you create a project in the Autodesk Revit software, do you work in 3D or 2D?

   a. You work in 2D in plan views and in 3D in non-plan views.

   b. You work in 3D almost all of the time, even when you are using what looks like a flat view.

   c. You work in 2D or 3D depending on how you toggle the 2D/3D control.

   d. You work in 2D in plan and section views and in 3D in isometric views.

2. What is the purpose of the Project Browser?

   a. It enables you to browse through the building project, similar to a walk through.

   b. It is the interface for managing all of the files that are required to create the complete architectural model of the building.

   c. It manages multiple Autodesk Revit projects as an alternative to using Windows Explorer.

   d. It is used to access and manage the views of the project.

3. Which parts of the interface change when you start a command such as **Wall** or **Doors**? (Select all that apply.)

   a. Ribbon

   b. View Control Bar

   c. Options Bar

   d. Properties Palette

4. What is the difference between Type Properties and Properties?

   a. Properties stores parameters that apply to the selected individual element(s). Type Properties stores parameters that impact every element of the same type in the project.

   b. Properties stores the location parameters of an element. Type Properties stores the size and identity parameters of an element.

   c. Properties only stores parameters of the view. Type Properties stores parameters of model components.

5. When you start a new project, how do you specify the base information in the new file?

   a. Transfer the base information from an existing project.

   b. Select the right template for the task.

   c. The Autodesk Revit software automatically extracts the base information from imported or linked file(s).

6. What is the main difference between a view made using

   (Default 3D View) and a view made using (Camera)?

   a. Use **Default 3D View** for exterior views and **Camera** for interior views.

   b. **Default 3D View** creates a static image and a **Camera** view is live and always updated.

   c. A **Default 3D View** is isometric and a **Camera** view is perspective.

   d. **Default 3D View** is used for the overall building and a **Camera** view is used for looking in tight spaces.

Command Summary

Button	Command	Location
General Tools		
	Home	• Quick Access Toolbar • **Shortcut:** <Ctrl>+<D>
	Modify	• **Ribbon:** All tabs>Select panel • **Shortcut:** MD
	New	• • *File* tab • **Shortcut:** <Ctrl>+<N>
	Open	• **Quick Access Toolbar** • *File* tab • **Shortcut:** <Ctrl>+<O>
	Open Documents	• *File* tab
	Properties	• **Ribbon:** *Modify* tab>Properties panel • **Shortcut:** PP
	Recent Documents	• *File* tab
	Save	• **Quick Access Toolbar** • *File* tab • **Shortcut:** <Ctrl>+<S>
	Synchronize and Modify Settings	• **Quick Access Toolbar**
	Synchronize Now	• **Quick Access Toolbar**>expand Synchronize and Modify Settings
	Type Properties	• **Ribbon:** *Modify* tab>Properties panel • **Properties palette**
Viewing Tools		
	Camera	• **Quick Access Toolbar**> Expand Default 3D View • **Ribbon:** *View* tab>Create panel> expand Default 3D View
	Close Inactive Views	• **Quick Access Toolbar** • **Ribbon:** *View* tab> Windows panel
	Default 3D View	• **Quick Access Toolbar** • **Ribbon:** *View* tab>Create panel
	Home	• ViewCube
N/A	Next Pan/Zoom	• **Navigation Bar** • **Shortcut Menu**

N/A	**Previous Pan/Zoom**	• **Navigation Bar** • **Shortcut Menu** • **Shortcut:** ZP
	Shadows On/Off	• **View Control Bar**
	Show Rendering Dialog/ Render	• **View Control Bar** • **Ribbon:** *View* tab>Graphics panel • **Shortcut:** RR
	Switch Windows	• **Quick Access Toolbar** • **Ribbon:** *View* tab> Windows panel
	Tab Views	• **Ribbon:** *View* tab> Windows panel • **Shortcut: TW**
	Tile Views	• **Ribbon:** *View* tab> Windows panel • **Shortcut: WT**
	Zoom All to Fit	• **Navigation Bar** • **Shortcut:** ZA
	Zoom in Region	• **Navigation Bar** • **Shortcut Menu** • **Shortcut:** ZR
	Zoom Out (2x)	• **Navigation Bar** • **Shortcut Menu** • **Shortcut:** ZO
	Zoom Sheet Size	• **Navigation Bar** • **Shortcut:** ZS
	Zoom to Fit	• **Navigation Bar** • **Shortcut Menu** • **Shortcut:** ZF, ZE

Visual Styles

	Consistent Colors	• **View Control Bar**:
	Hidden Line	• **View Control Bar** • **Shortcut:** HL
	Ray Trace	• **View Control Bar**:
	Realistic	• **View Control Bar**
	Shaded	• **View Control Bar** • **Shortcut:** SD
	Wireframe	• **View Control Bar** • **Shortcut:** WF

Basic Sketching and Modify Tools

Basic sketching, selecting, and modifying tools are the foundation of working with all types of elements in the Autodesk® Revit® software. Using these tools with drawing aids helps you to place and modify elements to create accurate building models.

Learning Objectives in This Chapter

- Sketch linear elements such as walls, beams, and pipes.
- Ease the placement of elements by incorporating drawing aids such as alignment lines, temporary dimensions, and snaps.
- Place reference planes as temporary guide lines.
- Use techniques to select and filter groups of elements.
- Modify elements using a contextual tab, Properties, temporary dimensions, and controls.
- Move, copy, rotate, and mirror elements and create array copies in linear and radial patterns.
- Align, trim, and extend elements with the edges of other elements.
- Split linear elements anywhere along their length.
- Offset elements to create duplicates a specific distance away from the original.

2.1 Using General Sketching Tools

When you start a command, the contextual tab on the ribbon, the Options Bar, and the Properties palette (as shown in Figure 2–1) enable you to set up features for each new element you are placing in the project. As you are working, several features called *drawing aids* display, as shown in Figure 2–1. They help you to create designs quickly and accurately.

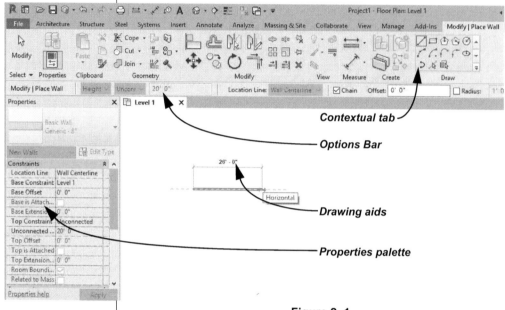

Contextual tab

Options Bar

Drawing aids

Properties palette

Figure 2–1

- In Autodesk Revit, you are most frequently creating 3D model elements rather than 2D sketches. These tools work with both 3D and 2D elements in the software.

Draw Tools

Many linear elements (such as walls, beams, ducts, pipes, and railings) are modeled using the tools on the contextual tab in the Draw panel. Other elements (such as floors, ceilings, roofs, and slabs) have boundaries that are sketched using many of the same tools. Draw tools are also used when you create details or schematic drawings.

Two methods are available:

- *Draw* the element using a geometric form.
- *Pick* an existing element (such as a line, face, or wall) as the basis for the new element's geometry and position.

The exact tools vary according to the element being modeled.

How To: Create Linear Elements

1. Start the command you want to use.
2. In the contextual tab>Draw panel (shown in Figure 2–2), select a drawing tool.

You can change from one Draw tool shape to another in the middle of a command.

Figure 2–2

3. Select points to define the elements or watch the Status Bar, in the lower-left corner, for hints on what to do.
4. Finish the command using one of the standard methods:

- Click  (Modify).
- Press <Esc> twice.
- Start another command.

Draw Options

When you are in Drawing mode, several options display in the Options Bar, as shown in Figure 2–3.

Figure 2–3

Different options display according to the type of element that is selected or the command that is active.

- **Chain:** Controls how many segments are created in one process. If this option is not selected, the **Line** and **Arc** tools only create one segment at a time. If it is selected, you can continue adding segments until you press <Esc> or select the command again.

- **Offset:** Enables you to enter values so you can create linear elements at a specified distance from the selected points or element.

- **Radius:** Enables you to enter values when using a radial tool or to add a radius to the corners of linear elements as you sketch them.

Draw Tools

/	**Line**	Draws a straight line defined by the first and last points. If **Chain** is enabled, you can continue selecting end points for multiple segments.
▱	**Rectangle**	Draws a rectangle defined by two opposing corner points. You can adjust the dimensions after selecting both points.
⬠	**Inscribed Polygon**	Draws a polygon inscribed in a hypothetical circle with the number of sides specified in the Options Bar.
⬠	**Circumscribed Polygon**	Draws a polygon circumscribed around a hypothetical circle with the number of sides specified in the Options Bar.
◯	**Circle**	Draws a circle defined by a center point and radius.
⌒	**Start-End-Radius Arc**	Draws a curve defined by a start, end, and radius of the arc. The outside dimension shown is the included angle of the arc. The inside dimension is the radius.
⌒	**Center-ends Arc**	Draws a curve defined by a center, radius, and included angle. The selected point of the radius also defines the start point of the arc.
⌒	**Tangent End Arc**	Draws a curve tangent to another element. Select an end point for the first point, but do not select the intersection of two or more elements. Then, select a second point based on the included angle of the arc.
⌒	**Fillet Arc**	Draws a curve defined by two other elements and a radius. Because it is difficult to select the correct radius by clicking, this command automatically moves to Edit mode. Select the dimension and then modify the radius of the fillet.
⋏	**Spline**	Draws a spline curve based on selected points. The curve does not actually touch the points (sketches, model, and detail lines only).
⬭	**Ellipse**	Draws an ellipse from a primary and secondary axis (walls, sketches, model, and detail lines only).
ᗐ	**Partial Ellipse**	Draws only one side of the ellipse, like an arc. A partial ellipse also has a primary and secondary axis (sketches, model, and detail lines only).

Pick Tools

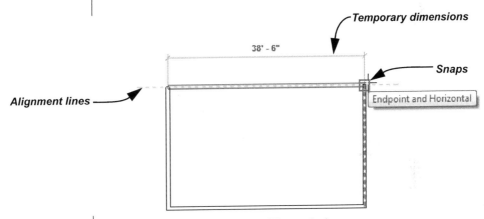⬈	**Pick Lines**	Use this option to select existing linear elements in the project. This is useful when you start the project from an imported 2D drawing.
⬀	**Pick Face**	Use this option to select the face of a 3D massing element (walls and 3D views only).
⬀	**Pick Walls**	Use this option to select an existing wall in the project to be the basis for a new sketch line (floors, ceilings, etc.).

Drawing Aids

As soon as you start sketching or placing elements, three drawing aids display, as shown in Figure 2–4:

- Alignment lines

- Temporary dimensions

- Snaps

These aids are available with most modeling and many modification commands.

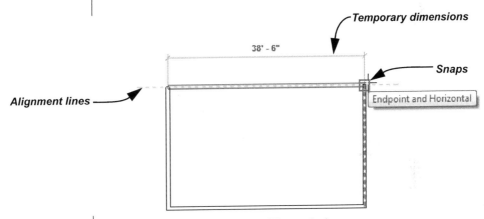

Temporary dimensions

38' - 6"

Snaps

Alignment lines

Endpoint and Horizontal

Figure 2–4

Alignment lines display as soon as you select your first point. They help keep lines horizontal, vertical, or at a specified angle. They also line up with the implied intersections of walls and other elements.

- Hold <Shift> to force the alignments to be orthogonal (90-degree angles only).

Temporary dimensions display to help place elements at the correct length, angle, and location.

- You can type in a value or move the cursor until you see the dimension you want, or you can place the element and then modify the value as needed.

- The length and angle increments shown vary depending on how far in or out the view is zoomed.

- For Imperial measurements (feet and inches), the software uses a default of feet. For example, when you type **4** and press <Enter>, it assumes 4'-0". For a distance such as 4'-6", you can type any of the following: **4'-6"**, **4'6**, **4-6**, or **4 6** (the numbers separated by a space). To indicate distances less than one foot, type the inch mark (") after the distance, or enter **0**, a space, and then the distance.

Hint: Temporary Dimensions and Permanent Dimensions

Temporary dimensions disappear as soon as you finish adding elements. If you want to make them permanent, select the dimension symbol ( ), as shown in Figure 2–5.

Figure 2–5

Snaps are key points that help you reference existing elements to exact points when modeling, as shown in Figure 2–6.

Figure 2–6

- When you move the cursor over an element, the snap symbol displays. Each snap location type displays with a different symbol.

Hint: Snap Settings and Overrides

In the *Manage* tab>Settings panel, click 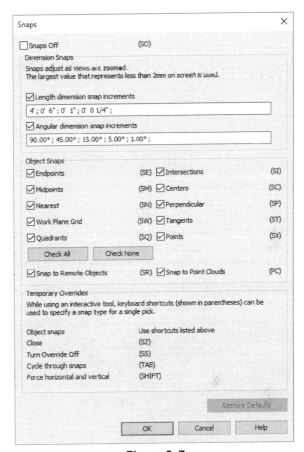 (Snaps) to open the Snaps dialog box, which is shown in Figure 2–7. The Snaps dialog box enables you to set which snap points are active, and set the dimension increments displayed for temporary dimensions (both linear and angular).

Figure 2–7

- Keyboard shortcuts for each snap can be used to override the automatic snapping. Temporary overrides only affect a single pick, but can be very helpful when there are snaps nearby other than the one you want to use.

Reference Planes

As you develop designs in the Autodesk Revit software, there are times when you need lines to help you define certain locations. You can sketch reference planes (displayed as dashed green lines) and snap to them whenever you need to line up elements. For the example shown in Figure 2–8, the lighting fixtures in the reflected ceiling plan are placed using reference planes.

Reference planes do not display in 3D views.

- To insert a reference plane, in the *Architecture, Structure,* or *Systems* tab>Work Plane panel, click 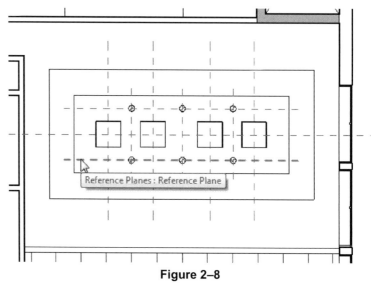 (Ref Plane) or type **RP**.

Figure 2–8

- Reference planes display in associated views because they are infinite planes and not just lines.

- You can name reference planes by clicking on **<Click to name>** and typing in the text box, as shown in Figure 2–9.

Figure 2–9

- If you sketch a reference pane in Sketch mode (used with floors and similar elements), it does not display once the sketch is finished.

- Reference planes can have different line styles if they have been defined in the project. In Properties, select a style from the Subcategory list.

Hint: Model Line vs. Detail Line

While most of the elements that you create are representations of actual building elements, there are times you may need to add lines to clarify the design intent. These can be either detail lines, as shown in Figure 2–10, or model lines. Detail lines are also useful as references because they are only reflected in the view in which you sketch them.

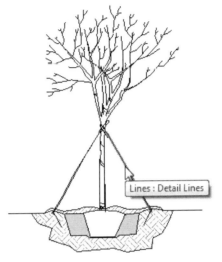

Figure 2–10

- A model line (*Architecture* or *Structure* tab>Model panel>

  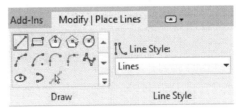 (Model Line)) functions as a 3D element and displays in all views. It can also be used as a path for extruded profiles.

- A detail line (*Annotate* tab>Detail panel> (Detail Line)) is strictly a 2D element that only displays in the view in which it is drawn.

- In the *Modify* contextual tab, as shown in Figure 2–11, select a *Line Style* and then the Draw tool that you want to use to draw the model or detail line.

Figure 2–11

2.2 Editing Elements

Building design projects typically involve extensive changes to the model. The Autodesk Revit software was designed to make such changes quickly and efficiently. You can change an element using the following methods, as shown in Figure 2–12:

- The Type Selector enables you to specify a different type. This is frequently used to change the size and/or style of the elements.

- The Properties palette enables you to modify the information (parameters) associated with the selected elements.

- The contextual tab in the ribbon contains the Modify commands and element-specific tools.

- Temporary dimensions enable you to change the element's dimensions or position.

- Controls enable you to drag, flip, lock, and rotate the element.

- Shape handles enable you to drag elements to modify their height or length.

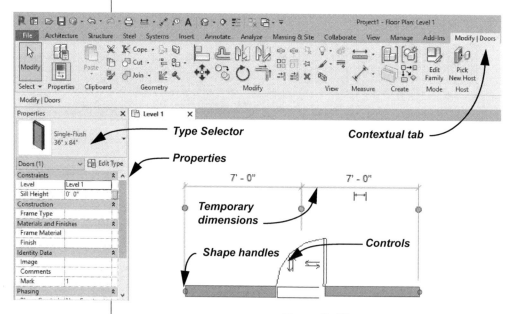

Figure 2–12

- To delete an element, select it and press <Delete>, right-click and select **Delete**, or in the Modify panel, click ✖ (Delete).

Working with Controls and Shape Handles

When you select an element, various controls and shape handles display depending on the element and view. For example, in plan view you can use controls to drag the ends of a wall and change its orientation. You can also drag the wall ends in a 3D view and use the arrow shape handles to change the height of the wall, as shown in Figure 2–13.

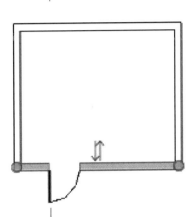 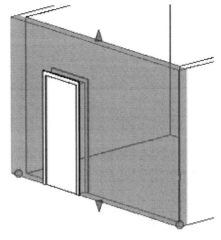

Figure 2–13

- If you hover the cursor over the control or shape handle, a tooltip displays showing its function.

Hint: Editing Temporary Dimensions

Temporary dimensions automatically link to the closest wall. To change this, drag the *Witness Line* control, as shown in Figure 2–14, to connect to a new reference. You can also click on the control to toggle between justifications in the wall.

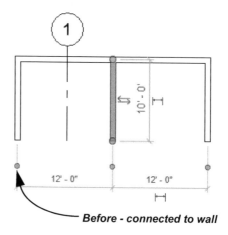

Before - connected to wall

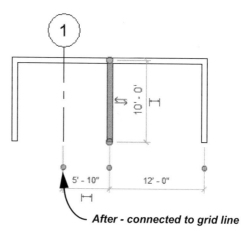

After - connected to grid line

Figure 2–14

- The new location of a temporary dimension for an element is remembered as long as you are in the same session of the software.

Selecting Multiple Elements

- Once you have selected at least one element, hold <Ctrl> and select another item to add it to a selection set.

- To remove an element from a selection set, hold <Shift> and select the element.

- If you click and drag the cursor to *window* around elements, you have two selection options, as shown in Figure 2–15. If you drag from left to right, you only select the elements completely inside the window. If you drag from right to left, you select elements both inside and crossing the window.

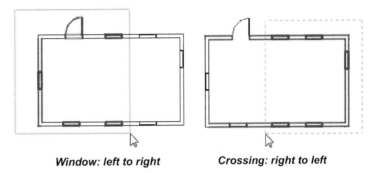

Window: left to right   **Crossing: right to left**

Figure 2–15

- If several elements are on or near each other, hover your cursor over an edge and press <Tab> to cycle through them before you click. If there are elements that might be linked to each other, such as walls that are connected, pressing <Tab> selects the chain of elements.

- Press <Ctrl>+<Left Arrow> to reselect the previous selection set. You can also right-click in the view window with nothing selected and select **Select Previous**.

- To select all elements of a specific type, right-click on an element and select **Select All Instances>Visible in View** or **In Entire Project**, as shown in Figure 2–16. For example, if you select a column of a specific size and use this command, only the columns of the same size are selected.

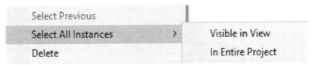

Figure 2–16

- You can save selections and use them again. For more information, see *A.1 Reusing Selection Sets*.

Hint: Measuring Tools

When modifying a model, it is useful to know the distance between elements. This can be done with temporary dimensions, or more frequently, by using the measuring tools found in the Quick Access Toolbar or in the *Modify* tab> Measure panel, as shown in Figure 2–17.

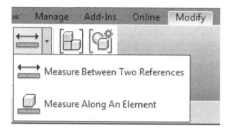

Figure 2–17

* (Measure Between Two References): Select two elements and the measurement displays.

* (Measure Along An Element): Select the edge of a linear element and the total length displays. Use <Tab> to highlight other elements and then click to measure along all of them, as shown in Figure 2–18.

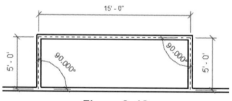

Figure 2–18

* References include any snap point, wall lines, or other parts of elements (such as door center lines).

Filtering Selection Sets

When multiple element categories are selected, the *Multi-Select* contextual tab opens in the ribbon. This gives you access to all of the Modify tools and the **Filter** command. The **Filter** command enables you to specify the types of elements to select. For example, you might only want to select columns, as shown in Figure 2–19.

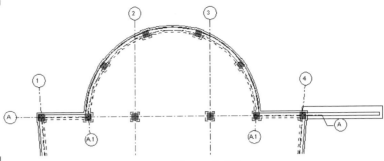

Figure 2–19

How To: Filter a Selection Set

1. Select everything in the area.
2. In the *Modify | Multi-Select* tab>Selection panel, or in the Status Bar, click ⏢ (Filter). The Filter dialog box opens, as shown in Figure 2–20.

The Filter dialog box displays all types of elements in the original selection.

Figure 2–20

3. Click **Check None** to clear all of the options or **Check All** to select all of the options. You can also select or clear individual categories as needed.
4. Click **OK**. The selection set is now limited to the elements you specified.

• The number of elements selected displays on the right end of the Status Bar and in the Properties palette.

Hint: Selection Options

You can control how the software selects specific elements in a project by toggling selection options on and off in the Status Bar, as shown in Figure 2–21. Alternatively, in any tab on the ribbon that has the Modify command, expand the Select panel's title and select the option.

Figure 2–21

- **Select links:** When toggled on, you can select linked CAD drawings or Autodesk Revit models. When it is toggled off, you cannot select them when using **Modify** or **Move**.

- **Select underlay elements:** When toggled on, you can select underlay elements. When toggled off, you cannot select them when using **Modify** or **Move**.

- **Select pinned elements:** When toggled on, you can select pinned elements. When toggled off, you cannot select them when using **Modify** or **Move**.

- **Select elements by face:** When toggled on, you can select elements (such as the floors or walls in an elevation) by selecting the interior face or selecting an edge. When toggled off, you can only select elements by selecting an edge.

- **Drag elements on selection:** When toggled on, you can hover over an element, select it, and drag it to a new location. When toggled off, the Crossing or Box select mode starts when you press and drag, even if you are on top of an element. Once elements have been selected, they can still be dragged to a new location.

Practice 2a

Sketch and Edit Elements

Practice Objective

- Use sketch tools and drawing aids.

In this practice, you will use the **Wall** command along with sketching tools and drawing aids, such as temporary dimensions and snaps. You will use the **Modify** command and modify the walls using grips, temporary dimensions, the Type Selector, and Properties. You will add a door and modify it using temporary dimensions and controls. The completed model is shown in Figure 2–22.

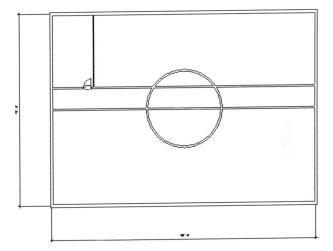

Figure 2–22

Task 1 - Use sketching tools and temporary dimensions to model and modify walls.

1. In the *File* tab, click (New)> (Project).

2. In the New Project dialog box, select **Imperial-Architectural Template** in the Template file drop-down list and click **OK**.

3. In the Quick Access Toolbar, click (Save). When prompted, name the project **Simple Building.rvt**.

4. In the *Architecture* tab>Build panel, click (Wall).

5. In the *Modify | Place Wall* tab>Draw panel, click
   ⬜ (Rectangle) and sketch a rectangle approximately
   100' x 70'. You do not have to be precise because you can
   change the dimensions later.

6. Note that the dimensions are temporary. Select the vertical
   dimension text and type **70'-0"**, as shown in Figure 2–23.
   Press <Enter>.

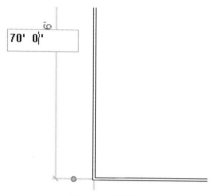

Figure 2–23

7. The dimensions are still displayed as temporary. Click the
   dimension controls of both the dimensions to make them
   permanent, as shown in Figure 2–24.

Figure 2–24

8. In the Select panel, click ▷ (Modify). You can also use one
   of the other methods to switch to **Modify**:

   • Type the shortcut **MD**.
   • Press <Esc> once or twice.

9. Select either vertical wall. The horizontal dimension becomes active (changes to blue). Click the dimension text and type **100'-0"**, as shown in Figure 2–25.

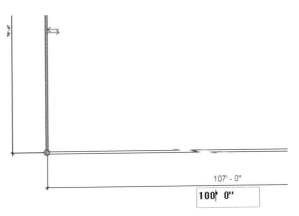

Figure 2–25

10. Click in an empty space in the view to end the selection. You are still in the **Modify** command.

11. In the *Architecture* tab>Build panel, click ⬚ (Wall). In the Draw panel, verify that ╱ (Line) is selected. Sketch a wall horizontally from midpoint to midpoint of the vertical walls.

12. Draw another horizontal wall **8'-0"** above the middle horizontal wall. You can use temporary dimensions to adjust it, if needed.

13. Draw a vertical wall exactly **16'-0"** from the left wall, as shown in Figure 2–26.

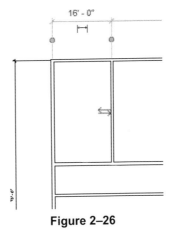

Figure 2–26

14. In the Draw panel, click 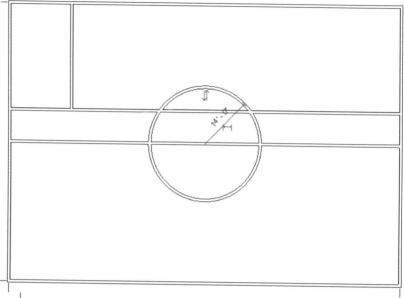 (Circle) and sketch a **14'-0"** radius circular wall at the midpoint of the lower interior horizontal wall, as shown in Figure 2–27.

Figure 2–27

15. Click 🔓 (Modify) to finish the command.

16. Hover the cursor over one of the outside walls, press <Tab> to highlight the chain of outside walls, and click to select the walls.

17. In the Type Selector, select **Basic Wall: Generic-12"**, as shown in Figure 2–28. The thickness of the outside walls changes.

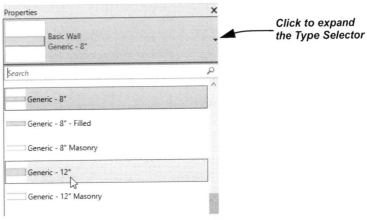

Figure 2–28

18. Click in an empty space in the view to release the selection.

19. Select the vertical interior wall. In the Type Selector, change the wall to one of the small interior partition styles.

20. Click in an empty space in the view to release the selection.

Task 2 - Add and modify a door.

---

1. Zoom in on the room in the upper left corner.

2. In the *Architecture* tab>Build panel, click ⬚ (Door).

3. In the *Modify | Place Door* tab>Tag panel, click ⬚ (Tag on Placement).

4. Place a door anywhere along the wall in the hallway.

5. Click ⬚ (Modify) to finish the command.

6. Select the door. Use temporary dimensions to move it so that it is **2'-6"** from the right interior vertical wall. If needed, use controls to flip the door so that it swings into the room, as shown in Figure 2–29.

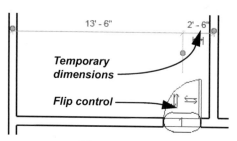

Figure 2–29

7. Type **ZE** to zoom out to the full view.

8. Save the project.

2.3 Working with Basic Modify Tools

The basic modify tools, **Move**, **Copy**, **Rotate**, **Mirror**, and **Array**, can be used with individual elements or any selection of elements. They are found in the Modify panel (shown in Figure 2–30), in the *Modify* tab, and in contextual tabs.

Figure 2–30

- For these modify commands, you can either select the elements and start the command, or start the command, select the elements, and press <Enter> to finish the selection and move to the next step in the command.

Moving and Copying Elements

The **Move** and **Copy** commands enable you to select the elements and move or copy them from one place to another. You can use alignment lines, temporary dimensions, and snaps to help place the elements, as shown in Figure 2–31.

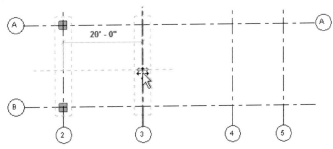

Figure 2–31

How To: Move or Copy Elements

1. Select the elements you want to move or copy.

2. In the Modify panel, click (Move) or (Copy). Alternatively, you can type **MV** for Move and **CO** for Copy. A boundary box displays around the selected elements.

3. Select a start point on or near the element.

4. Select a second point. Use alignment lines and temporary dimensions to help place the elements.

5. When you are finished, you can start another modify command using the elements that remain selected, or select ⬦ (Modify) to end the command.

- You can drag elements to new locations without starting the **Move** command. Holding <Ctrl> and dragging copies the element. This is quick but not very precise.

Move/Copy Elements Options

The **Move** and **Copy** commands have several options that display in the Options Bar, as shown in Figure 2–32.

☐ Constrain ☐ Disjoin ☐ Multiple

Figure 2–32

Constrain	Restricts the movement of the cursor to horizontal or vertical, or along the axis of an item that is at an angle. This keeps you from selecting a point at an angle by mistake. **Constrain** is off by default.
Disjoin (Move only)	Breaks any connections between the elements being moved and other elements. If **Disjoin** is on, the elements move separately. If it is off, the connected elements also move or stretch. **Disjoin** is off by default.
Multiple (Copy only)	Enables you to make multiple copies of one selection. **Multiple** is off by default.

- These commands only work in the current view, not between views or projects. To copy between views or projects, in the *Modify* tab>Clipboard panel, use 📋 (Copy to Clipboard), ✂ (Cut to the Clipboard), and 📋 (Paste from Clipboard).

Hint: Pinning Elements

If you do not want elements to be moved, you can pin them in place, as shown in Figure 2–33. Select the elements and in the

Modify tab>Modify panel, click 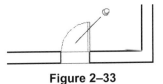 (Pin). Pinned elements can be copied, but not moved. If you try to delete a pinned element, a warning dialog displays reminding you that you must unpin the element before the command can be started.

Figure 2–33

Select the element and click (Unpin) or type the shortcut **UP** to free it.

Rotating Elements

The **Rotate** command enables you to rotate selected elements around a center point or origin, as shown in Figure 2–34. You can use alignment lines, temporary dimensions, and snaps to help specify the center of rotation and the angle. You can also create copies of the element as it is being rotated.

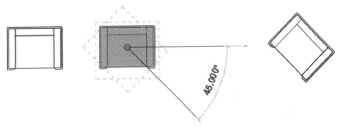

Figure 2–34

How To: Rotate Elements

1. Select the element(s) you want to rotate.

2. In the Modify panel, click ○ (Rotate) or type the shortcut **RO**.

3. The center of rotation is automatically set to the center of the element or group of elements, as shown on the left in Figure 2–35. To change the center of rotation, as shown on the right in Figure 2–35, use the following:

- Drag the ⟳ (Center of Rotation) control to a new point.
- In the Options Bar, next to **Center of rotation**, click **Place** and use snaps to move it to a new location.
- Press <Spacebar> to select the center of rotation and click to move it to a new location.

*To start the **Rotate** command with a prompt to select the center of rotation, select the elements first and type **R3**.*

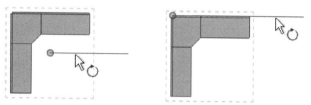

Figure 2–35

4. In the Options Bar, specify if you want to make a copy (select **Copy**), type an angle in the *Angle* field (shown in Figure 2–36), and press <Enter>. You can also specify the angle on screen using temporary dimensions.

Figure 2–36

5. The rotated element(s) remain highlighted, enabling you to start another command using the same selection, or click

⬉ (Modify) to finish.

- The **Disjoin** option breaks any connections between the elements being rotated and other elements. If **Disjoin** is on (selected), the elements rotate separately. If it is off (cleared), the connected elements also move or stretch, as shown in Figure 2–37. **Disjoin** is toggled off by default.

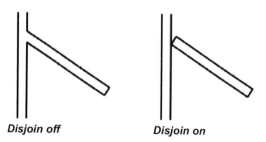

Disjoin off   **Disjoin on**

Figure 2–37

Mirroring Elements

The **Mirror** command enables you to mirror elements about an axis defined by a selected element, as shown in Figure 2–38, or by selected points.

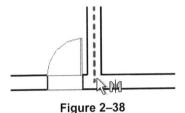

Figure 2–38

How To: Mirror Elements

1. Select the element(s) to mirror.
2. In the Modify panel, select the method you want to use:

   - Click ▣ (Mirror - Pick Axis) or type the shortcut **MM**. This prompts you to select an element as the **Axis of Reflection** (mirror line).

   - Click ▣ (Mirror - Draw Axis) or type the shortcut **DM**. This prompts you to select two points to define the axis about which the elements mirror.

3. The new mirrored element(s) remain highlighted, enabling you to start another command, or return to **Modify** to finish.

   - By default, the original elements that were mirrored remain. To delete the original elements, clear the **Copy** option in the Options Bar.

Hint: Scale

The Autodesk Revit software is designed with full-size elements. Therefore, not much should be scaled. For example, scaling a wall increases its length but does not impact the width, which is set by the wall type. However, you can use

▢ (Scale) in reference planes, images, and imported files from other programs.

Creating Linear and Radial Arrays

A linear array creates a straight line pattern of elements, while a radial array creates a circular pattern around a center point.

The **Array** command creates multiple copies of selected elements in a linear or radial pattern, as shown in Figure 2–39. For example, you can array a row of columns to create a row of evenly spaced columns on a grid, or array a row of parking spaces. The arrayed elements can be grouped or placed as separate elements.

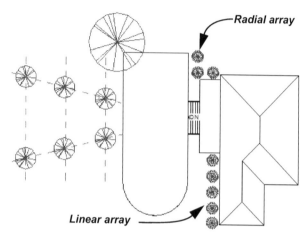

Figure 2–39

How To: Create a Linear Array

1. Select the element(s) to array.
2. In the Modify panel, click ⊞ (Array) or type the shortcut **AR**.
3. In the Options Bar, click 🔲 (Linear).
4. Specify the other options as needed.
5. Select a start point and an end point to set the spacing and direction of the array. The array is displayed.
6. If **Group and Associate** is selected, you are prompted again for the number of items, as shown in Figure 2–40. Type a new number or click on the screen to finish the command.

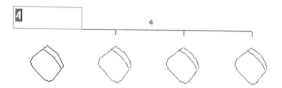

Figure 2–40

- To make a linear array in two directions, you need to array one direction first, select the arrayed elements, and then array them again in the other direction.

Array Options

In the Options Bar, set up the array options for **Linear Array** (top of Figure 2–41) or **Radial Array** (bottom of Figure 2–41).

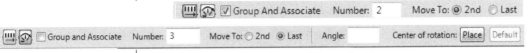

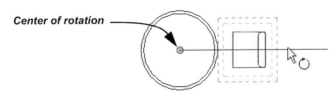

Figure 2–41

Group and Associate	Creates an array group element out of all arrayed elements. Groups can be selected by selecting any elements in the group.
Number	Specifies how many instances you want in the array.
Move To:	**2nd** specifies the distance or angle between the center points of the two elements. **Last** specifies the overall distance or angle of the entire array.
Constrain	Restricts the direction of the array to only vertical or horizontal (Linear only).
Angle	Specifies the angle (Radial only).
Center of rotation	Specifies a location for the origin about which the elements rotate (Radial only).

How To: Create a Radial Array

1. Select the element(s) to array.

2. In the Modify panel, click ⊞ (Array).

3. In the Options Bar, click ◺ (Radial).

4. Drag ↻ (Center of Rotation) or use **Place** to move the center of rotation to the appropriate location, as shown in Figure 2–42.

Remember to set the **Center of Rotation** *control first, before specifying the angle.*

Center of rotation —

Figure 2–42

5. In the Options Bar, type an angle and press <Enter>, or specify the rotation angle by selecting points on the screen.
6. Specify the other options as needed.

Modifying Array Groups

When you select an element in an array that has been grouped, you can change the number of instances in the array, as shown in Figure 2–43. For radial arrays, you can also modify the distance to the center.

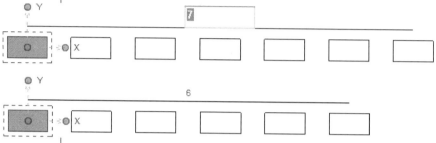

Figure 2–43

- Dashed lines surround the element(s) in a group, and the XY control lets you move the origin point of the group.

If you move one of the elements in the array group, the other elements move in response based on the distance and/or angle, as shown in Figure 2–44.

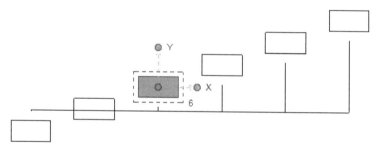

Figure 2–44

- To remove the array constraint on the group, select all of the elements in the array group and, in the *Modify* contextual tab>Group panel, click (Ungroup).

- If you select an individual element in an array and click (Ungroup), the element you selected is removed from the array, while the rest of the elements remain in the array group.

- You can use (Filter) to ensure that you are selecting only **Model Groups**.

Practice 2b

Work with Basic Modify Tools

Practice Objective

- Use basic modify tools such as Move, Copy, Rotate, and Array to modify elements.

In this practice, you will create a series of offices using the **Copy** and **Mirror** commands. You will array desks around a circular wall, then rotate and array a pair of columns across the front of a simple building, as shown in Figure 2–45.

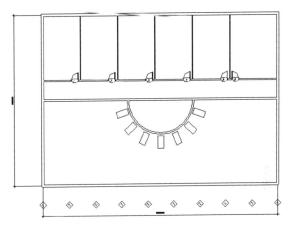

Figure 2–45

Task 1 - Modify walls and doors.

1. Open the project **Simple-Building-1.rvt** from the practice files folder.

2. In the **Floor Plans: Level 1** view, select the top arc of the circular wall.

*Remember that you can also press <Delete>, or right-click and select **Delete**.*

3. In the Modify panel, click ✖ (Delete). The walls that the circular wall crossed are automatically cleaned up.

4. Select the vertical interior wall, door, and door tag. Hold <Ctrl> to select more than one element or use a selection window.

5. In the Modify panel, click ⟳ (Copy).

6. In the Options Bar, select **Constrain** and **Multiple**. The **Constrain** option forces the cursor to move only horizontally or vertically.

7. Select the start point and, using the temporary dimensions, pick the end point **16'-0"** away from the start point, as shown in Figure 2–46. The wall, door, and door tag are copied to the right and the door tag displays **2**.

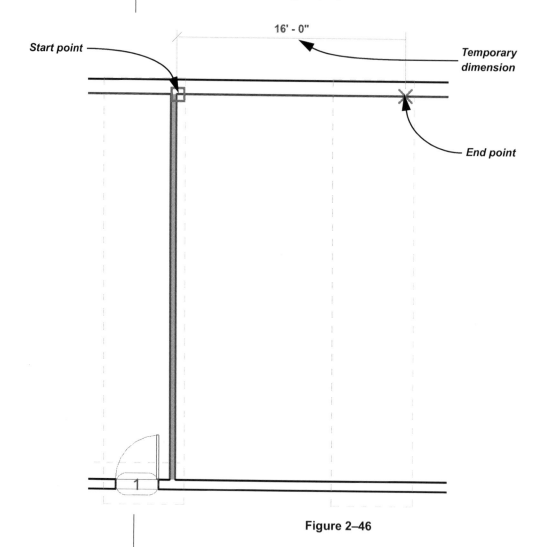

Figure 2–46

8. The new elements are still selected and you can continue to copy them. Use similar start and end points for the additional copies, or type **16** (16'-0") and press <Enter> to set the distance between each copy. The final layout is shown in Figure 2–47.

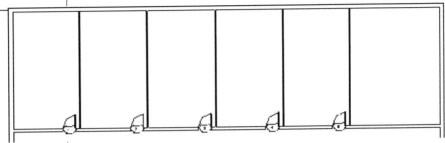

Figure 2–47

9. Click ⌖ (Modify) to finish the command.

10. Zoom in on the room to the far right.

11. Select door #5 and the associated door tag.

12. In the Modify panel, click ⊳⊲ (Mirror - Pick Axis). In the Options Bar, ensure that **Copy** is selected.

13. Select the vertical wall between the rooms as the mirror axis. An alignment line displays along the center of the wall. Place the new door, as shown in Figure 2–48.

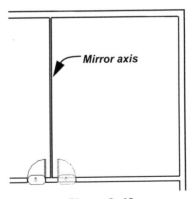

Mirror axis

Figure 2–48

14. Click in an empty space in the view to release the selection.

Task 2 - Add reference planes and use them to place a component.

1. In the *Architecture* tab>Work Plane panel, click 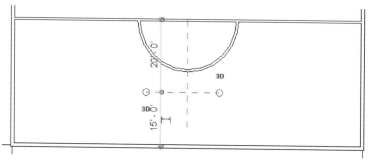 (Ref Plane).

2. Draw two reference planes, as shown in Figure 2–49. The vertical one starts at the midpoint of the wall. Place the horizontal plane 20'-0" from the horizontal wall, or place the reference plane at any distance and then use temporary dimensions to place it more exactly.

Figure 2–49

3. In the *Architecture* tab>Build panel, click (Component) or type **CM**.

4. In Properties, in the Type Selector, verify that **Desk: 60" x 30"** is selected, as shown in Figure 2–50.

Figure 2–50

5. As you move the cursor, you can see that the desk is horizontal. Press <Spacebar> to rotate the desk 90 degrees.

6. Place the desk at the intersection of the two reference planes, as shown in Figure 2–51. Zoom in as needed to ensure that you are connected to the reference planes and not to any other alignment lines.

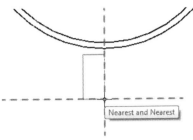

Nearest and Nearest

Figure 2–51

7. Click (Modify) and select the desk you just placed.

Use Snap Overrides, if needed.

8. In the Modify panel, click (Move). Select the start point of the move as the midpoint of the desk and the end point as the vertical reference plane, as shown in Figure 2–52.

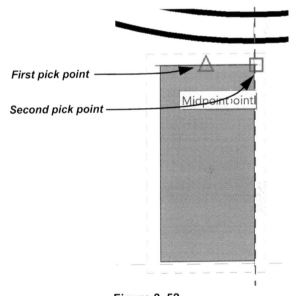

First pick point

Second pick point

Midpoint

Figure 2–52

9. Save the project.

Task 3 - Create a radial array.

1. Select the desk.

2. In the Modify panel, click ⬚⬚ (Array).

3. In the Options Bar, click 🗗 (Radial). Clear the **Group and Associate** option, set the *Number* field to **15**, and set the *Move to:* to **2nd**.

4. Drag the center of rotation from the center of the desk to the midpoint of the wall, as shown in Figure 2–53.

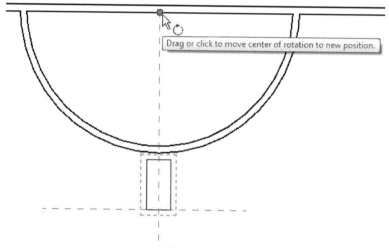

Drag or click to move center of rotation to new position.

Figure 2–53

5. Return to the Options Bar and set the *Angle* to **360**. Press <Enter>. The array displays as shown in Figure 2–54.

Sometimes it is easier to create more elements then you need, and then delete the ones that are not required, as is done in this example.

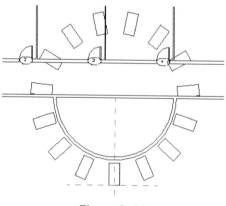

Figure 2–54

6. Delete all of the desks that are outside of the room.

7. Zoom out to display the entire view.

Task 4 - Place columns in appropriate locations.

1. Pan and zoom to the lower right side of the model. Two columns (one architectural and one structural) have been added to the project.

2. Select the square architectural column and drag it over so that it lines up with the wall, as shown in Figure 2–55. Use the temporary dimension to set the distance off the wall to **8'-0"**.

3. Place the structural column at the center of the architectural column, as shown in Figure 2–56, using the **Midpoint** and **Extension** snaps.

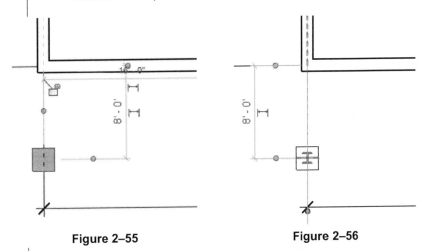

Figure 2–55   **Figure 2–56**

4. Save the project.

Task 5 - Rotate and array the columns.

1. Click ⌂ (Modify) and select the two columns.

2. In the *Modify | Multi-Select* tab>Modify panel, click ⟳ (Rotate).

3. For the start ray, click horizontally, as shown in Figure 2–57.

4. Move the ray line until you see the temporary dimension **45.000**, as shown in Figure 2–58.

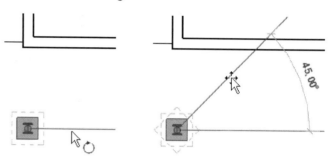

Figure 2–57   Figure 2–58

5. With the two columns still selected, in the *Modify |*
   Multi-Select tab>Modify panel, click ⬚⬚ (Array).

6. In the Options Bar, click ▥ (Linear), clear **Group and Associate**, set the *Number* to **10**, and set *Move To:* to **Last**.

7. For the start point, click the midpoint of the columns. For the endpoint of the array, select the **Horizontal and Extension** of the center of the far right wall, as shown in Figure 2–59.

Figure 2–59

8. Zoom out to display the entire building.

9. The columns are arrayed evenly across the front of the building, as shown in Figure 2–60.

Figure 2–60

10. Save the project.

2.4 Working with Additional Modify Tools

As you work on a project, some additional tools found in the *Modify* tab>Modify panel, as shown in Figure 2–61, can help you with placing, modifying, and constraining elements. **Align**, **Paint**, and **Split Face** can be used with a variety of elements, while **Split Element**, **Trim/Extend**, and **Offset** can only be used with linear elements.

Figure 2–61

Aligning Elements

The **Align** command enables you to line up one element with another, as shown in Figure 2–62. Most Autodesk Revit elements can be aligned. For example, you can line up the tops of windows with the top of a door, or line up furniture with a wall.

First pick   *Second pick*

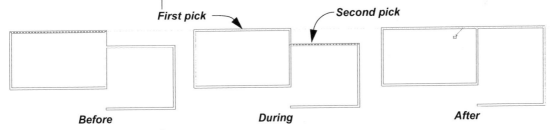

Before   *During*   *After*

Figure 2–62

How To: Align Elements

1. In the *Modify* tab>Modify panel, click ▣ (Align).
2. Select a line or point on the element that is going to remain stationary. For walls, press <Tab> to select the correct wall face.
3. Select a line or point on the element to be aligned. The second element moves into alignment with the first one.

- The **Align** command works in all model views, including parallel and perspective 3D views.

• You can lock alignments so that the elements move together if either one is moved. Once you have created the alignment, a padlock is displayed. Click on the padlock to lock it, as shown in Figure 2–63.

Locking elements enlarges the size of the project file, so use this option carefully.

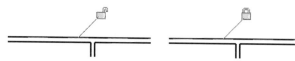

Figure 2–63

• From the Options Bar, select **Multiple Alignment** to select multiple elements to align with the first element. You can also hold <Ctrl> to select multiple elements to align.

• For walls, you can specify if you want the command to prefer **Wall centerlines**, **Wall faces**, **Center of core**, or **Faces of core**, as shown in Figure 2–64. The core refers to the structural members of a wall as opposed to facing materials, such as sheet rock.

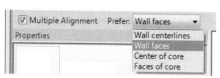

Figure 2–64

Applying Materials

You may want to apply information that is not in the model element, such as different materials on the face of a wall, as shown in Figure 2–65. The **Split Face** command divides an element face into smaller separate faces. You can then use the **Paint** command to apply different materials to the faces.

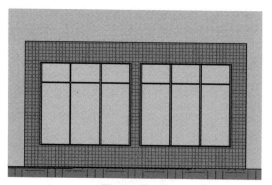

Figure 2–65

• The changes made with **Split Face** and **Paint** are displayed in elevations and 3D views.

- **Split Face** and **Paint** do not alter the structure of the wall.

- The area and other information about the materials can be used in a material takeoff schedule.

How To: Create a Split Face

1. Switch to an elevation view (a 3D view works as well).

2. In the *Modify* tab>Geometry panel, click 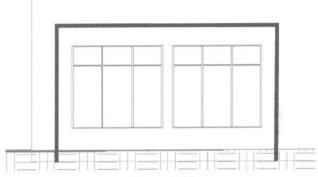 (Split Face).

3. Select the edge of the face that you want to modify. Use <Tab> to toggle through the available faces.

If the 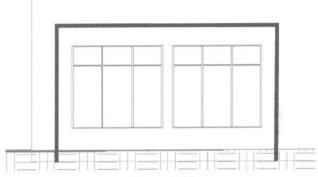 *(Select elements by face) option is toggled on in the lower-left corner of the Status Bar, you can click directly on the face.*

4. In the *Modify | Split Face>Create Boundary* tab>Draw panel, use the sketch tools to create a sketch to define the split, as shown in Figure 2–66.

Figure 2–66

- The split must be a closed shape completely inside the face, or an open shape that touches the face edges.

- Windows are cut out of faces automatically.

5. Click ✔ (Finish Edit Mode).

- Before you begin working with split faces, ensure that the walls are mitered. By default, the walls are butted to each other. This creates a problem when you select faces.

- To save time, use a wall style that includes the primary material you want to use on the split face. For example, if you are working with brick, set the wall to a type that has a brick face. This way, you can work with the brick courses when creating the split face.

- When using a material such as brick, you can snap to the pattern and even lock the split lines to the pattern, as shown in Figure 2–67.

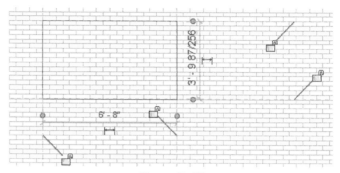

Figure 2–67

You can double-click on the edge of the split face lines to switch to Edit Boundary mode. If you double-click on the wall face (with the **Select elements by face** option toggled on), it switches to Edit Profile mode, which impacts the entire wall, not just the split face boundary.

How To: Apply Material with Paint

1. In the *Modify* tab>Geometry panel, click ⬚ (Paint) or enter **PT**.
2. In the Material Browser, select a material. You can run a search or filter the list using specific types of materials, as shown in Figure 2–68.

The browser remains open as you apply the paint.

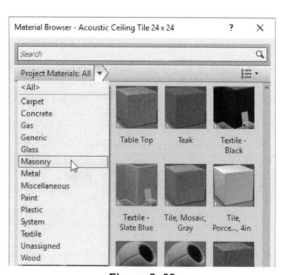

Figure 2–68

3. Hover the cursor over the face you want to paint. It should highlight, as shown in Figure 2–69. Click on the face to apply the material.

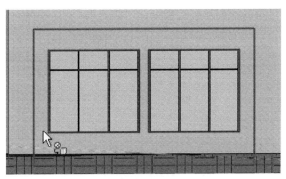

Figure 2–69

4. Continue selecting materials and painting other faces, if needed.
5. In the Material Browser, click **Done** to finish the command.

- Some material patterns display as shaded when you zoom out. Zoom in to display the pattern. Other material patterns only display when you are in the ⬛ (Realistic) visual style or when you render.

- To remove the material applied to a face, in the *Modify* tab> Geometry panel, expand 🔲 (Paint) and click 🔲 (Remove Paint). Select the face(s) from which you want to remove the material.

Splitting Linear Elements

The **Split Element** command enables you to break a linear element at a specific point. You can use alignment lines, snaps, and temporary dimensions to help place the split point. After you have split the linear element, you can use other editing commands to modify the two parts, or change the type of one part, as shown with walls in Figure 2–70. You can split walls in plan, elevation, or 3D views.

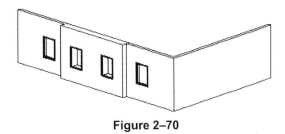

Figure 2–70

How To: Split Linear Elements

1. In the *Modify* tab>Modify panel, click 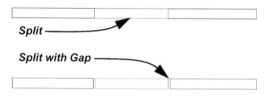 (Split Element) or type the shortcut **SL**.
2. In the Options Bar, select or clear the **Delete Inner Segment** option.
3. Move the cursor to the point you want to split and select the point.
4. Repeat for any additional split locations.
5. Modify the elements that were split, as needed.

- The **Delete Inner Segment** option is used when you select two split points along a linear element. When the option is selected, the segment between the two split points is automatically removed.

- An additional split tool found in the *Modify* tab>Modify panel is (Split with Gap). This tool splits the linear element at the point you select, as shown in Figure 2–71, but also creates a *Joint Gap*, which is specified in the Options Bar. This command is only available when splitting walls.

Split ——

Split with Gap ——

Figure 2–71

Trimming and Extending

There are three trim/extend methods that you can use with linear elements: **Trim/Extend to Corner**, **Trim/Extend Single Element**, and **Trim/Extend Multiple Elements**.

- When selecting elements to trim, click the part of the element that you want to keep. The opposite part of the line is then trimmed.

How To: Trim/Extend to Corner

1. In the *Modify* tab>Modify panel, click (Trim/Extend to Corner) or type the shortcut **TR**.
2. Select the first linear element on the side you want to keep.

3. Select the second linear element on the side you want to keep, as shown in Figure 2–72.

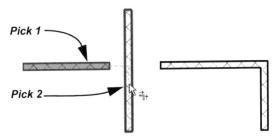

Figure 2–72

How To: Trim/Extend a Single Element

1. In the *Modify* tab>Modify panel, click ⊐╢ (Trim/Extend Single Element).
2. Select the cutting or boundary edge.
3. Select the linear element to be trimmed or extended, as shown in Figure 2–73.

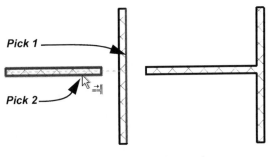

Figure 2–73

How To: Trim/Extend Multiple Elements

1. In the *Modify* tab>Modify panel, click ⊒ (Trim/Extend Multiple Elements).
2. Select the cutting or boundary edge.

3. Select the linear elements that you want to trim or extend by selecting one at a time or by using a crossing window, as shown in Figure 2–74. For trimming, select the side you want to keep.

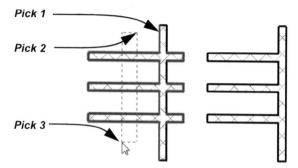

Figure 2–74

- You can click in an empty space in the view to clear the selection and select another cutting edge or boundary.

Offsetting Elements

The **Offset** command is an easy way of creating parallel copies of linear elements at a specified distance, as shown in Figure 2–75. Walls, beams, braces, and lines are among the elements that can be offset.

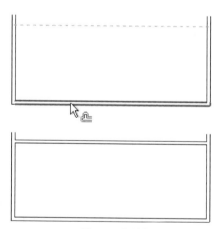

Figure 2–75

- If you offset a wall that has a door or window embedded in it, the elements are copied with the offset wall.

The offset distance can be set by typing the distance (**Numerical** method), as shown in Figure 2–76, or by selecting points on the screen (**Graphical** method).

○ Graphical ◉ Numerical   Offset: | 1' 0" | ☑ Copy

Figure 2–76

How To: Offset Using the Numerical Method

*The **Copy** option (which is on by default) makes a copy of the element being offset. If this option is not selected, the **Offset** command moves the element the set offset distance.*

1. In the *Modify* tab>Modify panel, click ⬛ (Offset) or type the shortcut **OF**.
2. In the Options Bar, select the **Numerical** option.
3. In the Options Bar, type the required distance in the *Offset* field.
4. Move the cursor over the element you want to offset. A dashed line previews the offset location. Move the cursor to flip the sides, as needed.
5. Click to create the offset.
6. Repeat Steps 4 and 5 to offset other elements by the same distance, or to change the distance for another offset.

- With the **Numerical** option, you can select multiple connected linear elements for offsetting. Hover the cursor over an element and press <Tab> until the other related elements are highlighted. Select the element to offset all of the elements at the same time.

How To: Offset Using the Graphical Method

1. Start the **Offset** command.
2. In the Options Bar, select **Graphical**.
3. Select the linear element to offset.
4. Select two points that define the distance of the offset and which side to apply it. You can type an override in the temporary dimension for the second point.

- Most linear elements connected at a corner automatically trim or extend to meet at the offset distance, as shown in Figure 2–77.

Figure 2–77

Practice 2c

Work with Additional Modify Tools

Practice Objective

- Use the Align, Split, Trim/Extend, and Offset commands to modify elements.

In this practice, you will split a wall into three parts and delete the middle portion. You will offset walls and then trim or extend them to form new rooms. You will then align the new walls to match existing walls, as shown in Figure 2–78.

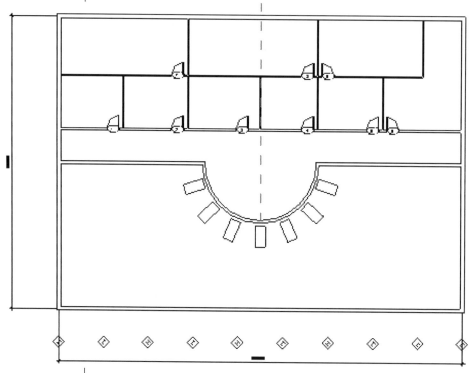

Figure 2–78

Task 1 - Split and remove walls.

1. Open the project **Simple-Building-2.rvt** from the practice files folder.

2. Verify that you are in the **Floor Plans: Level 1** view. In the *Modify* tab>Modify panel, click (Split Element).

3. In the Options Bar, select **Delete Inner Segment**.

4. Click on the horizontal wall where it intersects with the curved wall at both ends. The wall segment between these points is removed, as shown in Figure 2–79.

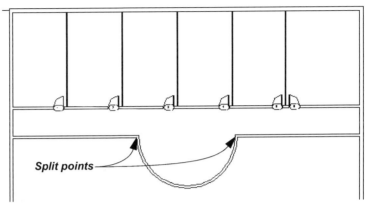

Figure 2–79

5. Click (Modify) to finish.

Task 2 - Offset and trim walls.

1. In the *Modify* tab>Modify panel, click ![offset icon] (Offset).

2. In the Options Bar, set the *Offset* to **14'-0"** and ensure that **Copy** is selected.

3. Select the top horizontal wall while ensuring that the dashed alignment line displays inside the building, as shown in Figure 2–80.

Figure 2–80

4. With **Offset** still active, change the *Offset* to **10'-0"** and offset the last vertical interior wall to the right, as shown in Figure 2–81.

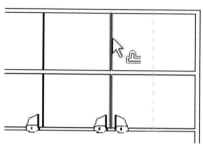

Figure 2–81

5. Click (Modify) and select the new horizontal wall that was created from the exterior wall. Change the wall type to **Basic Wall: Interior - 3 1/8" Partition (1-hr)**. The layout of the new walls should display as shown in Figure 2–82.

The vertical wall does not need to be changed because it was offset from an interior wall.

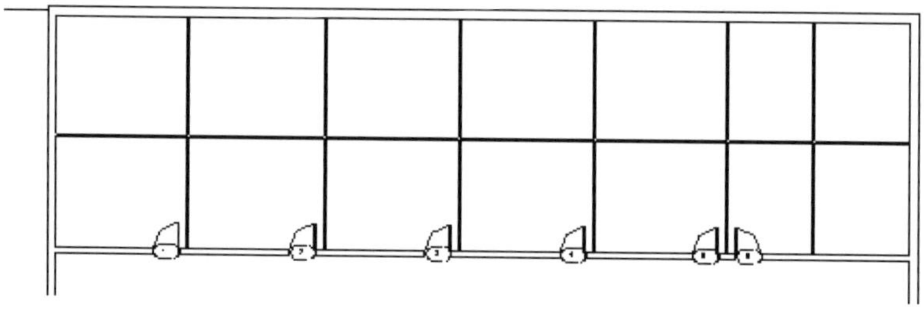

Figure 2–82

6. In the *Modify* tab>Modify panel, click (Trim/Extend Multiple Elements).

7. Select the new horizontal wall as the element to trim against.

8. Select every other wall *below* the new wall. (Remember, you select the elements that you want to keep.) The walls should display as shown in Figure 2–83.

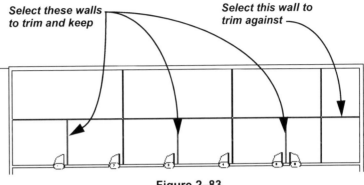

Select these walls to trim and keep

Select this wall to trim against

Figure 2–83

9. In the *Modify* tab>Modify panel, click 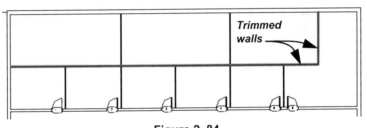 (Trim/Extend to Corner) and select the two walls to trim as shown in Figure 2–84.

Trimmed walls

Figure 2–84

10. Add doors into the three new rooms.

11. Save the project.

Task 3 - Align walls.

1. Select and extend the vertical reference plane. Use the control to drag the top end so it extends beyond the outer wall, as shown in Figure 2–85.

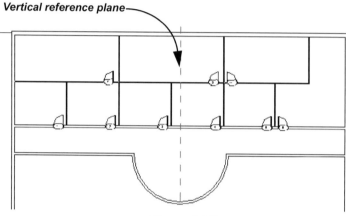

Figure 2–85

2. In the *Modify* tab>Modify panel, click ⬛ (Align).

3. Select the reference plane, and then select the wall to the left. The wall should line up with the reference plane.

4. Save and close the project.

Chapter Review Questions

1. What is the purpose of an alignment line?

   a. Displays when the new element you are placing or modeling is aligned with the grid system.

   b. Indicates that the new element you are placing or modeling is aligned with an existing element.

   c. Displays when the new element you are placing or modeling is aligned with a selected tracking point.

   d. Indicates that the new element is aligned with true north rather than project north.

2. You cannot change the distance of an element using temporary dimensions.

   a. True

   b. False

3. How do you select all the doors of various sizes, but no other elements in a view?

   a. In the Project Browser, select the *Door* category.

   b. Select one door, right-click, and select **Select All Instances>Visible in View**.

   c. Select all of the elements in the view and use 🔽 (Filter) to clear the other categories.

   d. Select one door and click ▣ (Select Multiple) in the ribbon.

4. What are the two methods for starting commands such as **Move**, **Copy**, **Rotate**, **Mirror**, and **Array**?

   a. Start the command from the *Modify* tab and select the elements, then start the command.

   b. Start the command from the *Modify* tab and select the elements, then select the command from the Status Bar.

   c. Start the command from the *Modify* tab and select the elements, then right-click and select the command from the list.

5. Where do you change the wall type for a selected wall, as shown in Figure 2–86?

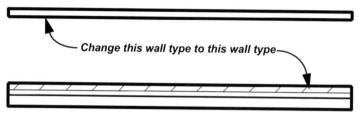

Change this wall type to this wall type

Figure 2–86

a. In the *Modify | Walls* tab>Properties panel, click 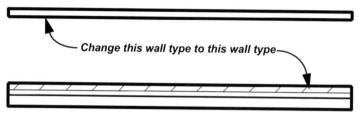 (Type Properties) and select a new wall type in the dialog box.

b. In the Options Bar, click **Change Element Type**.

c. Select the dynamic control next to the selected wall and select a new type in the drop-down list.

d. In Properties, select a new type in the Type Selector drop-down list.

6. Both ⟳ (Rotate) and ⊞ (Array) with 🔲 (Radial) have a center of rotation that defaults to the center of the element or group of elements you have selected. How do you move the center of rotation to another point, as shown in Figure 2–87? (Select all that apply.)

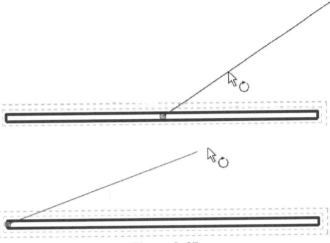

Figure 2–87

a. Select the center of rotation and drag it to a new location.

b. In the Options Bar, click **Place** and select the new point.

c. In the *Modify* tab>Placement panel, click ⊘ (Center) and select the new point.

d. Right-click and select **Snap Overrides>Centers** and select the new point.

7. Which command would you use to remove a part or a segment of a wall?

a. ⟷ (Split Element)

b. 📐 (Wall Joins)

c. ⬭ (Cut Geometry)

d. 🔨 (Demolish)

8. Which of the following are ways in which you can create additional parallel walls, as shown in Figure 2–88? (Select all that apply.)

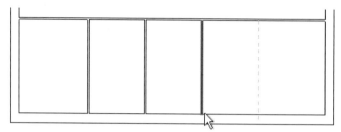

Figure 2–88

a. Use the **Trim/Extend Multiple Elements** tool.

b. Use the **Offset** tool in the *Modify* tab.

c. Select an existing wall, hold <Ctrl>, and drag the wall to a new location.

d. Use the **Align** command with an offset.

9. Which command do you use if you want two walls that are not touching to come together, as shown in Figure 2–89?

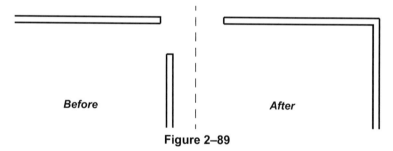

Before   *After*

Figure 2–89

a. (Edit Wall Joins)

b. (Trim/Extend to Corner)

c. (Join Geometry)

d. (Edit Profile)

Command Summary

Button	Command	Location
Draw Tools		
	Center-ends Arc	• **Ribbon:** *Modify	(various linear elements)* tab>Draw panel
	Circle	• **Ribbon:** *Modify	(various linear elements)* tab>Draw panel
	Circumscribed Polygon	• **Ribbon:** *Modify	(various linear elements)* tab>Draw panel
	Ellipse	• **Ribbon:** *Modify	Place Lines, Place Detail Lines, and various boundary sketches*>Draw panel
	Ellipse Arc	• **Ribbon:** *Modify	Place Lines, Place Detail Lines, and various boundary sketches*>Draw panel
	Fillet Arc	• **Ribbon:** *Modify	(various linear elements)* tab>Draw panel
	Inscribed Polygon	• **Ribbon:** *Modify	(various linear elements)* tab>Draw panel
	Line	• **Ribbon:** *Modify	(various linear elements)* tab>Draw panel
	Pick Faces	• **Ribbon:** *Modify	Place Wall*> Draw panel
	Pick Lines	• **Ribbon:** *Modify	(various linear elements)* tab>Draw panel
	Pick Walls	• **Ribbon:** *Modify	(various boundary sketches)*>Draw panel
	Rectangle	• **Ribbon:** *Modify	(various linear elements)* tab>Draw panel
	Spline	• **Ribbon:** *Modify	Place Lines, Place Detail Lines, and various boundary sketches*>Draw panel
	Start-End-Radius Arc	• **Ribbon:** *Modify	(various linear elements)* tab>Draw panel
	Tangent End Arc	• **Ribbon:** *Modify	(various linear elements)* tab>Draw panel
Modify Tools		
	Align	• **Ribbon:** *Modify* tab>Modify panel • **Shortcut:** AL
	Array	• **Ribbon:** *Modify* tab>Modify panel • **Shortcut:** AR
	Copy	• **Ribbon:** *Modify* tab>Modify panel • **Shortcut:** CO

	Copy to Clipboard	• **Ribbon:** *Modify* tab>Clipboard panel • **Shortcut:** <Ctrl>+<C>
	Delete	• **Ribbon:** *Modify* tab>Modify panel • **Shortcut:** DE
	Mirror - Draw Axis	• **Ribbon:** *Modify* tab>Modify panel • **Shortcut:** DM
	Mirror - Pick Axis	• **Ribbon:** *Modify* tab>Modify panel • **Shortcut:** MM
	Move	• **Ribbon:** *Modify* tab>Modify panel • **Shortcut:** MV
	Offset	• **Ribbon:** *Modify* tab>Modify panel • **Shortcut:** OF
	Paste	• **Ribbon:** *Modify* tab>Clipboard panel • **Shortcut:** <Ctrl>+<V>
	Pin	• **Ribbon:** *Modify* tab>Modify panel • **Shortcut:** PN
	Rotate	• **Ribbon:** *Modify* tab>Modify panel • **Shortcut:** RO, R3
	Scale	• **Ribbon:** *Modify* tab>Modify panel • **Shortcut:** RE
	Split Element	• **Ribbon:** *Modify* tab>Modify panel • **Shortcut:** SL
	Split with Gap	• **Ribbon:** *Modify* tab>Modify panel
	Trim/Extend Multiple Elements	• **Ribbon:** *Modify* tab>Modify panel
	Trim/Extend Single Element	• **Ribbon:** *Modify* tab>Modify panel
	Trim/Extend to Corner	• **Ribbon:** *Modify* tab>Modify panel • **Shortcut:** TR
	Unpin	• **Ribbon:** *Modify* tab>Modify panel • **Shortcut:** UP

Select Tools

	Drag elements on selection	• **Ribbon:** All tabs>Expanded Select panel • **Status Bar**
	Filter	• **Ribbon:** *Modify	Multi-Select* tab>Filter panel • **Status Bar**
	Select Elements By Face	• **Ribbon:** All tabs>Expanded Select panel • **Status Bar**

	Select Links	• **Ribbon:** All tabs>Expanded Select panel • **Status Bar**
	Select Pinned Elements	• **Ribbon:** All tabs>Expanded Select panel • **Status Bar**
	Select Underlay Elements	• **Ribbon:** All tabs>Expanded Select panel • **Status Bar**

Additional Tools

	Aligned Dimension	• **Ribbon:** *Modify* tab>Measure panel • Quick Access Toolbar
	Component	• **Ribbon:** *Architecture/Structure/ Systems* tab • **Shortcut:** CM
	Detail Line	• **Ribbon:** *Annotate* tab>Detail panel • **Shortcut:** DL
	Model Line	• **Ribbon:** *Architectural* tab>Model panel • **Shortcut:** LI
	Paint	• **Ribbon:** *Modify* tab>Geometry panel • **Shortcut:** PT
	Reference Plane	• **Ribbon:** *Architecture/Structure/ Systems* tab> Work Plane panel
	Split Face	• **Ribbon:** *Modify* tab>Geometry panel

Starting Architectural Projects

Starting a project in Autodesk Revit begins by using a template. From there, you can add the framework for a building, including levels to define vertical heights. You can also link in a CAD file.

Learning Objectives in This Chapter

- Add and modify levels to define floor-to-floor heights and other vertical references.
- Link and import CAD files to be used as a basis for developing a design.

3.1 Setting Up Levels

Levels define stories and other vertical heights, such as a parapet or other reference heights, as shown in Figure 3–1. The default template includes two levels, but you can define as many levels in a project as required. They can go below 0'-0" or in the negative (for basements) as well.

Figure 3–1

- You must be in an elevation or section view to define levels.

- Once you constrain an element to a level, it moves with the level when the level is changed.

How To: Create Levels

1. Open an elevation or section view.

2. In the *Architecture* tab>Datum panel, click (Level), or type **LL**.

3. In the Type Selector, set the Level Head type, if needed.

4. In the Options Bar, select or clear **Make Plan View**, as needed. You can also click **Plan View Types...** to select the types of views to create when you place the level.

5. In the *Modify | Place Level* tab>Draw panel, click either
 (Pick Lines) to select an element or (Line) to sketch a level.

6. Continue adding levels as needed.

- Level names are automatically incremented as you place them. This automatic numbering is most effective when you use names such as Floor 1, Floor 2, etc. (as opposed to First Floor, Second Floor, etc.). In addition, this makes it easier to find the view in the Project Browser.

- A fast way to create multiple levels is to use the ⬟ (Pick Lines) option. In the Options Bar, specify an *Offset,* select an existing level, and then pick above or below to place the new level, as shown in Figure 3–2.

You specify above or below the offset by hovering the cursor on the needed side.

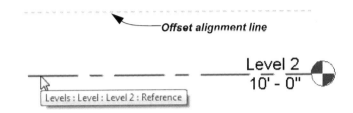

Figure 3–2

- When using the ✎ (Line) option, alignments and temporary dimensions help you place the line correctly, as shown in Figure 3–3.

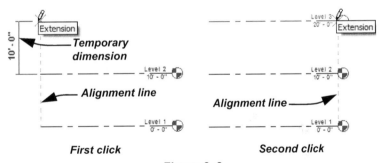

Figure 3–3

- Sketch the level lines from left to right or right to left to keep consistent.

- You can also use ⬓ (Copy) to duplicate level lines. The level names are incremented but a plan view is not created.

- Levels display in the default 3D view. They can be modified and copied, but cannot be created in this view.

- Levels can be hidden in any view.

Modifying Levels

You can change levels using standard controls and temporary dimensions, as shown in Figure 3–4. You can also make changes in the Properties palette.

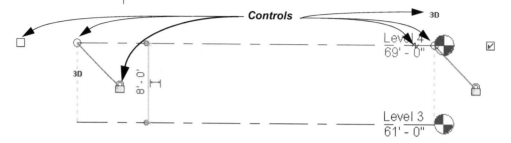

Figure 3–4

- ☑ ☐ (Hide / Show Bubble) displays on either end of the level line and toggles the level head symbol and level information on or off.

- 2D 3D (Switch to 3d / 2d extents) controls whether any movement or adjustment to the level line is reflected in other views (3D) or only affects the current view (2D).

- ↻ (Modify the level by dragging its model end) at each end of the line enables you to drag the level head to a new location.

- 🔒 🔓 (Create or remove a length or alignment constraint) controls whether the level is locked in alignment with the other levels. If it is locked and the level line is stretched, all of the other level lines stretch as well. If it is unlocked, the level line stretches independent of the other levels.

- Click ⌁ (Add elbow) to add a jog to the level line, as shown in Figure 3–5. Drag the shape handles to new locations as needed. This is a view-specific change.

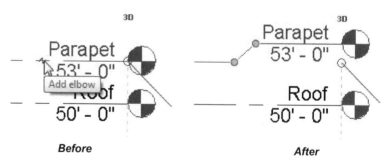

Figure 3–5

- To change the level name or elevation, select the level and modify the *Name* or *Elevation* fields in Properties, as shown in Figure 3–6. Alternatively, you can do one of the following:

  - Slowly click twice on the information next to the level head and type in a new name or elevation.
  - Right-click on the level name in the Project Browser and select **Rename**. Type in a new name for the level and press <Enter>.
  - Slowly click twice on the name in the Project Browser and type in a new name.

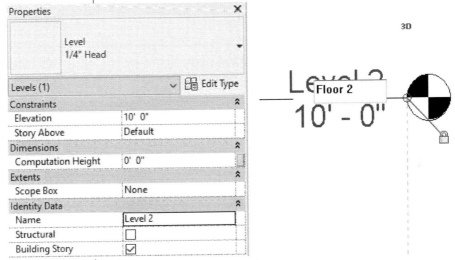

Figure 3–6

- When you rename a level, an alert box opens prompting you to rename the corresponding views, as shown in Figure 3–7.

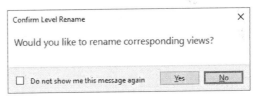

Figure 3–7

- The view is also renamed in the Project Browser.

> **Hint: Copying Levels and Grids from Other Projects**
>
> Levels and grid lines can be added by drawing over existing levels or grids in an imported or linked CAD file. They can also be copied and monitored from a linked Autodesk Revit file. Some projects might require both methods.
>
> • For more information on using the Copy/Monitor tools, see the ASCENT guide *Autodesk Revit: Collaboration Tools*.

• If you delete a level, the views related to that level are also deleted. A warning displays, as shown in Figure 3–8.

Autodesk Revit

Warning

Along with the selection, 6 elements and 3 views will be deleted.
View Floor Plan : Floor 4 will be deleted.
View Ceiling Plan : Floor 4 will be deleted.
View Structural Plan : Floor 4 will be deleted.

Show   More Info   Expand >>

OK   Cancel

Figure 3–8

Creating Plan Views

By default, when you place a level, plan views for that level are automatically created. If **Make Plan View** was toggled off when adding the level, or if the level was copied, you can create plan views to match the levels.

• Level heads with views are blue and level heads without views are black, as shown in Figure 3–9.

Typically, you do not need to create plan views for levels that specify data, such as the top of a storefront window or the top of a parapet.

Figure 3–9

How To: Create Plan Views

1. In the *View* tab>Create panel, expand 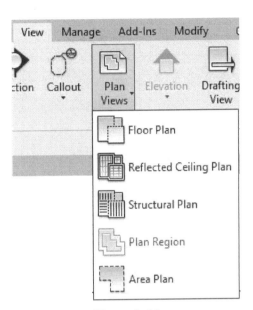 (Plan Views) and select the type of plan view you want to create, as shown in Figure 3–10.
2. In the New Plan dialog box (shown in Figure 3–11), select the levels for which you want to create plan views. Hold <Ctrl> to select more than one level.

- Clear **Do no duplicate existing views** to create a copy of an existing view.

Figure 3–10

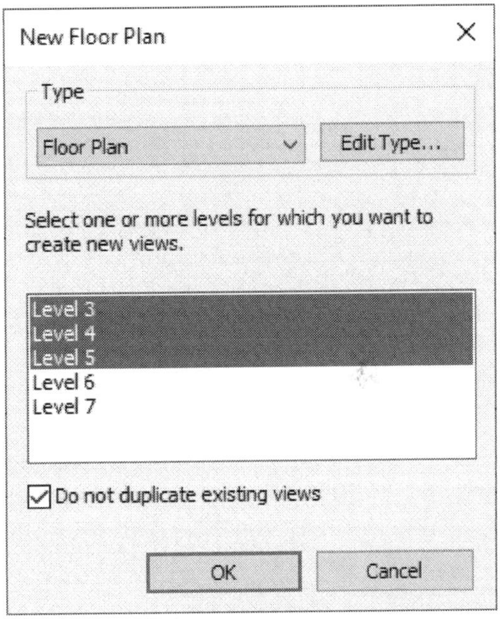

Figure 3–11

3. Click **OK**.

- Once a plan view is made from a level, you can double-click on the level head to open the related plan view.

Hint: Temporary Hide/Isolate

You might want to temporarily hide elements from a view, modify the project, and then restore the elements. Instead of completely toggling the elements off, you can use

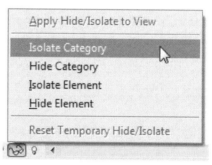 (Temporary Hide/Isolate) in the View Control Bar. The Temporary Hide/Isolate status is not saved with the project.

Select the elements you want to hide (make invisible) or isolate (keep displayed while all other elements are hidden) and click

(Temporary Hide/Isolate). Select the method you want to use, as shown in Figure 3–12.

Apply Hide/Isolate to View

Isolate Category
Hide Category
Isolate Element
Hide Element

Reset Temporary Hide/Isolate

Figure 3–12

The elements or category are hidden or isolated. A cyan border displays around the view with a note in the upper-left corner, as shown in Figure 3–13. It indicates that the view contains temporarily hidden or isolated elements.

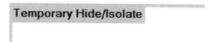

Figure 3–13

- Click (Temporary Hide/Isolate) again and select **Reset Temporary Hide/Isolate** to restore the elements to the view.

- If you want to permanently hide the elements in the view, select **Apply Hide/Isolate to View**.

- Any elements that are temporarily hidden still print.

Practice 3a

Set Up Levels

Practice Objective

- Add and modify levels.

In this practice, you will set up the levels required in the residential project, including the floors, the top of the footing, and the roof, as shown in Figure 3–14.

Roof Peak
32' - 0"

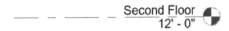

Second Floor
12' - 0"

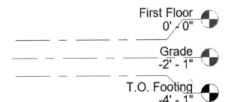

First Floor
0' - 0"

Grade
-2' - 1"

T.O. Footing
-4' - 1"

Figure 3–14

1. In the *File* tab, expand (New) and click (Project).

   - If you are on the Home page, click the **New** button under the *Model* section.

2. In the New Project dialog box, expand the *Template file* list and select the default **Imperial-Architectural** template.

3. Click **OK**.

4. Save the project as **Residential_*your initials*.rvt**.

5. Open the **Elevations (Building Elevation): South** view.

6. The project view has two existing levels, named **Level 1** and **Level 2**, that were defined in the template.

7. Zoom in on the level names.

8. Slowly click twice on the name *Level 1* and rename it to **First Floor**, as shown in Figure 3–15. Press <Enter>.

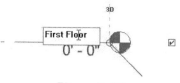

Figure 3–15

9. Click **Yes** (you can also press <Enter> or type **Y**) when prompted to rename the corresponding views.

10. Do the same for *Level 2* and name it **Second Floor**. Click **Yes** to rename the corresponding views.

11. For the Second Floor, select *10'-0"* and change it to **12'-0"** (type **12** for 12'), as shown in Figure 3–16.

Figure 3–16

12. In the *Architecture* tab>Datum panel, click 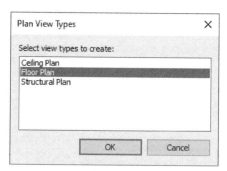 (Level).

13. In the Options Bar, verify that **Make Plan View** is selected. Click **Plan View Types...** and select **Floor Plan**, as shown in Figure 3–17. Click **OK**.

Plan View Types ✕

Select view types to create:
Ceiling Plan
Floor Plan
Structural Plan

OK   Cancel

Figure 3–17

14. Create another level **32'-0"** above **Floor 1**.

15. Draw the level from left to right so the level head is on the correct side of the view.

16. Rename it as **Roof Peak**.

17. Click ⌖ (Modify).

18. Select the **First Floor** level and click on the ⤳ (Add elbow) symbol, as shown in Figure 3–18. This is to make room for the grade level.

19. Use the grip to adjust the level name above the level line, as shown in Figure 3–19.

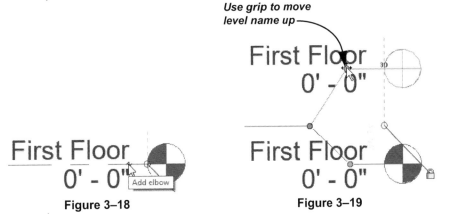

Figure 3–18

Figure 3–19

20. Click ⌖ (Modify).

21. Start the **Level** command again.

22. In the Options Bar, select the **Make Plan View** option and set the *Offset* to **2'-1"**. Click **Plan View Types...** and select **Floor Plan**. Click **OK**. In the *Modify | Place Level* tab>Draw panel, click ✏ (Pick Lines).

23. Hover the cursor over the **First Floor** level line and move the cursor slightly downward so that the offset level line is displayed below the **First Floor** level. Click to create the new level.

24. Rename the bottom level as **Grade**, as shown in Figure 3–20.

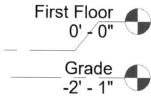

First Floor
0' - 0"

Grade
-2' - 1"

Figure 3–20

25. Click (Modify).

26. In the *Architecture* tab>Datum panel, click (Level).

27. In the *Modify | Place Level* tab>Draw panel, click (Pick Lines).

28. In the Options Bar, clear the **Make Plan View** option, set the *Offset* to **2'-0"**, and create another level below the Grade level called **T.O. Footing**. (This level does not need a plan view.) Figure 3–21 shows the new level.

29. Click (Modify).

30. Select the **T.O. Footing** level. Click on the (Add elbow) symbol and use the grip to move the level name below the level line. This helps to make the levels more clear, as shown in Figure 3–21.

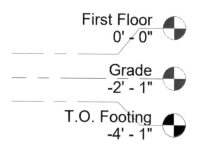

First Floor
0' - 0"

Grade
-2' - 1"

T.O. Footing
-4' - 1"

Figure 3–21

31. Click (Modify).

32. In the Project Browser, select **Floor Plans: Site**, right-click, and select **Delete**.

33. Zoom out to display the entire project.

34. Open the default **3D** view. You can see the levels display in this view as well.

35. Save and close the project.

3.2 Linking and Importing CAD Files

Many firms have legacy drawings from vector-based CAD programs, or could be working with consultants that use such programs. For example, you may want to link a DWG plan into your project, as shown in Figure 3–22, that you would then trace over using the Autodesk Revit tools. You can print a hybrid drawing - part Autodesk Revit project and part imported/ linked drawing.

When you select an imported or linked CAD file, you can see that it is called an Import Symbol.

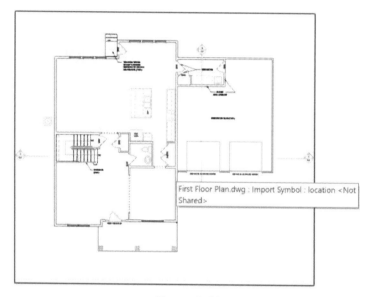

First Floor Plan.dwg : Import Symbol : location <Not Shared>

Figure 3–22

CAD file formats that can be imported or linked include AutoCAD® (DWG and DXF), MicroStation (DGN), 3D ACIS modeling kernel (SAT), and Trimble® SketchUp (SKP).

Linking vs. Importing

- **Link:** A connection is maintained with the original file and the link updates if the original file is updated.

- **Import:** No connection is maintained with the original file. It becomes a separate element in the Autodesk Revit model.

How To: Link or Import a CAD File

1. Open the view into which you want to link or import the file.
   - For a 2D file, this should be a 2D view. For a 3D file, open a 3D view.

2. In the *Insert* tab>Link panel, click 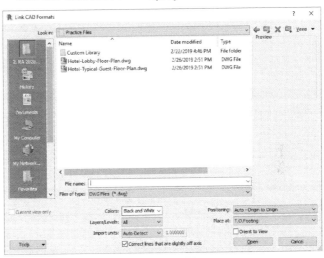 (Link CAD), or in the *Insert* tab>Import panel, click (Import CAD).

3. In the Link CAD Formats or Import CAD Formats dialog box, shown in Figure 3–23, select the file that you want to import.
   - Select a file format in the Files of type drop-down list to limit the files that are displayed.

The dialog boxes for Link CAD Formats and Import CAD Formats are the same.

Figure 3–23

4. Set the other options, as shown in Figure 3–24.

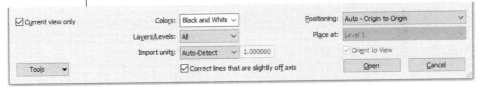

Figure 3–24

5. Click **Open**.

Hint: Link or Import PDFs

You can link or import a PDF into Autodesk Revit as a raster image. If the PDF contains vector data, you can snap to the elements in the PDF.

- From the *Insert* tab>Import panel, click (Import PDF).
- From the *Insert* tab>Link panel, click (Link PDF).

Link and Import Options

Current view only	Determine whether the CAD file is placed in every view or only in the current view. This is especially useful if you are working with a 2D floor plan that you only need to have in one view.
Colors	Specify the color settings. Typical Autodesk Revit projects are mainly black and white. However, other software frequently uses color. You can **Invert** the original colors, **Preserve** them, or change everything to **Black and White**.
Layers/Levels	Indicates which CAD layers are going to be brought into the model. Select how you want layers to be imported: **All**, **Visible**, or **Specify...**.
Import units	Select the units of the original file, as required. **Auto-Detect** works in most cases.
Correct Lines...	If lines in a CAD file are off axis by less than 0.1 degrees, selecting this option straightens them. It is selected by default.
Positioning	Specify how you want the imported file to be positioned in the current project: **Auto-Center to Center**, **Auto-Internal Origin to Internal Origin**, **Auto - By Shared Coordinates**, **Auto - Project Base Point to Project Base Point**, **Manual - Internal Origin**, **Manual - Base Point**, or **Manual - Center**. The default position is **Auto - Internal Origin to Internal Origin**.
Place at	Select a level in which to place the imported file. If you selected **Current view only**, this option is grayed out.
Orient to View	Used to orient the CAD file on import/link.

- When a file is positioned **Auto - Internal Origin to Internal Origin**, it is pinned in place and cannot be moved. To move the file, click on the pin to unpin it, as shown in Figure 3–25.

For more information on importing and linking CAD files, see the ASCENT guide Autodesk Revit: Collaboration Tools.

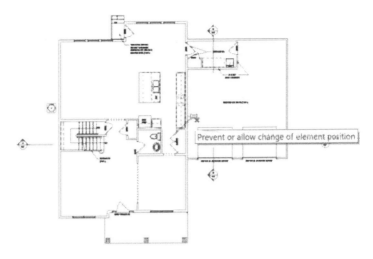

Figure 3–25

Setting an Imported or Linked File to Halftone

To see the difference between the host model elements and the linked or imported file, you can set the linked/imported file to halftone, as shown in Figure 3–26.

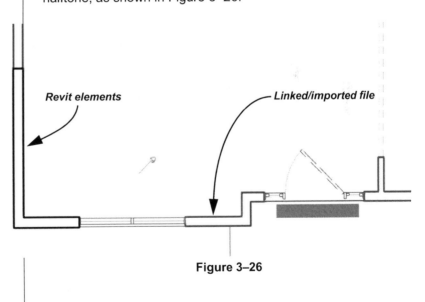

Figure 3–26

How To: Set an Element to Halftone

1. Select the imported file.
2. Right-click and select **Override Graphics in View>By Element...**.
3. In the View Specific Element Graphics dialog box, select **Halftone**, as shown in Figure 3–27.

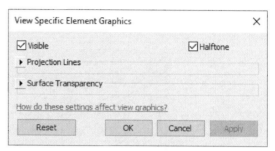

Figure 3–27

4. Click **OK**.

- You can use this method to set any element or category to halftone.

Hint: Draw Layer

Linked CAD files are typically in the background of a view. To change this, select the CAD file and in the Options Bar or in Properties in the *Other* area, change the *Draw Layer* to **Foreground**.

Managing Links

The Manage Links dialog box (shown in Figure 3–28) enables you to reload, unload, add, and remove links, and it also provides access for you to set other options. To open the Manage Links dialog box, in the *Insert* tab>Link panel, click 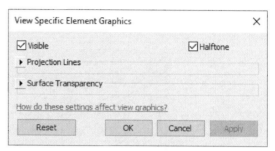 (Manage Links). Alternatively, you can go to the *Manage* tab>Manage Projects panel and click (Manage Links).

- You can also select the link and click (Manage Links) in the *Modify | DWG File Name.dwg* tab>Link panel.

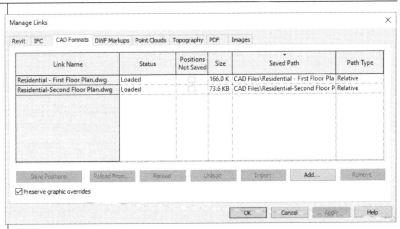

Figure 3–28

The following options are available:

- **Reload From:** Opens the Find Link dialog box, which enables you to select the file you want to reload. Use this if the linked file location or name has changed.

- **Reload:** Reloads the file without additional prompts.

- **Unload:** Unloads the file so that the link is kept, but the file is not displayed or calculated in the project. Use **Reload** to restore it.

- **Add:** Opens the Link CAD Format dialog box, which enables you to link additional files into the host project.

- **Remove:** Deletes the link from the file.

The option in the *Path Type* column controls how the location of the link is remembered.

- **Relative**
    - Searches the root folder of the current project.
    - If the file is moved, the software still searches for it.

- **Absolute**
    - Searches the entire file path where the file was originally saved.
    - If the original file is moved, the software is not able to find it.

- Other options control how the linked file interfaces with worksets and shared positioning.

Hint: Visibility Graphics and Linked Files

When you open the Visibility/Graphic Overrides dialog box (type **VV** or **VG**), you can modify the graphic overrides for DWG linked files, as shown in Figure 3–29. This can help you clean up the view or assign a view to build on.

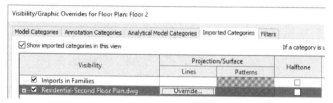

Figure 3–29

Practice 3b | Link CAD Files

Practice Objective

- Link a CAD file.

In this practice, you will import floor plans created in the Autodesk AutoCAD software. You will use the linked DWG as a base layout for the first and second floors, as shown in Figure 3–30.

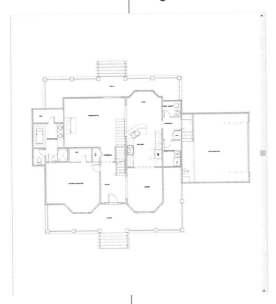 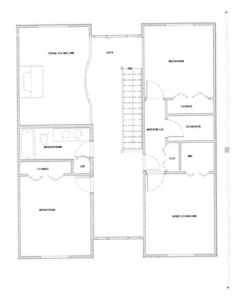

Figure 3–30

1. Open the project **Residential-Linking.rvt** from the practice files folder. (There are no elements in this file.)

2. Open the **Floor Plans: First Floor** view.

3. In the *Insert* tab>Link panel, click (Link CAD).

4. In the Link CAD Formats dialog box, navigate to the practice files *CAD Files* folder and select the file **Residential-First Floor Plan.dwg** and set the following options:

   - Select **Current view only**
   - *Colors:* **Black and White**
   - *Layers/Levels:* **All**
   - *Import Units:* **Auto-Detect**
   - *Positioning:* **Auto - Internal Origin to Internal Origin**

The DWG is all in one element and pinned in place because it was linked in using Auto - Internal Origin to Internal Origin.

5. Click **Open**. The linked CAD file is placed in the project on the **Floor Plans: First Floor** view.

6. Select the linked CAD file. In the Options Bar, change *Background* to **Foreground**.

7. With the DWG still selected, right-click and select **Override Graphics in View>By Element...**.

8. In the View-Specific Element Graphics dialog box, select **Halftone** and click **OK**.

9. Click in an empty space in the view to release the selection. The linked file displays in halftone, as shown in Figure 3–31.

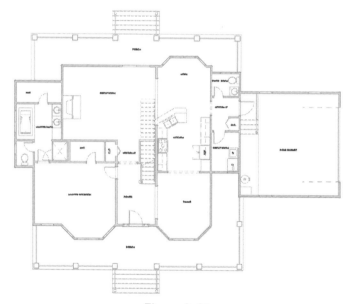

Figure 3–31

As you are drawing walls, floors, ceilings, and roofs within your project, you will want to change how the DWG is displaying in your view from Foreground to Background, depending on what you need to see.

10. Open the **Floor Plans: Second Floor** view. The CAD file linked in *First Floor* does not display because we specified to link the CAD file with **Current view only** selected.

11. Link the CAD file **Residential-Second Floor Plan.dwg** using the options that were used for the First Floor.

12. Override the graphics and set the linked file to **Halftone** and set the DWG to **Foreground**.

13. Save and close the project.

Chapter Review Questions

1. What type of view do you need to be in to add a level to your project?

   a. Any non-plan view.

   b. As this is done using a dialog box, the view does not matter.

   c. Any view except for 3D.

   d. Any section or elevation view.

2. Which of the following types of CAD formats can you import into the Autodesk Revit software? (Select all that apply.)

   a. .DWG

   b. .XLS

   c. .SAT

   d. .DGN

3. When creating a new level, you have to change all corresponding views.

   a. True

   b. False

4. Where can you change a level's name?

   a. From the Options Bar.

   b. Within the plan view and from the Options Bar.

   c. From the Project Browser, in Properties, or in an elevation view by clicking on the level's name.

   d. You cannot change the name after the level has been placed in the view.

5. You can set the imported DWG to be in the foreground or background throughout the project's life cycle.

   a. True

   b. False

Command Summary

Button	Command	Location
	Import CAD	• **Ribbon:** *Insert* tab>Import panel
	Import PDF	• **Ribbon:** *Insert* tab>Import panel
	Level	• **Ribbon:** *Architecture* tab>Datum panel • **Shortcut:** LL
	Link CAD	• **Ribbon:** *Insert* tab>Link panel
	Link PDF	• **Ribbon:** *Insert* tab>Link panel
	Temporary Hide/Isolate	• **View Control Bar**

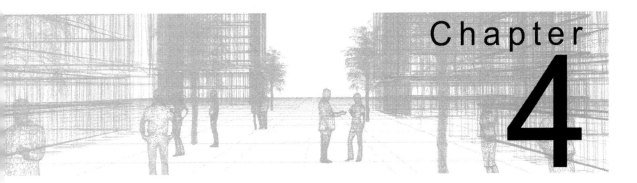

Modeling Walls

Walls are the primary elements that define rooms in buildings. Revit contains a variety of wall types that are available in different widths and materials. You can change the height, length, and type as needed. After you have added walls, you can add room elements to areas defined by the walls.

Learning Objectives in This Chapter

- Model walls using specific wall types.
- Modify walls by changing the wall type, height, and length.
- Define how walls join at intersections.
- Add wall openings that are not cased or filled with a door or window.
- Add room elements and tags that display the room name and square footage.

4.1 Modeling Walls

Walls in the Autodesk® Revit® software are more than just two lines on a plan. They are full 3D elements that store detailed information, including height, thickness, and materials. This means they are useful in 2D and 3D views, and also impact material takeoff schedules, as shown in Figure 4–1.

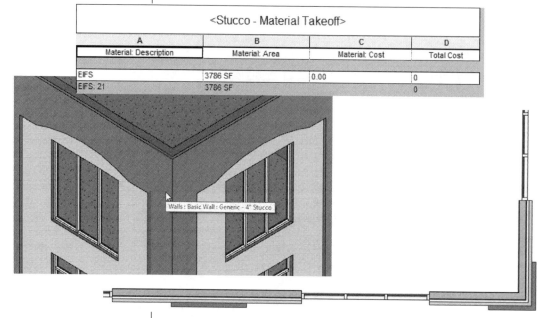

<Stucco - Material Takeoff>			
A	B	C	D
Material: Description	Material: Area	Material: Cost	Total Cost
EIFS	3786 SF	0.00	0
EIFS: 21	3786 SF		0

Walls : Basic Wall : Generic - 4" Stucco

Figure 4–1

There are three broad categories of walls:

- *Basic walls:* Compound walls that contain one or more layers (e.g., blocks, air space, bricks, etc.).

- *Curtain walls:* Non-bearing walls made of glass with mullions, such as a large window system or custom shower enclosure.

- *Stacked walls:* Includes one wall type above another wall type, such as a stud wall over a masonry stem wall.

The *Cross-Section* for these three categories can be modified to be **Vertical** or **Slanted**, as shown in Figure 4–2.

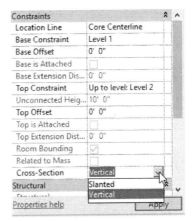

Figure 4–2

- To display the hatching in the walls in plan views, in the View Control Bar, set the *Detail Level* to **Medium** or **Fine**, as shown in Figure 4–3.

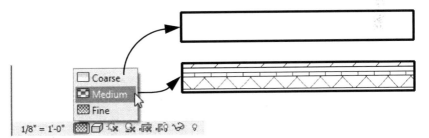

Figure 4–3

How To: Model a Wall

1. In the *Architecture* tab>Build panel, click 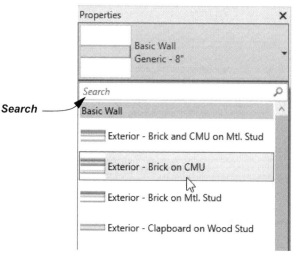 (Wall) or type the shortcut **WA**.
2. In the Type Selector, select a wall type, as shown in Figure 4–4. You can use the *Search* box to quickly find specific types of walls.

Figure 4–4

3. In the Options Bar, shown in Figure 4–5, specify the following information about the wall before you start modeling:

   - *Height:* Set the height of a wall either to **Unconnected** (with a specified height) or to a level.
   - *Location Line:* Set the justification of the wall using the options shown in Figure 4–5.
   - *Chain:* Enables you to model multiple connected walls.
   - *Offset:* Enables you to enter the distance at which a new wall is created from an existing element.
   - *Radius:* Adds a curve of a specified radius to connected walls as you model.
   - *Join Status:* **Allow** or **Disallow** automatic wall joins.

Figure 4–5

4. In the *Modify | Place Wall* tab>Draw panel (shown in Figure 4–6), select one of the options to create the wall.

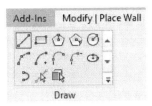

Figure 4–6

- Use alignment lines, temporary dimensions, and snaps to place the walls.
- As you are sketching, you can press <Spacebar> to flip the orientation of compound walls.
- When using the **Chain** option, press <Esc> to finish the string of walls and remain in the Wall command.

4.2 Modifying Walls

There are several methods of modifying walls. You can change the type of wall using the Type Selector, modify the Properties, use controls and shape handles to modify the length and wall orientation, and use temporary and permanent dimensions to change the location or length of a wall in 2D and 3D, as shown in Figure 4–7. Additional tools enable you to modify wall joins, edit the profile of a wall, control elevations of individual layers of walls, and add wall openings.

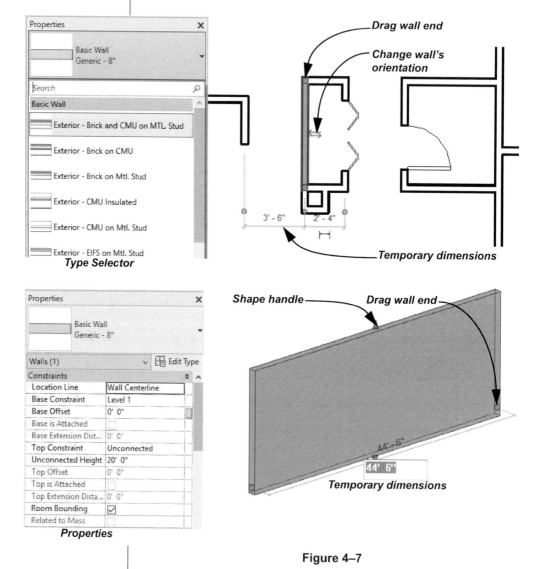

Figure 4–7

Wall Joins

The software automatically joins walls with common materials when they come together at an intersection, as shown on the left in Figure 4–8. However, there are times when you do not want the walls to clean up, such as when one fire-rated wall butts into another or when a wall touches a column surround, as shown on the right in Figure 4–8.

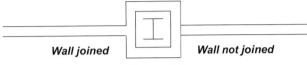

Wall joined   *Wall not joined*

Figure 4–8

- While you are creating walls, change the *Join Status* to **Disallow** in the Options Bar.

- If a wall is already placed, select the wall, right-click on the control at the end of the wall, and select **Disallow Join**, as shown on the left in Figure 4–9. Once the end is not joined, you can drag it to the appropriate location, as shown on the right in Figure 4–9.

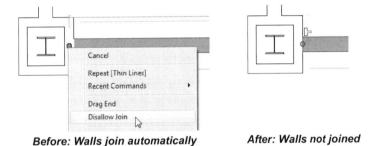

Before: Walls join automatically   *After: Walls not joined*

Figure 4–9

- To rejoin the walls, click ⬐ (Allow Join) or right-click on the end control and select **Allow Join**. Manually drag the wall back to where you want it to touch the target wall.

Hint: Using Thin Lines

The software automatically applies line weights to views, as shown for a section on the left in Figure 4–10. If a line weight seems heavy or obscures your work on the elements, toggle off the line weights. In the Quick Access Toolbar or in the *View* tab>Graphics panel, click 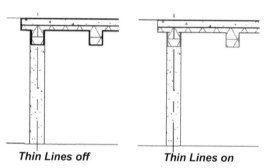 (Thin Lines) or type **TL**. The lines display with the same weight, as shown on the right in Figure 4–10.

Thin Lines off   *Thin Lines on*

Figure 4–10

- The **Thin Line** setting is remembered until you change it, even if you shut down and restart the software.

Editing Wall Profiles

Walls often follow the contours of a site or an angle, such as following a line of stairs (as shown in Figure 4–11). If needed, you can edit the profile of a wall.

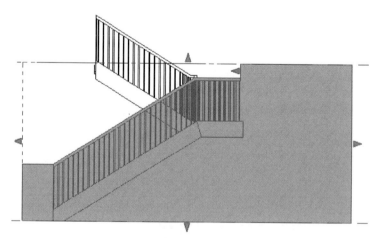

Figure 4–11

How To: Edit the Profile of a Wall

1. Open an elevation or section view in which you can see the face of the wall that you want to edit.
2. Select the wall (by highlighting the wall boundary). You can also double-click on a wall to edit the profile.
3. In the *Modify | Walls* tab>Model panel, click 🖍 (Edit Profile). The wall is outlined in magenta indicating the profile of the wall.
4. In the *Modify | Walls>Edit Profile* tab>Draw panel, use the tools to modify the profile sketch of the wall, as shown on the top in Figure 4–12.

   - The sketch must form a continuous loop. Verify that the lines are clean without any gaps or overlaps. Use any of the tools in the Modify panel to clean up the sketch.

5. Once the profile is complete, click ✔ (Finish Edit Mode). The wall now follows the new profile, as shown on the bottom in Figure 4–12.

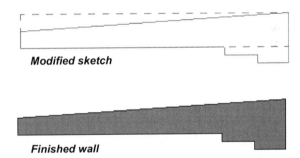

Modified sketch

Finished wall

Figure 4–12

Joining Geometry

Join Geometry is a versatile command used to clean up intersections. The elements remain separate, but the intersections are cleaned up. It can be used with many types of elements, including floors, walls, and roofs. In Figure 4–13, the wall on the left and the floor have been joined, but the wall on the right has not been joined with the floor and therefore does not display the lines that define the intersection edges.

Cutting a section through the objects you want to join helps to display them more clearly.

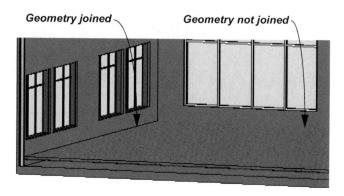

Geometry joined ⟍   Geometry not joined ⟍

Figure 4–13

How To: Join Geometry

1. In the *Modify* tab>Geometry panel, expand (Join) and click (Join Geometry).
2. Select the elements to join.

- If you toggle on the **Multiple Join** option in the Options Bar, you can select several elements to join to the first selection.

- To remove the join, expand (Join), click (Unjoin Geometry), and select the elements to unjoin.

Editing Wall Layer Elevations

Individual layers of walls can have their height modified to better control elevations of finishes, such as brick veneer extending to a foundation (as shown in Figure 4–14), while the other layers rest on the floor slab.

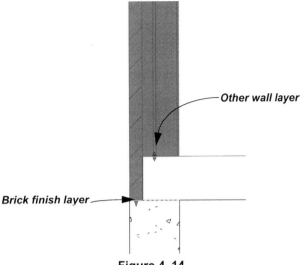

Other wall layer

Brick finish layer

Figure 4–14

How To: Edit Wall Layers

1. In any view, select a wall. From Properties, click **Edit Type**.
2. In the Type Properties dialog box, click the **Edit...** button next to *Structure* in the *Construction* section.
3. In the Edit Assembly dialog box, click the **<<Preview** button to expand the preview window, as shown in Figure 4–15.

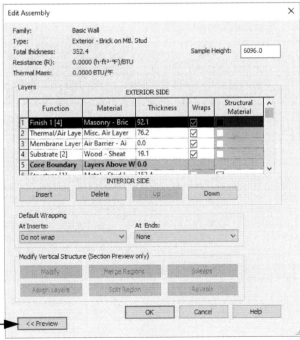

Click to expand the preview window

Figure 4–15

4. Set the *View:* to **Section: Modify type attributes**, as shown in Figure 4–16.

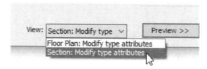

Figure 4–16

5. In the preview window, zoom in to the bottom edge of the wall, as shown in Figure 4–17, and from the *Modify Vertical Structure* area, click **Modify**. The brick layer will turn from blue to red.

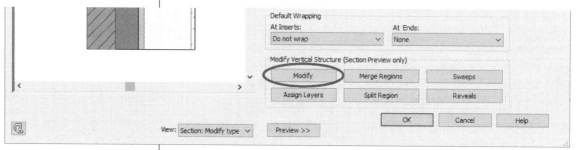

Figure 4–17

If doing this to multiple layers in a wall, all the layers must be adjacent to each other.

6. Click on the outer boundary at bottom of the brick layer, as shown on the right in Figure 4–18. A lock will display, as shown on the left in Figure 4–18.

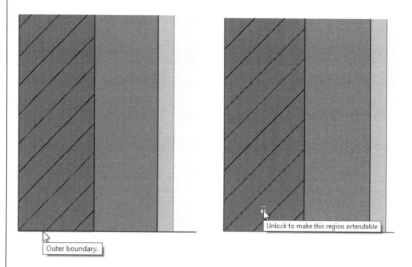

Figure 4–18

7. Click the lock to make the brick layer or region extendable.
   • Note: Make sure the lock displayed shows as unlocked, as shown in Figure 4–19, before you proceed.

Figure 4–19

8. Click **OK** twice.
9. In a section view, you can select the wall and use the grips to extend the brick layer, as shown in Figure 4–20.

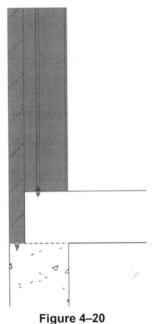

Figure 4–20

Sections are talked about in 6.3 Creating Elevations and Sections.

- An alternative option for adjusting the extension is in the instance properties of the wall. Set the *Base Extension Distance* to adjust unlocked layers, as shown in Figure 4–21.

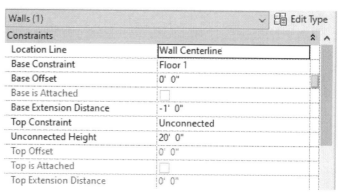

Figure 4–21

- If the layers were unlocked at the top instead of the bottom, you would be able to adjust the top extension distance in Properties or by dragging grips in a section view.

Wall Openings

You can add openings in walls that are not windows or doors by using the **Wall Opening** tool. This creates rectangular openings for both straight and curved walls, as shown in Figure 4–22.

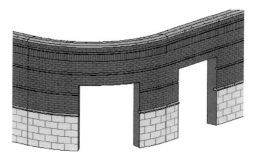

Figure 4–22

How To: Add Wall Openings

1. Open a plan, elevation, section, or 3D view.
2. In the *Architecture* tab>Openings panel, click ⊟ (Wall Opening).
3. Select the wall.
4. Pick two points on the diagonal to determine the opening size if in an elevation, section, or 3D view. If you are in a plan view, you need to pick the start and stop points for the wall opening.

- You can use temporary dimensions to size the opening while in the command and both temporary dimensions and shape handles to modify the opening when it is selected, as shown in Figure 4–23.

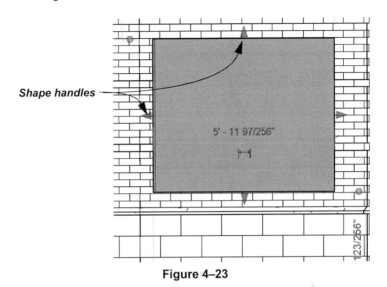

Figure 4–23

Hint: Matching Properties

You can select an existing wall and use it to assign the wall type and instance properties to other walls by using the **Match Type** command. This command also works with all elements that have types.

1. In the *Modify* tab>Clipboard panel, click [icon] (Match Type) or type **MA**. The cursor changes to an arrow with a clean paintbrush.
2. Select the source element that you want all of the others to match. The paintbrush changes to look as if it has been dipped in black paint, as shown in Figure 4–24.

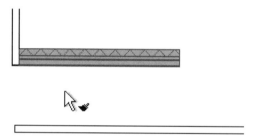

Figure 4–24

3. To select more than one element, in the *Modify | Match Type* tab>Multiple panel, click [icon] (Select Multiple). You can then use windows, crossings, <Ctrl>, and <Shift> to create a selection set of elements to change.

4. Click [icon] (Finish) to apply the type to the selection.

• Click in an empty space in the view to empty the brush so that you can repeat the command with a different element.

• Elements to be matched must be of the same type (e.g., all walls, all doors, etc.).

5. Click [icon] (Modify) to end the command.

Editing Wall Joins

Use **Wall Joins** to modify the configuration of the intersections, as shown in Figure 4–25. Do not use this command if you have complex wall joins; instead, modify the length of the wall in relation to the adjoining walls.

Figure 4–25

How To: Modify the Configuration of a Wall Join

1. In the *Modify* tab>Geometry panel, click 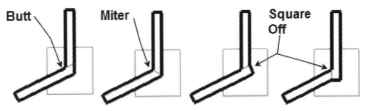 (Wall Joins).
2. Click on the wall join that you want to edit. There is a square box around the join. Hold <Ctrl> to select multiple joins.
3. In the Options Bar, the configuration options display, as shown in Figure 4–26. Select the required option.

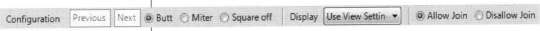

Figure 4–26

- Select from three configurations: **Butt**, **Miter**, and **Square off**, as shown in Figure 4–27.

Figure 4–27

- Click **Previous** and **Next** to toggle the butt or squared-off corner configurations through the various intersection options.
- **Allow Join** automatically cleans up the join while **Disallow Join** breaks the connection.

4. The **Wall Joins** command remains active until you select another command.

How To: Modify Display Options of Wall Joins

1. In the *Modify* tab>Geometry panel, click 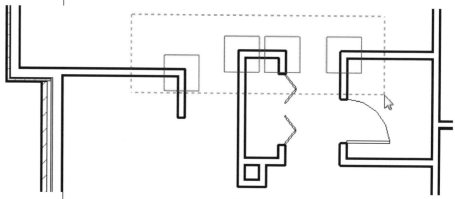 (Wall Joins).
2. Click on the wall join that you want to edit.
   - To modify multiple joins at the same time, draw a window around several wall intersections (as shown in Figure 4–28), or hold <Ctrl> and pick additional intersections. A square box displays around each join.

Figure 4–28

- The *Display* controls whether or not wall joins are displayed. The options are **Use View Setting** (set up in View Properties), **Clean Join**, and **Don't Clean Join**, as shown in Figure 4–29.

Figure 4–29

3. If you select the end of a wall that is not joined to another wall, you can change the option to **Allow Join** in the Options Bar, as shown in Figure 4–30. Reselect the wall join to make the configurations available.

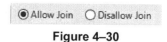

Figure 4–30

4.3 Applying Finish Carpentry

The Autodesk Revit software includes a series of commands that enable you to modify walls, roofs, and floors by sweeping a profile along an element. For example, you can quickly add a fascia (shown in Figure 4–31) along the full length of a roof or trim carpentry at the edge of a floor. The element modified by the sweep is called the host. Therefore, all of these operations are known as host sweeps.

Figure 4–31

The process of creating reveals, floor slab edges, etc. is similar.

- The software comes with a few standard profiles for the sweeps. You can also create your own custom profiles.

- Open a 3D or other elevation view if you are working with walls. You can be in a plan or elevation view for working with roof and floor sweeps.

- There are specific commands to create wall sweeps and reveals, roof fascias and gutters, and floor slab edges. These are located by expanding the associated command in the *Architecture* tab>Build panel, as shown in Figure 4–32. For walls and floors, they are also located in the *Structure* tab> Structure panel.

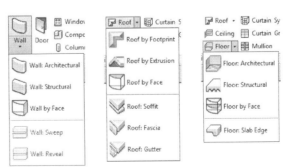

Figure 4–32

- Wall sweeps and wall reveals can only be applied in elevation, section, or 3D views, and can only be horizontal or vertical.

How To: Set Up Sweep Profiles

1. In the *Insert* tab>Load from Library panel, click 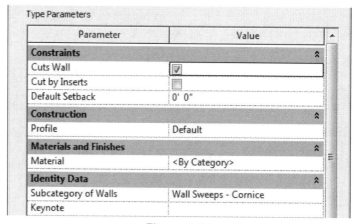 (Load Family).
2. In the Load Family dialog box, select the profile you want to use (in the *Profiles* folder) or select a custom profile.
3. Start the related host sweep command. For example, if you are working with a gutter, click ⬙ (Roof: Gutter), or if you are working with a wall reveal, click ▭ (Wall: Reveal).
4. In Properties, select a Sweep type and click ▦ (Edit Type).
5. In the Type Properties dialog box, click **Duplicate...**.
6. Enter a new name for the type.
7. In the Type Properties dialog box, under *Construction*, select the *Profile*. You can also apply *Constraints* (for wall reveals and wall sweeps), *Materials and Finishes*, and *Identity Data*, as shown in Figure 4–33.

Type Parameters	
Parameter	**Value**
Constraints	
Cuts Wall	☑
Cut by Inserts	☐
Default Setback	0' 0"
Construction	
Profile	Default
Materials and Finishes	
Material	\<By Category>
Identity Data	
Subcategory of Walls	Wall Sweeps - Cornice
Keynote	

Figure 4–33

- Click **OK** to close the dialog box. The new type is set to be current.

Constraints

The following constraints give you more control over how the sweep works.

Cuts Wall	If selected, cuts the geometry out of the host wall where it overlaps. Toggling this off might increase the performance if the project contains a large amount of sweeps.
Cut by Inserts	If selected, when doors or windows are inserted into a wall with a wall sweep, the insert cuts the sweep.
Default Setback	Specify the distance that the sweep is set back from interacting wall inserts.

How To: Use the Wall Sweep Command

1. Open an elevation or 3D view.

2. In the *Architecture* tab>Build panel, expand (Wall) and click (Wall Sweep).

3. In Properties, select a Wall Sweep type.

- The Wall Sweep type should be set up before you start the command. If you do not have it loaded, you can stay in the command and go to the *Insert* tab>Load from Library panel and click (Load Family). In the Load Family dialog box, select the profile you want to use (in the *Profiles* folder) or select a custom profile.

4. In the *Modify | Place Wall Sweep* tab>Placement panel, click either (Horizontal) or (Vertical). (This is only for walls.)

To specify a precise location for the sweep element, select it after you have created it and modify the dimensions as needed.

5. Move the cursor over the element where you want to add the sweep and click to place it.

6. If you are doing horizontal sweeps, continue selecting elements. The sweep is placed at the same height as the first element.

7. To change sweep styles or the height, in the Placement panel, click (Restart Wall Sweep), or return to the **Modify** command to finish.

Hint: Transferring Project Standards

Some elements (such as wall types) are not accessible from a specific library. However, you can copy them from other projects.

1. Open the project from which you want to copy information.
2. Open the project you want to copy the information to.

3. In the *Manage* tab>Settings panel, click 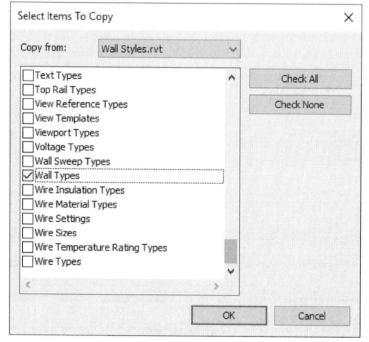 (Transfer Project Standards).
4. In the Select Items To Copy dialog box, select an option in the Copy from drop-down list and then select the settings you want to copy into the current file, as shown in Figure 4–34. Click **OK**.

Figure 4–34

5. In the Duplicate Types dialog box, click either **Overwrite** or **New Only** to apply the settings to the current project.

Practice 4a

Model the Exterior Shell

Practice Objective

- Add walls by tracing over lines in the linked DWG file.

In this practice, you will add exterior walls to create the exterior shell of the project. You will use the linked DWG file to help establish the location of the walls. The completed model is shown in Figure 4–35.

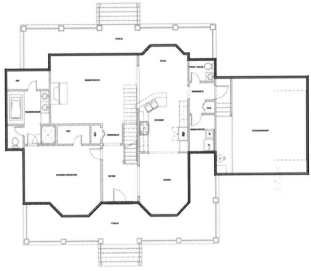

Figure 4–35

Task 1 - Add walls using Pick Lines.

1. Open the project **Residential-Walls Ext.rvt** from the practice files folder.

2. Verify that you are in the **Floor Plans: First Floor** view.

3. In the View Control Bar, set the *Detail Level* to ▨ (Fine). Doing so enables the multiple layers of the wall that is going to be added to be displayed.

4. Select the DWG. In Properties, set the *Draw Layer* to **Background**. As you work on this project, you can adjust how the DWG displays, as needed.

5. In the *Architecture* tab>Build panel, click ⬭ (Wall).

---

6. In the Type Selector, select **Basic Wall: Exterior - Wood Siding on Wood Stud**.

7. In the Draw panel, click 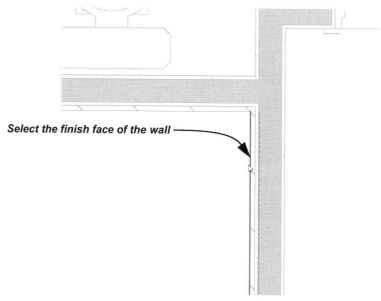 (Pick Lines).

Offset in the Options Bar offsets the wall from where you are drawing it and not from a level perspective, like Base and Top Offset do.

8. In Properties, set the following:

   • *Base Constraint:* **First Floor**
   • *Location Line:* **Finish Face: Exterior**
   • *Base Offset:* (negative) **-0'-4"**
   • *Base Extension Distance:* (negative) **-0'-4 3/4"**
   • *Top Constraint:* **Unconnected**
   • *Top Offset:* **10'-0"**

9. Click **Apply**.

10. Select one of the lines of exterior walls in the DWG file, as shown in Figure 4–36. Ensure the dashed line displays inside the wall. This wall is a compound wall and you want the siding to display on the outside.

Use ⇆ (Flip) to change the wall's orientation if the siding side of the wall is not on the outside. Hint: Use the default {3D} view to verify.

Select the finish face of the wall ——

Figure 4–36

11. Click (Modify).

12. For walls that have windows on them, like the one shown in Figure 4–37, you will need to select the wall and use the Drag Wall End control to extend the selection to the entire length wall.

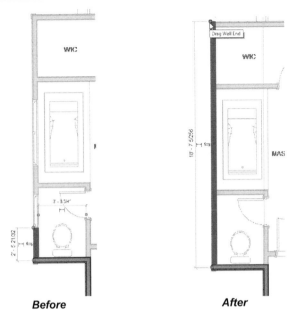

Before　　　　　　　　**After**

Figure 4–37

13. Continue selecting the finish face exterior lines around the exterior of the house. When you get to the bay windows, switch to the ✎ (Line) tool and snap to the corners of the walls. Figure 4–38 shows all the exterior walls highlighted.

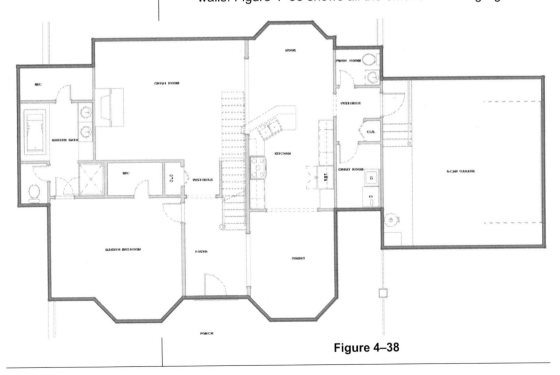

Figure 4–38

14. Click 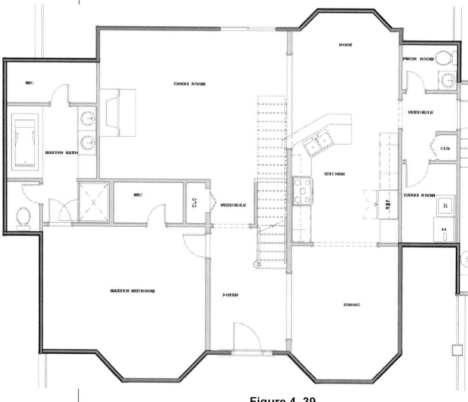 (Modify).

Task 2 - Modify walls.

1. Select the walls shown in Figure 4–39 and modify their properties as follows:

- *Base Constraint:* **First Floor**
- *Location Line:* **Finish Face: Exterior**
- *Base Offset:* (negative) **-0'-4"**
- *Base Extension Distance:* **0'-0"**
- *Top Constraint:* **Up to Level: Second Floor**
- *Top Offset:* **0'-0"**

Figure 4–39

2. Select the three garage walls shown in Figure 4–40 and modify their properties as follows:

- *Base Constraint:* **Grade**
- *Location Line:* **Finish Face: Exterior**
- *Base Offset:* **0'-0"**
- *Base Extension Distance:* **0'-0"**
- *Top Constraint:* **Up to Level: Second Floor**
- *Top Offset:* **0'-0"**

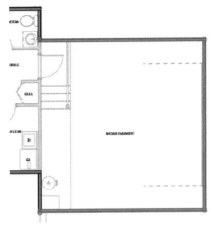

Figure 4–40

3. Save the project.

Task 3 - Clean up the wall connections.

After all the exterior walls have been added to the first floor, you need to clean up the walls that join.

1. Zoom in to the corner of the master bathroom below the water closet.

2. Select one of the walls.

3. From the *Modify | Walls* tab>Geometry panel, click (Wall Joins).

4. Hover over the corner of the walls, as shown in Figure 4–41, and click when the square is around the two walls.

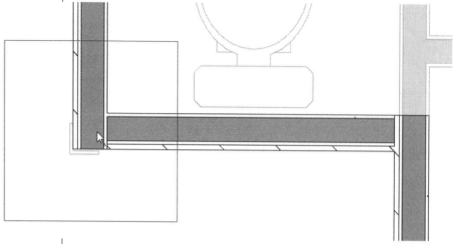

Figure 4–41

5. In the Options Bar, select **Miter**. The walls join, as shown in Figure 4–42.

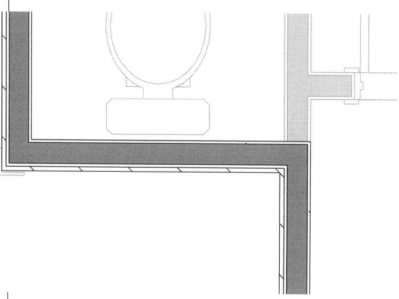

Figure 4–42

6. Stay in the **Wall Joins** command.

7. Draw a selection box around the entire house. All of the corners now display a square.

8. In the Options Bar, select **Miter**.

9. Click ⌖ (Modify).

10. Save the project.

Task 4 - Add second floor walls.

---

1. Open the **Floor Plans: Second Floor** view.

2. Select the DWG. In Properties, set the *Draw Layer* to **Background**.

3. Continue to model the exterior walls the same way you did on the first floor with the **Basic Wall: Exterior - Wood Siding on Wood Stud**.

4. In the Options Bar, do the following:

   • Select **Chain** if using the ⟋ (Line) draw tool and select the exterior corners of the walls.
   • Set the *Join Status* to **Allow**.

5. In Properties, set the following:

   • *Location Line:* **Core Face: Exterior**
   • *Base Offset:* **0'-0"**
   • *Base Extension Distance:* **0'-0"**
   • *Unconnected Height:* **10'-0"**
   • *Top Extension Distance:* **0'-0"**

6. Clean up the walls using the **Align** or **Move** command, as well as the **Wall Joins** command.

7. Save and close the project.

Practice 4b | Add Interior Walls

Practice Objectives

- Model and modify walls.
- Use **Split Element** to change wall types.

In this practice, you will add interior walls to the first floor plan, as shown in Figure 4–43, and use **Split Element** and the Modify tools to help create them.

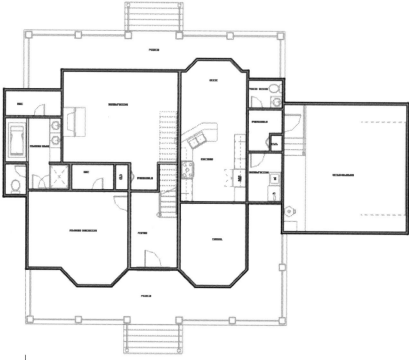

Figure 4–43

Task 1 - Add interior walls.

1. Open the project **Residential-Walls Int.rvt** from the practice files folder.

2. Open the **Floor Plans: First Floor** view.

3. In the *Architecture* tab>Build panel, click ⬙ (Wall).

4. In the Type Selector, select **Basic Wall: Interior 6 1/2" Partition**.

5. In the Options Bar, set the following:

- *Location Line:* **Finish Face: Interior**
- *Join Status:* **Allow**
- Clear **Chain**

6. In Properties, set the following:

- *Base Constraint:* **First Floor**
- *Base Offset:* **0'-0"**
- *Base Extension Distance:* **0'-0"**
- *Top Constraint:* **Unconnected**
- *Top Offset:* **10'-0"**
- *Top Extension Distance:* **0'-0"**
- The wall types will be different depending on where they are on the plan.

7. In the Draw panel, click 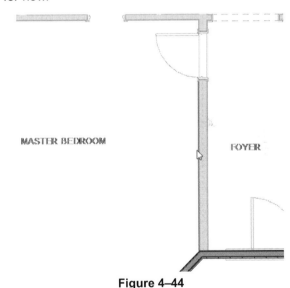 (Pick Lines).

8. Select the wall separating the master bedroom and the entry in the DWG file, as shown in Figure 4–44. Ensure the dashed line displays inside the wall.

- Remember to disregard the door and trimmed openings for now.

MASTER BEDROOM

FOYER

Figure 4–44

9. Ensure that the gypsum finish flushes with the exterior walls, as shown in Figure 4–45. If necessary, use the Drag Wall End control to temporarily unjoin the walls, then align the finishes before rejoining the walls.

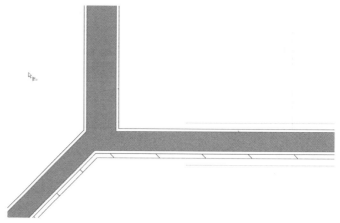

Figure 4–45

10. Click ⌕ (Modify) and zoom out to see the remainder of the plan.

11. Note that several different interior wall sizes have been used in the plan.

12. In the *Modify* tab>Measure panel, use the **Measure** tool to measure partition thicknesses on the linked floor plan to help determine the correct wall type for a given wall.

   • If needed, you can use the **Align** command to ensure that the walls are in the right place. You can also use the **Trim** tool, if needed.

13. Continue to add the remaining interior walls.

14. Save the project.

Task 2 - Modify the first floor walls.

---

1. Start the **Wall** command and set the following properties:

   • *Wall Type:* **Basic Wall: Interior - 4" Chase**
   • *Location Line:* **Finished Face: Interior**
   • *Top Constraint:* **Unconnected**
   • *Unconnected Height:* **5'-3"**

2. Draw the wall behind the stairs shown in Figure 4–46.

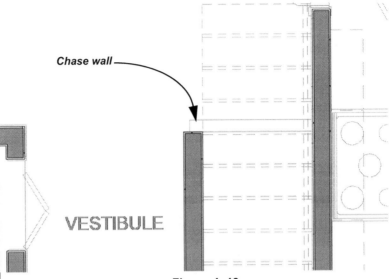

Chase wall

VESTIBULE

Figure 4–46

3. Pan over to the master bathroom. Start the **Wall** command again and set the following properties:

- *Wall Type:* **Basic Wall: Interior - 4" Chase**
- *Height:* **Unconnected**
- *Location Line:* **Finish Face: Interior**
- *Top Offset:* **1'-7 1/2"**

4. Draw the wall shown in Figure 4–47, being sure to follow the edge of the tub surface. The end should be flush with the vertical wall below it.

- This wall will become hidden under the tub surface later on.

Figure 4–47

5. Zoom out to the wall containing the fireplace.

6. Still in the Wall command, in the *Modify | Place Wall* tab> Modify panel, click (Split Element).

7. Select either point at the corner of the fireplace where the firebox meets the wall, as shown in Figure 4–48.

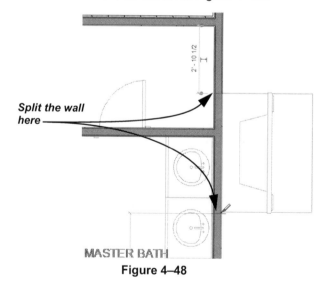

Figure 4–48

- The wall should now be in three parts.

8. Click ⌖ (Modify).

9. Select the wall directly behind the firebox.

10. In the Type Selector, change the wall type to **Basic Wall: Interior - 4" Chase**.

11. Ensure that the split (middle) part of the wall is flush on the bathroom side, as shown in Figure 4–49. Depending on wall location lines, when the wall is changed, the wall may need to be flipped. Before flipping the wall, change the location line to **Wall Centerline**, so the flip occurs in the center of the wall.

   - If needed, use the **Align** tool to get the wall into the correct location.

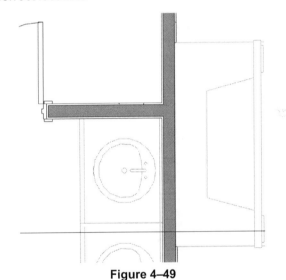

Figure 4–49

Task 3 - Add the second floor walls.

1. Open the **Floor Plan: Second Floor** view.

2. Start the **Wall** command.

3. In the Type Selector, select **Basic Wall: Interior 6 1/2" Partition**.

4. In the Options Bar, set the following:

- *Location Line:* **Finish Face: Interior**
- *Join Status:* **Allow**
- Clear **Chain**

5. In Properties, set the following:

- *Base Constraint:* **Second Floor**
- *Base Offset:* **0'-0"**
- *Top Constraint:* **Up to Level: Roof Peak**
- *Top Extension Distance:* **0'-0"**

6. In the Draw panel, click (Pick Lines).

7. Select the walls in the DWG file.

8. Zoom out, then save and close the project.

4.4 Adding Room Elements

Room elements are important for room names and square footage, as well as adding room information to schedules. You can place a room element in any space bounded by walls (as shown in Figure 4–50) or by room separation lines. Room separation lines enable you to divide an open space into more rooms.

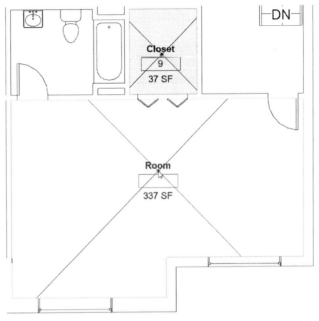

Figure 4–50

- To remove a room from a project, it must be deleted in the view and deleted from the room schedule.

- Room separation lines will typically show in views and print.

How To: Add Rooms

1. In the *Architecture* tab>Room & Area panel, click ⊠ (Room) or type **RM**.
2. Move the cursor inside a boundary and click to place a room element. If you have **Tag on Placement** active, it also places the tag at the point you selected.
3. Continue clicking inside boundaries to add other rooms.

- To add multiple rooms at once, in the *Modify | Place Room* tab>Room panel, click 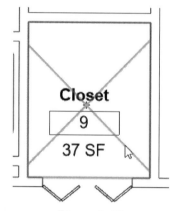 (Place Rooms Automatically). Rooms are added in every bounded area that does not already have a room.

- Rooms are inserted with the default name of *Room*. Room numbers increment automatically as you place rooms. Select the first room on a floor, change the number as needed, and then add the rest of the room locations.

- You can change the name and/or number of the room at any time in Properties or in the room schedule.

- To select rooms, hover the cursor near the room tag or move the cursor around slowly until you find the X to highlight the room element, as shown in Figure 4–51.

Closet

9

37 SF

Figure 4–51

- To change the names of several rooms to the same name, select the room elements and, in Properties, change the *Name* parameter, as shown in Figure 4–52.

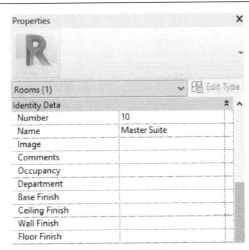

Figure 4–52

- Another option for changing the name or number of a single room is to select the tag, then select the tag name and type the name or number of the room.

- Other information, such as finishes, can also be added in the room properties. This information is made available to schedules.

Hint: Making Rooms Visible

If rooms are not visible in a view, in the Visibility/Graphic Overrides dialog box, expand **Rooms** and select **Interior Fill** and/or **Reference**, as shown in Figure 4–53.

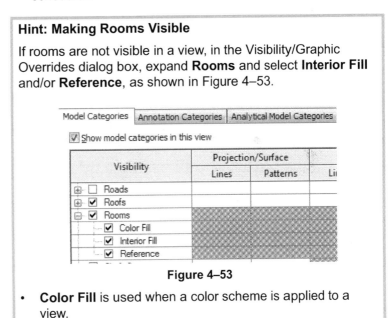

Figure 4–53

- **Color Fill** is used when a color scheme is applied to a view.

How To: Add Room Separation Lines

1. In the *Architecture* tab>Room & Area panel, click  (Room Separator).
2. Use the Draw tools to place lines that divide the spaces.
3. After creating the room separation lines, use the **Room** command to add the rooms, as shown in Figure 4–54.

Before room separation lines   *With room separation lines*

Figure 4–54

Practice 4c | Add Room Elements

Practice Objectives

- Set up a view that displays rooms.
- Add rooms and room separation lines.

In this practice, you will add rooms to the model. You will change the names and numbers of rooms using tags and Properties. You will also add room separation lines to break up the larger open areas, as shown in Figure 4–55. (The DWG has been hidden in the image for clarity.)

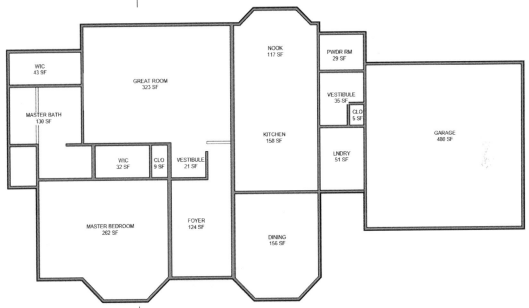

Figure 4–55

Task 1 - Add rooms and room tags.

1. Open the project **Residential-Rooms.rvt** in the practice files folder.

2. Open the **Floor Plans: First Floor** view.

3. Open the Visibility/Graphic Overrides dialog box by typing **VV**.

4. Verify the *Model Categories* tab is selected.

5. Scroll down the list and verify that room elements are turned on.

6. Click **OK**.

7. In the *Architecture* tab>Room & Area panel, click ⊠ (Room).

8. In the *Modify | Place Room* tab>Tag panel, verify that 🏷① (Tag on Placement) is selected.

9. Place a room element inside the garage area, as shown in Figure 4–56.

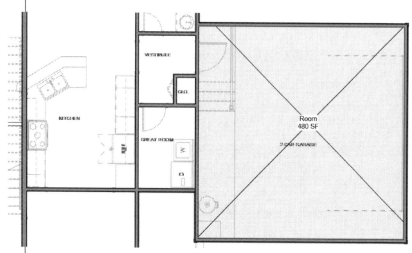

Figure 4–56

10. Zoom in on the room tag.

11. Click ▹ (Modify). Click on the tag and change the room name to **Garage**, as shown in Figure 4–57.

Figure 4–57

12. Click **OK**.

13. Zoom out and start the **Room** command again.

14. In the *Modify | Place Room* tab>Room panel, click ⊠ (Place Rooms Automatically). The rest of the rooms are added to the model. Click **Close** in the dialog box, as shown in Figure 4–58.

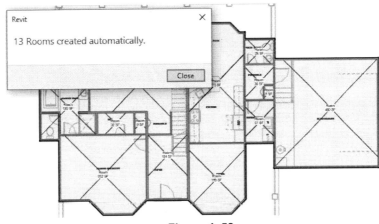

Figure 4–58

15. Select the room where the fireplace shows. Do not select the tag.

16. In Properties, in the *Identity Data* area, note that the *Number* is automatically incremented. Rooms must have unique numbers; however, the tag used will not display this information. Set the *Name* to **Great Room** (as shown in Figure 4–59) and click **Apply**.

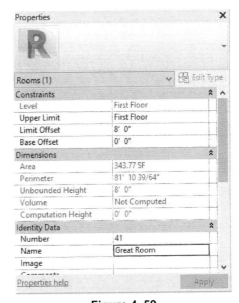

Figure 4–59

17. Rename the rest of the rooms by using the tag or by selecting the room and changing the name in Properties.

18. Save the project.

Task 2 - Add room separation lines and additional rooms.

1. In the *Architecture* tab>Room & Area panel, click 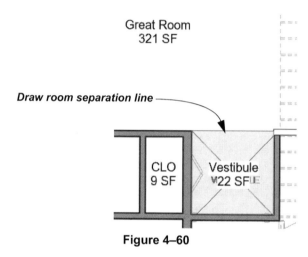 (Room Separator).

2. Draw room separation lines to separate the great room from the vestibule, as shown in Figure 4–60.

Great Room
321 SF

Draw room separation line

CLO
9 SF

Vestibule
V22 SF

Figure 4–60

3. Start the **Room** command and verify that **Tag on Placement** is toggled on. In Properties, in the *Name* field, type **Vestibule**, and then place the room in the location shown in Figure 4–60.

4. Move tags around, as needed.

    *   Toggle on **Leader** if you want to move a tag outside of its room. If you try to move it without leader toggled on, you will get a warning that the tag will be orphaned from the room.

5. Scroll over to the kitchen area.

6. In the *Architecture* tab>Room & Area panel, click 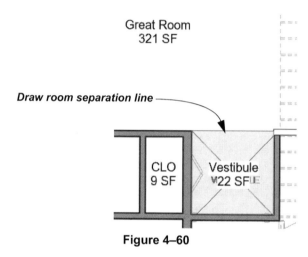 (Room Separator).

7. Draw a room separation line to separate the kitchen from the nook, then place a room in the nook location, as shown in Figure 4–61.

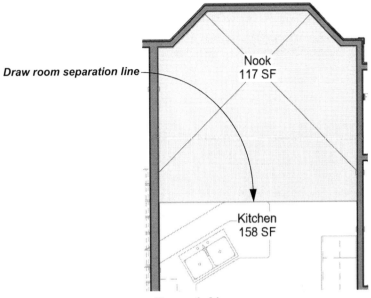

Draw room separation line

Nook
117 SF

Kitchen
158 SF

Figure 4–61

8. In the master bathroom, select the walls surrounding the water closet. In Properties, ensure that **Room Bounding** is unchecked, as shown in Figure 4–62. This will make the water closet a part of the overall master bathroom.

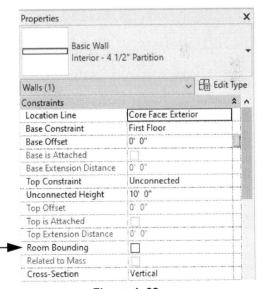

Figure 4–62

Task 3 - Add rooms to the second floor.

1. Open the **Floor Plans: Second Floor** view.

2. Start the **Room** command and place room elements inside the bedrooms.

3. At the loft area, draw room separation lines to separate the open-to-below area from the loft.

4. In the *Architecture* tab>Room & Area panel, click 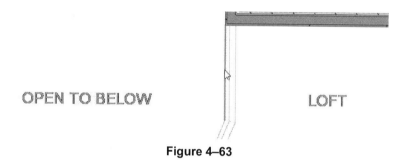 (Room Separator).

5. In the Draw panel, click (Pick Lines).

6. Hover your cursor over the center of the DWG edge of the loft, as shown in Figure 4–63.

OPEN TO BELOW   LOFT

Figure 4–63

7. Press <Tab> until the entire line highlights, then click to place a separation line, as shown in Figure 4–64.

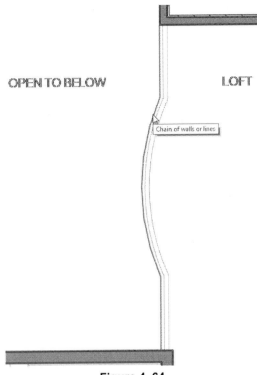

OPEN TO BELOW   LOFT

Chain of walls or lines

Figure 4–64

• Do not place a room tag where the DWG shows OPEN TO BELOW.

8. Save and close the project.

Practice 4d

(Optional) Add Finish Carpentry

Practice Objectives

- Model finish carpentry, including baseboards.
- Modify finish carpentry for clean edges.

If time permits, you can add baseboards to the first floor (as shown in Figure 4–65). You can then add other trim, such as chair rails or cornices, the same way.

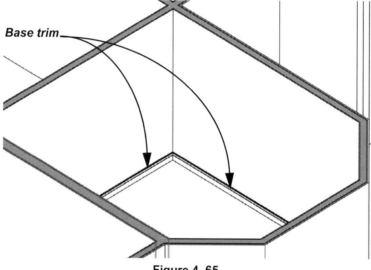

Base trim

Figure 4–65

1. Open the project **Residential-Finish Carpentry.rvt** from the practice files folder.

2. Open the default **{3D}** view.

3. Below the ViewCube, click ▽ (Context Menu).

4. Scroll down the list to select **Orient to View>Floor Plans> Floor Plan: First Floor**, as shown in Figure 4–66.

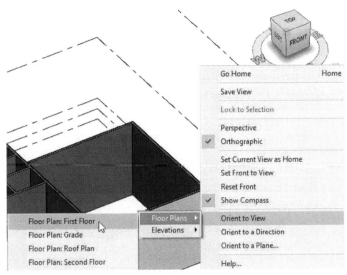

Figure 4–66

5. Select the bottom-left corner of the ViewCube. The view is orbited to a south-west isometric view, as shown in Figure 4–67.

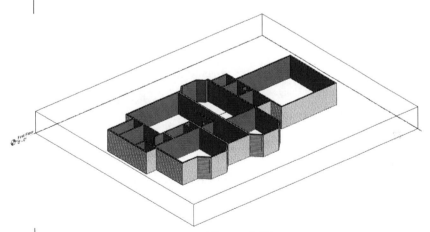

Figure 4–67

6. Zoom in to a wall in the dining room area.

7. In the *Architecture* tab>Build panel, expand ⬜ (Wall) and select ⬛ (Wall:Sweep).

8. In the Type Selector, select **Wall Sweep: Wall Sweep - Base**.

9. In the *Modify | Place Wall Sweep* tab>Placement panel, click ▱ (Horizontal).

10. Place the trim somewhere on the wall, as shown in Figure 4–68.

The image's visual style has been set to Hidden Line for clarity.

- You can choose to select adjacent walls as part of the chain.

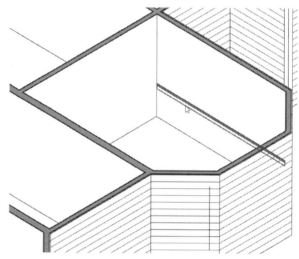

Figure 4–68

11. Press <Esc> to finish the command.

12. Select the newly created trim.

13. In Properties, ensure that *Offset From Level* is set to **0'-0"**.

14. In the *Modify | Wall Sweeps* tab>Wall Sweeps panel, select ▱ (Add/Remove Walls).

15. Select additional walls in the room to chain the newly created trim together.

16. Zoom in to a corner of the room, as shown in Figure 4–69. Note that the ends of the trim do not meet up.

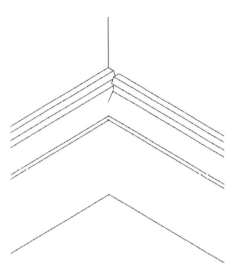

Figure 4–69

17. Select the trim, and click and drag the Drag Wall Sweep End control from the trim that is short over the other end, as shown in Figure 4–70.

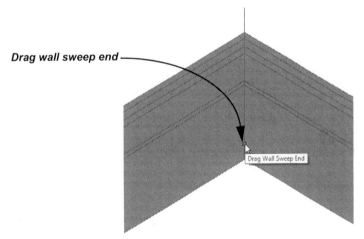

Drag wall sweep end

Drag Wall Sweep End

Figure 4–70

18. Continue to modify the finish trim in the dining room as necessary.

19. Save and close the project.

Chapter Review Questions

1. Where do you specify the height of a wall before you start modeling it?

   a. In the *Modify | Place Wall* tab.

   b. In the Options Bar.

   c. In the Status Bar.

   d. In the Quick Access Toolbar.

2. Some walls are made from multiple layers of materials, such as brick, block, and drywall, as shown on the bottom in Figure 4–71. If the hatching for these materials is not displayed (as shown at the top in Figure 4–71), how do you change this?

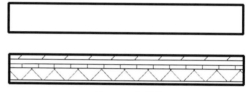

   Figure 4–71

   a. Set the *Visual Style* to **Realistic**.

   b. Set the *Detail Level* to **Medium**.

   c. Set the *View Scale* to be higher.

   d. Set the *Phase* to **New**.

3. Which of the following tools enables you to change a wall from one made out of studs and brick to one made out of concrete?

   a. Properties

   b. Change Wall

   c. Type Selector

   d. Edit Wall

4. Match the names for the following controls with the numbers shown in Figure 4–72.

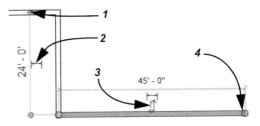

Figure 4–72

Control	Number
Drag wall end	
Flip	
Move witness line	
Make this temporary dimension permanent	

5. Which of the following would be true if you changed the top constraint of a wall from an unconnected height to a level?

   a. All walls of that type would also change height.

   b. Only that wall would change height.

6. When you want to add rooms with the same name, you need to modify each one separately.

   a. True

   b. False

Command Summary

Button	Command	Location
	Detail Level: Coarse	• **View Control Bar**
	Detail Level: Fine	• **View Control Bar**
	Detail Level: Medium	• **View Control Bar**
	Edit Profile	• **Ribbon:** (when a wall is selected) *Modify	Walls* tab>Mode panel
	Match Type	• **Ribbon:** *Modify* tab>Clipboard panel • **Shortcut:** MA
	Properties	• **Ribbon:** *Modify* tab>Properties panel • **Shortcut:** PP
N/A	**Type Selector**	• **Properties palette** • **Ribbon:** *Modify* tab (*Optional*) • **Quick Access Toolbar** (*Optional*)
	Wall	• **Ribbon:** *Architecture* tab>Build panel
	Wall Opening	• **Ribbon:** *Architecture* tab>Opening panel
	Room	• **Ribbon:** *Architecture* tab>Room & Area panel • **Shortcut:** RM
	Room Separator	• **Ribbon:** *Architecture* tab>Room & Area panel

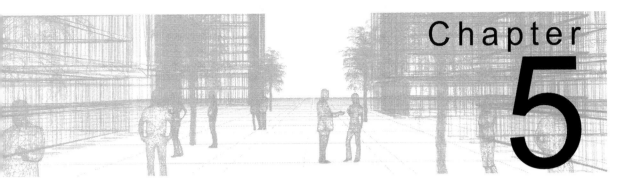

Working with Doors and Windows

Doors and windows are host elements that are placed in walls. There are many different types of doors and windows available in the Autodesk® Revit® libraries, and you can easily create additional sizes of the types that come with the software to meet your design requirements.

Learning Objectives in This Chapter

- Insert doors and windows in walls.
- Modify door and window locations and properties that can be referenced in schedules.
- Load additional door and window types from the library.
- Create additional door and window sizes of a selected type.

5.1 Inserting Doors and Windows

Doors and windows in the Autodesk Revit software are designed to be hosted by walls. You can use temporary dimensions (as shown in Figure 5–1), as well as alignment lines and snaps, to help place the openings exactly where you need them in the walls.

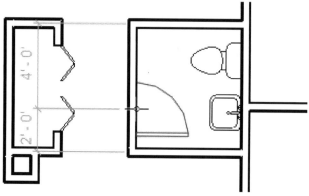

Figure 5–1

How To: Add a Door or Window

1. In the *Architecture* tab>Build panel, click 🚪 (Door) or
   🪟 (Window). The keyboard shortcuts are **DR** for doors and **WN** for windows.

2. To insert a tag with each door or window, verify that 🏷️ (Tag on Placement) is toggled on. You can specify the tag options using the Options Bar, as shown in Figure 5–2.

Figure 5–2

3. In the Type Selector, select the type of door or window.
4. Hover over the wall that you want to place the door or window in.
   - Use temporary dimensions and/or other drawing aids to properly locate where you want the door or window.
   - Press <Spacebar> to change the swing of the door before placing it.

5. Once you are in the correct location, select the wall to place the door or window.
6. Continue adding other doors or windows, as needed.

- While placing or modifying doors or windows, you can adjust the element using temporary dimensions and the **Flip the instance facing** and **Flip the instance hand** controls to change the swing and hinge locations, as shown in Figure 5–3. With windows, you can flip the interior and exterior using the same technique.

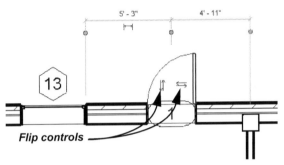

Figure 5–3

- If you are including window tags, select a point close to the outside of the wall when inserting the window so that the tag is placed on the outside.

- To move a door or window tag, select the tag. A control displays, as shown in Figure 5–4, which enables you to drag the tag to a new location.

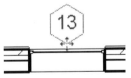

Figure 5–4

Modifying Door and Window Properties

The door or window types control most of their properties. To change the property information, you change the type in the Type Selector. You can also change instance parameters (as shown in Figure 5–5) that impact the specific door or window in the associated schedule. Instance parameters include things such as the swing angle, masonry, drywall frame, etc.

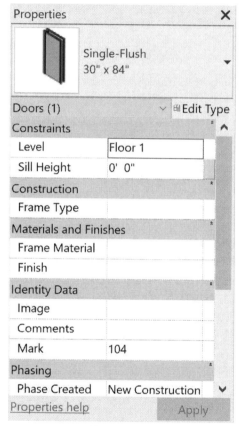

Figure 5–5

- The exact properties vary according to the door or window selected.

- Often, custom door and window families will have very different instance and/or type parameters.

Hint: Copying Elements to Levels

The standard Windows commands 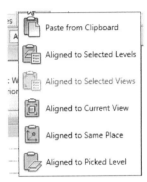 (Cut or <Ctrl>+<X>),
(Copy To Clipboard or <Ctrl>+<C>), and (Paste From Clipboard or <Ctrl>+<V>) work in the Autodesk Revit software just as they do in other Windows-compatible software. They are available in the *Modify* tab>Clipboard panel, but not in the shortcut menu.

In the software, you can also paste elements aligned to various views or levels, as shown in Figure 5–6.

Paste from Clipboard

Aligned to Selected Levels

Aligned to Selected Views

Aligned to Current View

Aligned to Same Place

Aligned to Picked Level

Figure 5–6

- **Aligned to Selected Levels** opens a dialog box where you can select the level to which you want to copy. This enables you to copy items on one level and paste them to the same location on another level (e.g., windows in a high-rise building).

- **Aligned to Selected Views** copies view-specific elements (such as text or dimensions) into a view that you select in a dialog box. Only the floor plan and reflected ceiling plan views are available.

- **Aligned to Current View** pastes elements copied in one view to the same location in another view.

- **Aligned to Same Place** pastes elements to the same location in the same view.

- **Aligned to Picked Level** pastes elements to the level you select in an elevation or section view.

Practice 5a

Insert Doors and Windows

Practice Objective

- Add doors and windows.

In this practice, you will add doors and windows to a model, as shown in Figure 5–7. You will use controls and temporary dimensions to help you place the doors and windows.

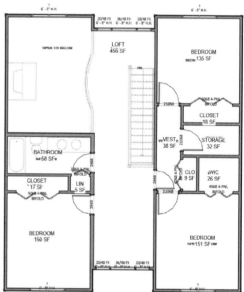

Figure 5–7

Task 1 - Insert doors.

1. Open the project **Residential-Doors.rvt** from the practice files folder.

2. Verify that you are in the **Floor Plans: First Floor** view.

3. Select the DWG file. In Properties, change the *Draw Layer* to **Foreground**.

4. In the *Architecture* tab>Build panel, click (Door).

5. In the Type Selector, select **Door-Interior-Single-2_Panel-Wood: 30" x 80"**.

6. In the *Modify | Place Door* tab>Tag panel, select 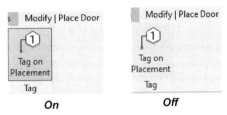 (Tag on Placement). It will be highlighted in the ribbon if it is on, as shown Figure 5–8.

On   Off

Figure 5–8

7. Place the door in the master bedroom, as shown in Figure 5–9. Use the flip arrows to make it swing in the right direction and use temporary dimensions to place it at the correct location on the wall.

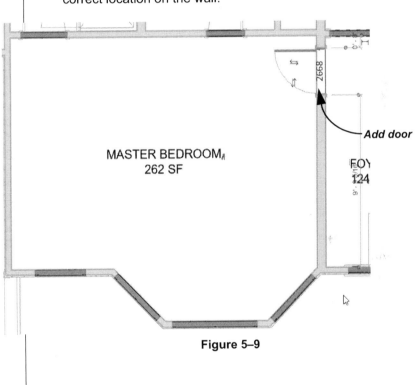

MASTER BEDROOM
262 SF

Add door

FOY
124

Figure 5–9

8. Add another **Door-Interior-Single-2_Panel-Wood: 30" x 80"** door leading to the master bathroom, as shown in Figure 5–10. Press <Spacebar> to flip it into the correct position.

   - Alternatively, after placing the door, click the flip icons to flip the door to have the correct swing.

MASTER BEDROOM

Figure 5–10

9. Pan over to the laundry room (LNDRY) and add a **Door-Interior-Single-2_Panel-Wood: 30" x 80"** door.

10. Stay in the **Door** command.

11. In the Type Selector, change the door type to **Door-Interior-Single-2_Panel-Wood: 36" x 80"**.

12. Place a door that leads to the garage, as shown in Figure 5–11.

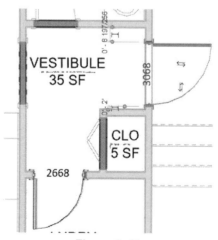

Figure 5–11

13. In the Type Selector, change the door type to **Door-Interior-Single-2_Panel-Wood: 24" x 80"**.

14. Add a door to the powder room (PWDR RM), as shown in Figure 5–12.

Figure 5–12

15. Stay in the **Door** command. Pan back to the master bathroom.

16. Verify that **Door-Interior-Single-2_Panel-Wood: 24" x 80"** is the current style. Place doors leading into both the walk-in closet (WIC) and the water closet (WC) in the master bathroom, as shown Figure 5–13.

Figure 5–13

17. Click ⌖ (Modify).

18. Click 🚪 (Door) and in the Type Selector, select **Bifold-2 Panel: 30" x 80"**.

19. Place the door both at the closet near the great room and next to the laundry area, as shown in Figure 5–14.

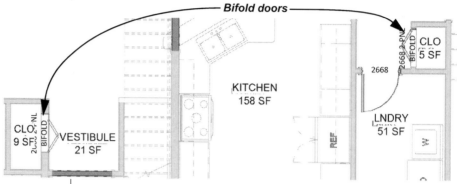

Figure 5–14

20. Zoom out to see the full floor plan.

21. Save the project.

Task 2 - Add windows.

1. Verify that you are in the **Floor Plans: First Floor** view.

2. Pan and zoom in to the garage area.

3. The windows will show as a darker gray than the rest. This is how you will know where to place the windows.

4. In the *Architecture* tab>Build panel, click ▦ (Window).

5. In the *Modify | Place Window* tab>Tag panel, verify that ⌐① (Tag on Placement) is toggled on.

6. In the Type Selector, select **Window-Single-Hung: 36" x 56"**.

7. Place a window on top of where it is located in the DWG, as shown in Figure 5–15.

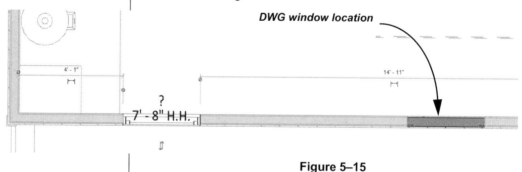

Figure 5–15

8. Continue to place windows on both garage walls, as shown in Figure 5–16.

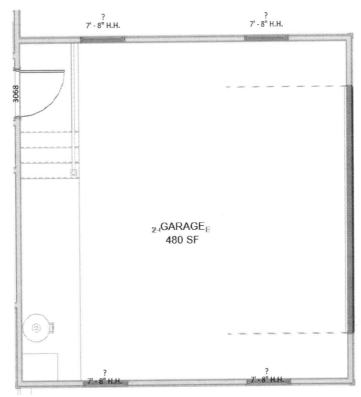

Figure 5–16

9. Click ⌂ (Modify).

10. Select the four windows in the garage.

11. In Properties, change the *Sill Height* to **4'-0 1/2"**. Note that this changes the *Head Height* to **8'-8 1/2"**.

    • Note that the window tags also change.

12. In the *Architecture* tab>Build panel, click ▦ (Window).

13. In the *Modify | Place Window* tab>Tag panel, verify that

    ⌐① (Tag on Placement) is toggled on.

14. In the Type Selector, select **Window-Single-Hung-Double: 60" x 56"**.

15. In Properties, in the *Other* section, set the *Head Height* to **6'-8"**.

16. Add the window to the lower wall in the dining room, as shown in Figure 5–17.

- Ignore the question marks for now; they will be addressed in *Chapter 15: Adding Tags and Schedules.*

DINING
156 SF

?
6'-8" H.H.

Figure 5–17

17. Pan over to the master bedroom and place the same window in the bay, then pan to the nook in the back of the house and again place the same window in the bay.

18. While still in the **Window** command, pan back to the dining room and add windows to either side of the larger window using the **Window-Single-Hung: 42" x 56"** window type with a head height of **6'-8"**, as shown in Figure 5–18.

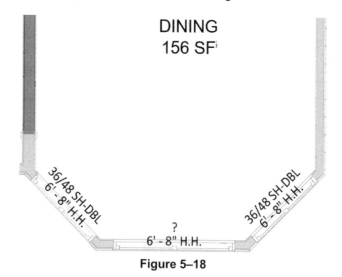

DINING
156 SF

36/48 SH-DBL
6'-8" H.H.

36/48 SH-DBL
6'-8" H.H.

?
6'-8" H.H.

Figure 5–18

19. Pan over to the master bedroom and add the same two windows to the bay window area.

20. Select the windows you just added. In Properties, in the *Other* section, change the *Head Height* to **6'-8"**.

21. Use the following table and Figure 5–19 to place the rest of the windows in the house. (Image tags have been removed for clarity.)

Marker	Window Type	Sill Height
A	Window-Single-Hung_Double: 60" x 56"	2'-0"
B	Window-Single-Hung_Double: 42" x 56"	2'-0"
C	Window-Single-Hung: 36" x 56"	2'-0"
D	Window-Single-Hung: 30" x 44"	3'-0"
E	Window-Single-Hung: 26" x 56"	2'-0"
F	Window-Single-Hung-Double: 60" x 44"	3'-0"

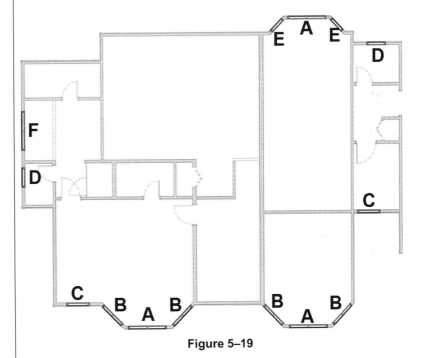

Figure 5–19

22. Save the project.

Task 3 - (Optional) Add doors and windows to the second floor.

1. Open the **Floor Plans: Second Floor** view.

2. Select the DWG file. In Properties, change the *Draw Layer* to **Foreground**.

3. In the *Architecture* tab>Build panel, click (Door).

4. In the *Modify | Place Door* tab>Tag panel, select (Tag on Placement).

5. Use the DWG to place the correct door and closet door sizes. Figure 5–20 shows all the doors placed.

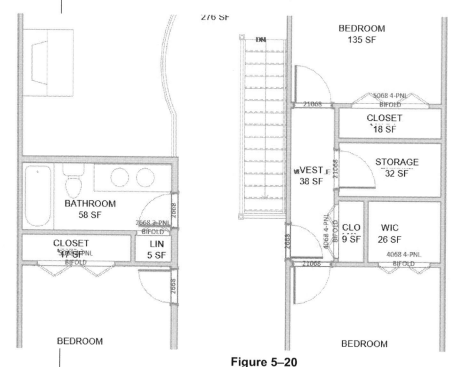

Figure 5–20

6. Click (Modify).

7. Select the DWG. In Properties, change the *Draw Layer* to **Foreground**. The windows will show as a darker gray than the rest. This is how you will know where to place the windows.

8. In the *Architecture* tab>Build panel, click 🔲 (Window).

9. In the *Modify | Place Window* tab>Tag panel, verify that
   ⌐① (Tag on Placement) is toggled on.

10. Use the table below and Figure 5–21 to place the windows.

Marker	Second Floor Window Type	Sill Height
A	Window-Single-Hung_Double: 60" x 56"	2'-0"
B	Window-Fixed-Transom: 24" x 56"	2'-0"
C	Window-Single-Hung: 42" x 56"	2'-0"

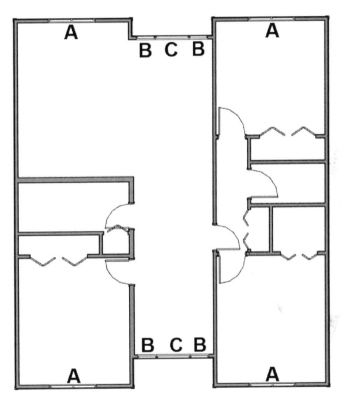

Figure 5–21

11. Save and close the project.

5.2 Loading Door and Window Types from the Library

A variety of door and window styles are available in the Autodesk Revit Library, as shown in Figure 5–22. They are grouped in *Family* files with the extension .RFA. For example, when you load the family **Door-Double-Glass.rfa**, you can then select various sizes of this door to use in your project.

- The process is similar for loading all types of families.

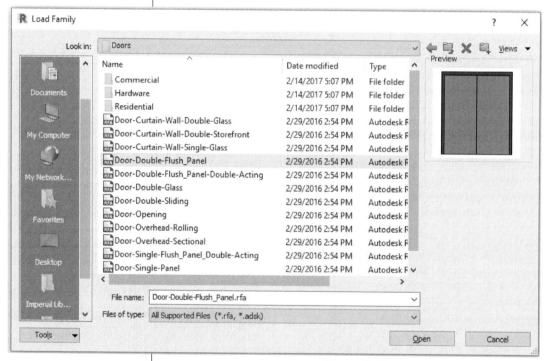

Figure 5–22

How To: Load a Family

1. In the *Insert* tab>Load from Library panel, click 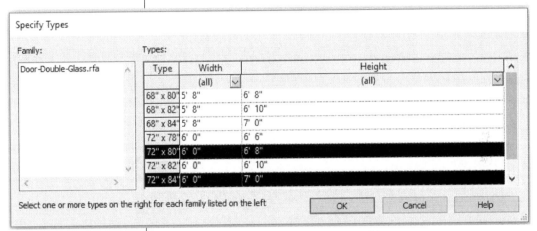 (Load Family). Alternatively, start a family-based command such as **Door** or **Window** and in the *Modify | <contextual>* tab>Mode panel, click (Load Family).
2. In the Load Family dialog box, navigate to the folder that contains the family you want to load and select the family.
3. Click **Open**.
4. For some families, the Specify Types dialog box displays, as shown for a door in Figure 5–23. Select the types you want to include in your project and click **OK**.

Figure 5–23

- To select more than one type, hold <Ctrl> as you select.
- You can use the drop-down lists under the columns to filter the sizes.

5. Once the family is loaded, in the Type Selector, select the type you want to use.

- When you are working with a command such as **Door** or **Window**, you can only load families that are from that category of elements. For example, you cannot load window families while working in the Door command.

- There are several families used for openings:

  - In the *Doors* folder: **Door-Opening.rfa**
  - In the *Windows* folder: **Window-Round Opening.rfa** and **Window-Square Opening.rfa**

5.3 Creating Additional Door and Window Sizes

You can easily add additional sizes to existing families of doors or windows that have been loaded into a project. To do this, you create a new type of the needed size based on an existing type, as shown in Figure 5–24.

You can specify materials for door and window sub-elements in the Type Properties.

The parameters might be different depending on the door or window you selected.

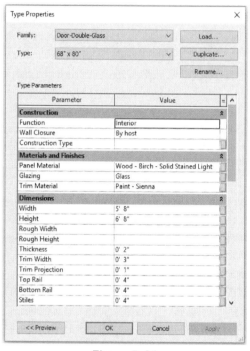

Figure 5–24

How To: Create Additional Door and Window Sizes

1. Start the **Door** or **Window** command.
2. In the Type Selector, select the type you want to modify. In Properties, click ⊞ (Edit Type) or in the *Modify* tab> Properties panel, click ⊞ (Type Properties).
3. In the Type Properties dialog box, click **Duplicate**.
4. Type a new name for the element and click **OK**.
5. In the Type Properties dialog box, change the *Height* and *Width* parameters to match the size.
6. Click **OK** to close the dialog box. The new window or door type is now available for use.

Practice 5b | Load and Create Door Types

Practice Objectives

- Load door types.
- Duplicate and modify a door type.

In this practice, you will load specialty door types used in the garage, create a new door size, and add doors to the second floor, as shown in Figure 5–25.

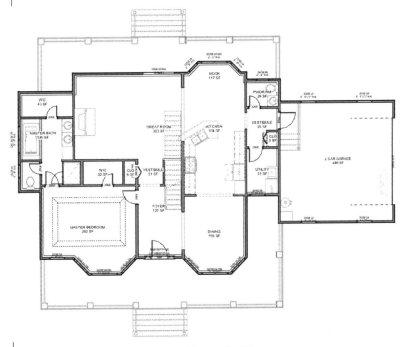

Figure 5–25

Task 1 - Load and place door types.

1. Open the project **Residential-Load.rvt** from the practice files folder.

2. Open the **Floor Plans: First Floor** view and zoom in on the garage area.

3. In the *Architecture* tab>Build panel, click (Door).

4. In the *Modify | Place Door* tab>Mode panel, click (Load Family).

5. In the Load Family dialog box, navigate to the Revit Library's *Doors>Residential* folder and select **Door Garage-Embossed_Panel.rfa**. Click **Open**.

6. In the Type Selector, change the type to **Door-Garage-Embossed_Panel: 192" x 84"**.

7. Place the door on the east garage wall, as shown in Figure 5–26. The dashed lines should line up with the DWG.

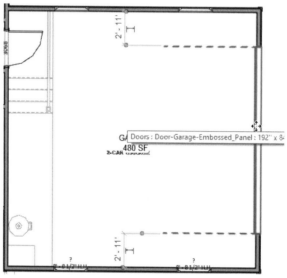

Figure 5–26

8. In Properties, click (Edit Type) or in the *Modify | Place Door* tab>Properties panel, click (Type Properties).

9. In the Type Properties dialog box, click **Duplicate**.

10. In the Name dialog box, enter **192" x 96"** for the name and click **OK**.

11. In the Type Properties dialog box, in the *Dimension* area, change the *Height* value to **8'-0"**. You can type either **8** or **8'-0"**, but you must add the " symbol to the value if you are using inches.

12. In the *Identity Data* area, change the *Type Comment* value to **16/80 O.H.**.

13. Click **OK** to close the dialog box. The garage door updates to the new type and the door tag updates.

14. Click  (Modify).

15. In the *Insert* tab>Load from Library panel, click (Load Family).

16. In the Load Family dialog box, navigate to the practice files *Custom Families* folder and select **Single-Raised Panel with Sidelights.rfa** and **Sliding-2 panel_without trim.rfa**.

17. Click **Open**.

18. Pan over to the front door.

19. In the *Architecture* tab>Build panel, click (Door).

20. In the Type Selector, select **Single-Raised Panel with Sidelights: 36" x 80"**.

21. In Properties, change the *Frame Type* to **PT-WOOD**.

22. Place the door and stay in the **Door** command.

23. Pan to the north wall in the great room.

24. In the Type Selector, select **Sliding-2 panel_without trim 72" x 80"**.

25. In Properties, change the *Frame Type* to **VINYL CLAD**.

26. Click to place the sliding door, as shown in Figure 5–27.

6068 GLASS SLIDING

1' - 3"

Figure 5–27

27. Click (Modify).

28. Save the project.

Task 2 - Load door openings and change types.

1. In the *Insert* tab>Load from Library panel, click 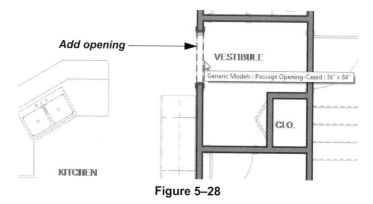 (Load Family).

2. In the Load Family dialog box, navigate to the Revit Library's *Openings* folder and select **Passage Opening-Cased.rfa**. Click **Open**.

3. In the *Architecture* tab>Build panel, click (Component).

4. In the Type Properties, select **Passage Opening-Cased.rfa: 36" x 80"**.

5. Place this opening on the wall between the kitchen and vestibule areas, as shown in Figure 5–28.

Figure 5–28

6. Ensure this opening is aligned on center with the door leading to the garage.

7. Click (Modify).

8. Start the **Component** command again.

9. In Properties, click (Edit Type), or in the *Modify | Place Door* tab>Properties panel, click (Type Properties).

10. In the Type Properties dialog box, click **Duplicate**.

11. Create the following opening types with these properties:

   • *Name:* **120" x 80"**
   • *Width:* **10'-0"**
   • *Type Comments:* **1068**

- *Name:* **84" x 80"**
- *Width:* **7'-0"**
- *Type Comments:* **7068**

- *Name:* **48" x 80"**
- *Width:* **4'-0"**
- *Type Comments:* **4068**

12. Place openings of these types in the locations specified in Figure 5–29.

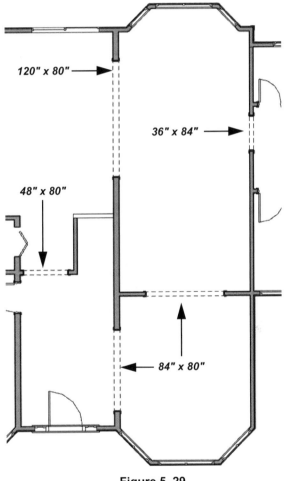

120" x 80"

36" x 84"

48" x 80"

84" x 80"

Figure 5–29

13. Save and close the project.

Chapter Review Questions

1. How do you change the swing direction of a door, as shown in Figure 5–30? (Select all that apply.)

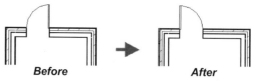

Before　　　　**After**

Figure 5–30

a. When placing the door, press <Spacebar>.

b. When placing the door, right-click and select **Change Swing**.

c. Select an existing door and select the flip arrows.

d. Select an existing door, right-click and select **Change Swing**.

2. How do you add additional window or door families to a project?

a. Find the window or door family using Windows Explorer, right-click and select **Import into Revit Project**.

b. Import them from the Window or Door Catalog.

c. Load them from the Revit Library.

d. Use the Window/Door tool to create new families.

3. How do you include a tag with a door or window, as shown in Figure 5–31?

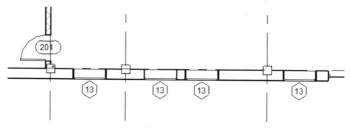

Figure 5–31

a. Select a door or window family that includes a tag.

b. Select the Tag box in the Options Bar before placing the door or window.

c. Tags can only be used after placing the door or window.

d. Select **Tag on Placement** in the contextual tab.

4. Where are the door and window sizes stored?

   a. In Properties.

   b. In Type Properties.

   c. In Door/ Window Settings.

   d. In the template file.

5. How do you create additional door or window sizes, as shown in Figure 5–32?

Figure 5–32

   a. Select the required door or window and use the Size tool to specify a new size.

   b. In Properties, select the required door or window and click **Edit Type**, then select **Duplicate** and modify it.

   c. Find the existing door or window family in the Project Browser, right-click and select **New Size**.

   d. Select the door or window in the view, and edit it using size controls to the needed size.

Command Summary

Button	Command	Location
Clipboard		
	Copy to Clipboard	• **Ribbon:** *Modify* tab>Clipboard panel • **Shortcut:** <Ctrl>+<C>
	Cut to the Clipboard	• **Ribbon:** *Modify* tab>Clipboard panel • **Shortcut:** <Ctrl>+<X>
	Paste - Aligned to Current View	• **Ribbon:** *Modify* tab>Clipboard panel> expand Paste
	Paste - Aligned to Same Place	• **Ribbon:** *Modify* tab>Clipboard panel> expand Paste
	Paste - Aligned to Selected Levels	• **Ribbon:** *Modify* tab>Clipboard panel> expand Paste
	Paste - Aligned to Selected Views	• **Ribbon:** *Modify* tab>Clipboard panel> expand Paste
	Paste - Aligned to Picked Level	• **Ribbon:** *Modify* tab>Clipboard panel> expand Paste
	Paste from Clipboard	• **Ribbon:** *Modify* tab>Clipboard panel • **Shortcut:** <Ctrl>+<V>
Doors and Windows		
	Door	• **Ribbon:** *Architecture* tab>Build panel • **Shortcut:** DR
	Edit Type/ Type Properties	• **Properties palette:** Edit Type • **Ribbon:** *Modify* tab>Properties panel
	Measure	• **Quick Access Toolbar** • **Ribbon:** *Modify* tab>Measure panel
	Window	• **Ribbon:** *Architecture* tab>Build panel • **Shortcut:** WN

Working with Views

Views are the cornerstone of working with Autodesk® Revit® models as they enable you to see the model in both 2D and 3D. As you are working, you can duplicate and change views to display different information based on the same view of the model. Callouts are especially important views for construction documents.

Learning Objectives in This Chapter

- Change the way elements display in different views to show required information and set views for construction documents.
- Duplicate views so that you can modify the display as you are creating the model and for construction documents.
- Establish building and interior elevations that can be used to demonstrate how the house will be built.
- Create building sections to help you create the model and to include in construction documents.
- Create callout views of parts of plans, sections, or elevations for detailing.

6.1 Modifying the View Display

Views are powerful tools that enable you to create multiple versions of a model without having to recreate building elements. For example, you can have views that are specifically used for working on the model, while other views are annotated and used for construction documents. Different disciplines can have different views that show only the features they require, as shown in Figure 6–1. Properties of one view can be independent of the properties in other views.

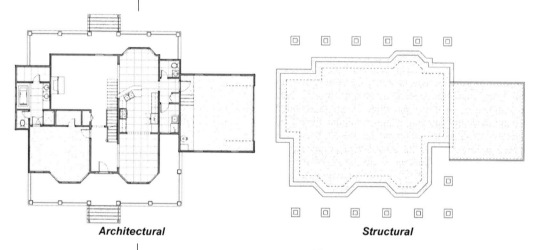

Architectural *Structural*

Figure 6–1

The view display can be modified in the following locations:

- View Control Bar
- Properties
- Shortcut menu
- Visibility/Graphic Overrides dialog box

View Properties

The most basic properties of a view are accessed using the View Control Bar (shown in Figure 6–2). These include the *Scale*, *Detail Level*, and *Visual Style* options. Additional options include temporary overrides and other advanced settings.

Figure 6–2

- The **Detail Level** controls whether you see schematic elements (Coarse or Medium detail) or full scale elements (Fine detail), as shown in Figure 6–3.

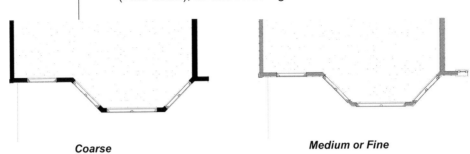

Coarse   *Medium or Fine*

Figure 6–3

Other modifications to views are available in Properties, as shown in Figure 6–4. These properties include *Underlays* and *View Range* as well as many others. The *Discipline* of a view can also be set here. Disciplines are hard-coded into the software and cannot be changed.

The options in Properties vary according to the type of view. A plan view has different properties than a 3D view.

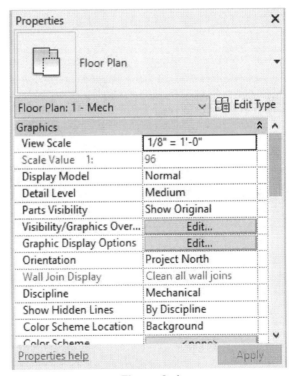

Figure 6–4

Setting an Underlay

Setting an *Underlay* is helpful if you need to display elements on a different level, such as the second floor plan shown with an underlay of the first floor plan in Figure 6–5. You can then use the elements to trace over or even copy them to the current level of the view.

Underlays are only available in floor plan and ceiling plan views.

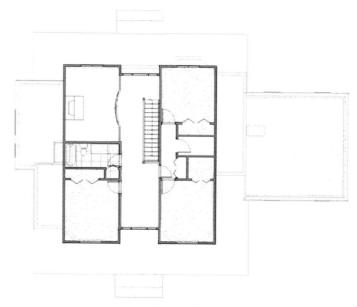

Figure 6–5

In Properties, in the *Underlay* area, specify the *Range: Base Level* and the *Range: Top Level*. You can also specify the *Underlay Orientation* to **Look down** or **Look up**, as shown in Figure 6–6.

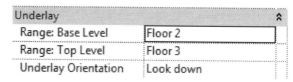

Figure 6–6

- To prevent moving elements in the underlay by mistake, in the Select panel, expand the panel title and clear **Select underlay elements**. You can also toggle this on/off using

   (Select Underlay Elements) in the Status Bar.

Setting the View Range

The View Range controls the cut planes that control the visibility of plan views, as shown in the Sample View Range key in Figure 6–7. Elements outside the cut planes do not display unless you include an underlay.

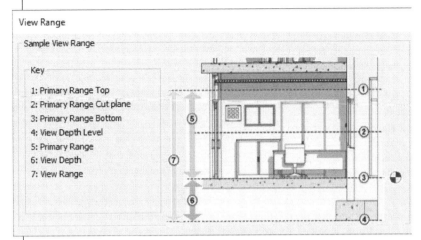

Figure 6–7

How To: Set the View Range

1. In Properties, in the *Extents* area, beside *View Range*, select **Edit…** or type **VR**.
2. In the View Range dialog box, as shown in Figure 6–8, modify the levels and offsets for the *Primary Range* and *View Depth*.
   - Click **<<Show** to display the Sample View Range key.

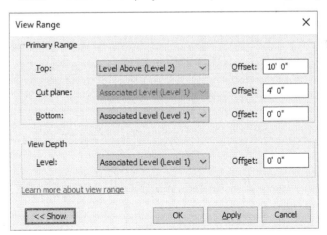

Figure 6–8

3. Click **OK**.

- If the settings used cannot be represented graphically, a warning displays, stating the inconsistency.

- A reflected ceiling plan (RCP) is created, as if the ceiling is reflected by a mirror on the floor, so that the ceiling is the same orientation as the floor plan. The cutline is placed just below the ceiling to ensure that any windows and doors below do not display.

Hint: Setting View Ranges for Roofs

Most plan views are typically cut at 3'-0" to 4'-0" above the bottom of the level, as shown in Figure 6–9. However, this does not work with pitched roofs, whose structures can reach 20'-0" high or more. To change the height of the area shown in the roof plan, change the *View Range*.

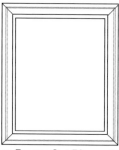 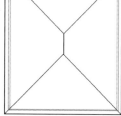

View Range Cut Plane at 4'-0"   *View Range Cut Plane at 30'-0"*

Figure 6–9

- Roofs are discussed in *Chapter 9: Modeling Roofs*.

Hiding and Overriding Graphics

Two common ways to customize a view are:

- Hiding individual elements or categories

- Modifying how graphics display for elements or categories (e.g., altering lineweight, color, or pattern)

An element is an individual item, such as one wall in a view, while a category includes all instances of a selected element, such as all walls in a view.

In the example shown in Figure 6–10, a foundation plan has been created by toggling off pochéd walls and other architectural components, leaving only the foundation slab and necessary structural elements.

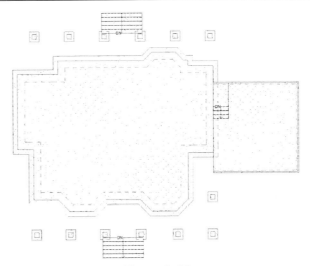

Figure 6–10

How To: Hide Elements or Categories in a View

1. Select the elements or categories you want to hide.
2. Right-click and select **Hide in View>Elements** or **Hide in View>Category**, as shown in Figure 6–11.

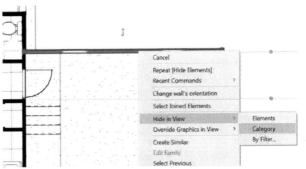

Figure 6–11

The elements or categories are hidden in the current view only.

3. A quick way to hide entire categories is to select an element(s) and type **VH**.

How To: Override Graphics of Elements or Categories in a View

1. Select the element(s) you want to modify.
2. Right-click and select **Override Graphics in View>By Element** or **By Category**. The View Specific Element (or Category) Graphics dialog box opens, as shown in Figure 6–12.

The exact options in the dialog box vary depending on the type of elements selected.

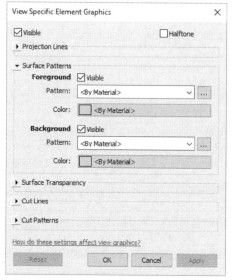

Figure 6–12

3. Select the changes you want to make and click **OK**.

View Specific Options

- Clearing the **Visible** option is the same as hiding the elements or categories.

- Selecting the **Halftone** option grays out the elements or categories.

- The options for *Projection Lines* and *Cut Lines* include **Weight**, **Color**, and **Pattern**. The options for *Surface Patterns* and *Cut Patterns* include **Visibility**, **Pattern**, and **Color** for the *Foreground* and *Background*, as shown previously in Figure 6–12.

- **Surface Transparency** can be set by moving the slider bar, as shown in Figure 6–13.

Figure 6–13

- The View Specific Category Graphics dialog box includes **Open the Visibility Graphics dialog...**, which opens the full dialog box of options.

The Visibility/Graphic Overrides Dialog Box

The options in the Visibility/Graphic Overrides dialog box (shown in Figure 6–14) control how every category and sub-category of elements is displayed per view. You can toggle categories on and off, override the *Projection/Surface* and *Cut* information, set categories to **Halftone**, and change the *Detail Level*.

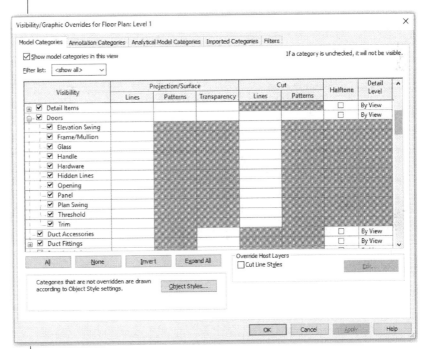

Figure 6–14

To open the Visibility/Graphic Overrides dialog box, type **VV** or **VG**. It is also available in Properties: in the *Graphics* area, beside *Visibility/Graphic Overrides*, click **Edit...**.

- The Visibility/Graphic Overrides are divided into *Model Categories*, *Annotation Categories*, *Analytical Model Categories*, *Imported Categories,* and *Filters*.

- Other categories might be available if specific data has been included in the project, including *Design Options*, *Linked Files*, and *Worksets*.

- To limit the number of categories showing in the dialog box, select a discipline from the *Filter list,* as shown in Figure 6–15.

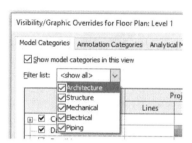

Figure 6–15

- To help you select categories, use the **All**, **None**, and **Invert** buttons. The **Expand All** button displays all of the sub-categories.

Hint: Restoring Hidden Elements or Categories

If you have hidden categories, you can display them using the Visibility/Graphic Overrides dialog box. To display hidden elements, however, you must temporarily reveal the elements first.

1. In the View Control Bar, click ⌕ (Reveal Hidden Elements). The border and all hidden elements are displayed in magenta, while visible elements in the view are grayed out, as shown in Figure 6–16.

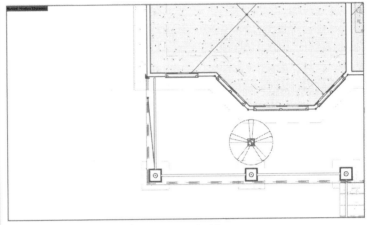

Figure 6–16

2. Select the hidden elements you want to restore, right-click, and select **Unhide in View>Elements** or **Unhide in View>Category**. Alternatively, in the *Modify | <contextual>* tab>Reveal Hidden Elements panel, click ⬚ (Unhide Element) or ⬚ (Unhide Category).

3. When you are finished, in the View Control Bar, click ⬚ (Close Reveal Hidden Elements) or, in the *Modify | <contextual>* tab>Reveal Hidden Elements panel, click ⨯ (Toggle Reveal Hidden Elements Mode).

Using View Templates

A powerful way to use views effectively is to set up a view and then save it as a view template. You can apply view templates to views individually or through Properties. Setting the view template using Properties helps to ensure that you do not accidentally modify the view while interacting with it.

How To: Create a View Template from a View

1. Set up a view, as needed.
2. In the Project Browser, right-click on the view and select **Create View Template from View**.
3. In the New View Template dialog box, type in a name and click **OK**.
4. The new view template is listed in the View Templates dialog box. Make any modifications needed in the *View properties* section.
5. Click **OK**.

How To: Specify a View Template for a View

1. In the Project Browser, select the view or views to which you want to apply a view template.
2. In Properties, scroll down to the *Identity Data* section and click the button beside *View Template*.
3. In the Apply View Template dialog box, select the view template from the list, as shown in Figure 6–17.

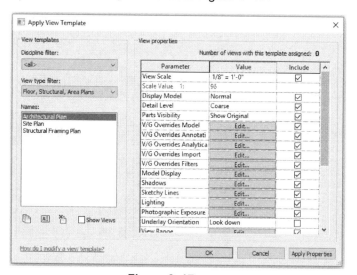

Figure 6–17

4. Click **OK**.

- In the View Control Bar, use 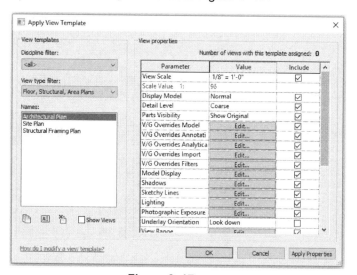 (Temporary View Properties) to temporarily apply a view template to a view.

6.2 Duplicating Views

Once you have created a model, you do not recreate the elements at different scales or copy them so that they can be used on more than one sheet. Instead, you duplicate the required view and modify the view to suit your needs.

Duplication Types

Duplicate creates a copy of the view that only includes the building elements and view properties, as shown in Figure 6–18. Annotation and detailing are not copied into the new view. Building model elements automatically change in all views, but view-specific changes made to the new view are not reflected in the original view.

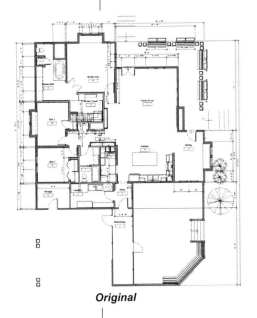

Original

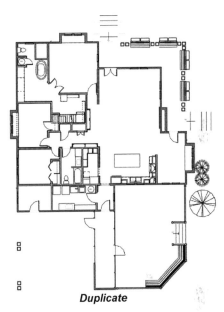

Duplicate

Figure 6–18

Duplicate with Detailing creates a copy of the view and includes all annotation and detail elements (such as tags), as shown in Figure 6–19. Any annotation or view-specific elements created in the new view are not reflected in the original view.

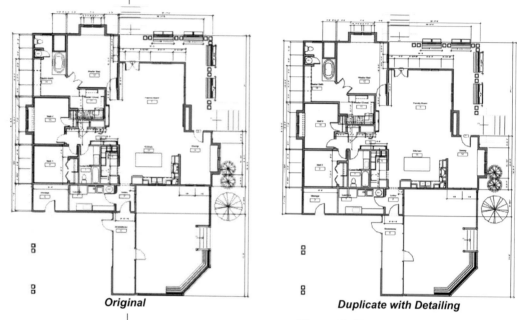

Original   *Duplicate with Detailing*

Figure 6–19

Duplicate as a Dependent creates a copy of the view and links it to the original (parent) view, as shown in the Project Browser in Figure 6–20. View-specific changes made to the overall view, such as changing the *Scale*, are also reflected in the dependent (child) views and vice-versa.

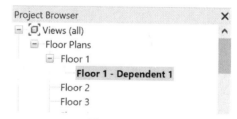

Figure 6–20

- Use dependent views when the building model is so large that you need to split the building onto separate sheets, while ensuring that the views are all the same scale.

- If you want to separate a dependent view from the original view, right-click on the dependent view and select **Convert to independent view**.

How To: Create Duplicate Views

1. Open the view you want to duplicate.
2. In the *View* tab>Create panel, expand **Duplicate View** and select the type of duplicate view you want to create, as shown in Figure 6–21.

Most types of views can be duplicated.

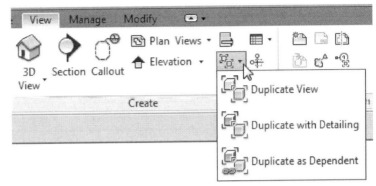

Figure 6–21

- Alternatively, you can right-click on a view in the Project Browser and select the type of duplicate that you want to use, as shown in Figure 6–22.

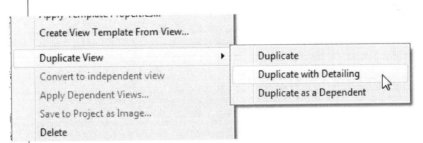

Figure 6–22

- To rename a view, slowly click twice on the view name so the text highlights and enter a new name, as shown in Figure 6–23. You can also right-click on a view name and select **Rename...** or press <F2>.

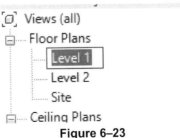

Figure 6–23

Practice 6a

Duplicate Views and Set the View Display

Practice Objectives

- Duplicate and rename views.
- Hide elements in views.
- Modify the graphic display of elements in views.

In this practice, you will duplicate views and then modify them by changing the scale, hiding some elements, and changing other elements to halftone to prepare them to be used in construction documents. The finished views of the first floor are shown in Figure 6–24.

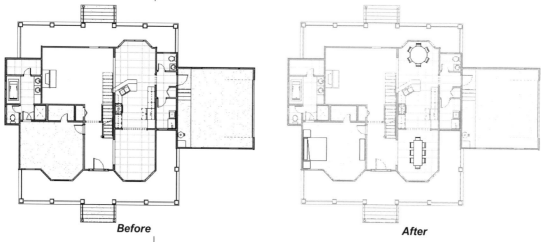

Before　　　　　　　　　　　　　　*After*

Figure 6–24

Furniture and dimensions have been added to the nook and kitchen area in this model to show what happens when you duplicate.

Task 1 - Duplicate and modify the first floor plan view.

1. Open the project **Residential-Display.rvt** from the practice files folder.

2. Close any other projects you may have open.

3. In the Project Browser, expand **Floor Plans** and rename the *Roof Peak* view to **Roof Plan**.

4. In the Confirm Plan View Rename dialog box (shown in Figure 6–25), click **No**.

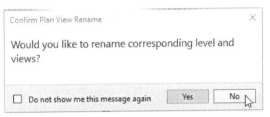

Figure 6–25

5. Open the **Floor Plans: First Floor** view.

6. Select the DWG and set it to **Background**.

7. In the Project Browser, right-click on the **Floor Plans: First Floor** view and select **Duplicate View>Duplicate**.

8. Type **ZA** to zoom all. Only the elevation markers on the exterior will carry over to the new view.

9. In the Project Browser, slowly click twice on the duplicated view name. Rename it **First Floor-Furniture Plan**. You will use this view later on to place components.

10. Open the Visibility/Graphic Overrides dialog box by typing **VV** or **VG**.

11. In the dialog box, set the *Filter list* to **Architecture** (by clearing the check marks for the other options).

12. In the *Visibility* column, select the **Furniture** category (as shown in Figure 6–26).

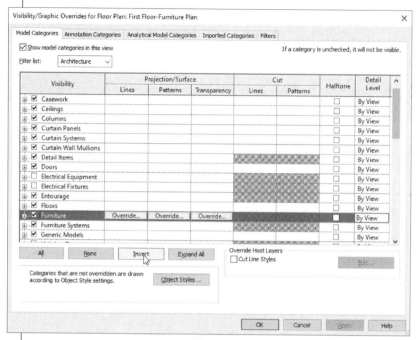

Figure 6–26

13. Click **Invert**. This selects everything except the Furniture category (as shown in Figure 6–27). In the *Halftone* column, click on just one of the highlighted categories. This places a check on all of the selected categories.

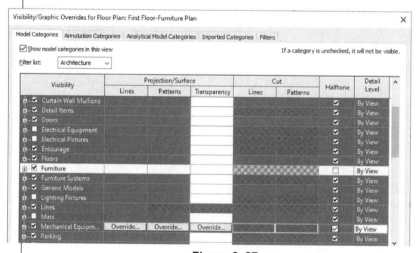

Figure 6–27

14. Click **None** to clear all of the selected categories.

15. Click **Apply** to set the changes without exiting the dialog box.

16. In the *Annotation Categories* tab, clear **Show annotation categories in this view**. All the categories will gray out, as shown in Figure 6–28.

   • No annotation elements will display in this view, even if they are added in other views of this part of the model.

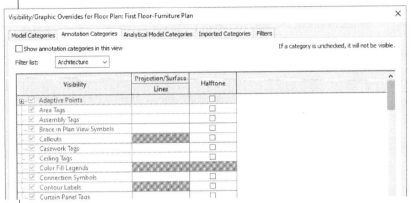

Figure 6–28

17. Click **OK**.

18. In the Project Browser, right-click on the **Floor Plans: First Floor** view and select **Duplicate View>Duplicate with Detail**.

19. Rename the new view to **First Floor-Dimension Plan**. You will use this view later on to place annotations.

20. In the Visibility/Graphics Overrides dialog box, in the *Model category* tab, uncheck the **Furniture** category.

21. Click **OK**.

22. Save the project.

Task 2 - Duplicate and modify a second floor plan view.

1. Open the **Floor Plans: Second Floor** view.

2. Close any other opened views by clicking 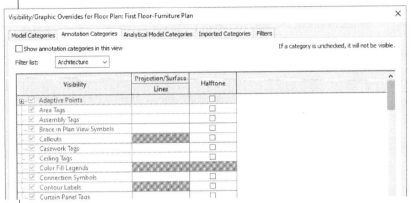 (Close Inactive Views) from the Quick Access Toolbar.

3. Select the DWG and set it to **Background**.

4. In the Project Browser, right-click on the **Second Floor** view and select **Duplicate View>Duplicate**. Rename this view **Second Floor-Furniture Plan**.

5. Open the Visibility/Graphic Overrides dialog box by typing **VV** or **VG**. Set the view settings similar to what was used for the Floor Plans: First Floor-Furniture Plan.

6. Click **OK**.

7. In the Project Browser, right-click on the **Second Floor** view and select **Duplicate View>Duplicate with Detail**. Rename this view **Second Floor-Dimension Plan**.

8. In the Visibility/Graphic Overrides dialog box, set the view settings similar to what was used for the Floor Plans: First Floor-Dimension Plan.

9. Click **OK**.

10. Save and close the project.

6.3 Creating Elevations and Sections

Elevations and sections are critical elements of construction documents and can assist you as you are working on a model. Any changes made in one of these views (such as the section in Figure 6–29) changes the entire model, and any changes made to the project model are also displayed in the elevations and sections.

Figure 6–29

- In the Project Browser, elevations are separated by elevation type and sections are separated by section type, as shown in Figure 6–30.

Figure 6–30

- To open an elevation or section view, double-click on the marker arrow or on its name in the Project Browser.

- To give the elevation or section a new name, in the Project Browser, slowly click twice on the name or right-click on it and select **Rename...**.

Elevations

Elevations are *face-on* views of the interiors and exteriors of a building. Four **Exterior Elevation** views are defined in the default template: **North**, **South**, **East**, and **West**. You can create additional building elevation views at other angles or interior elevation views, as shown in Figure 6–31.

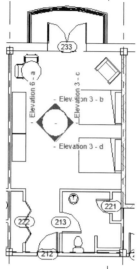

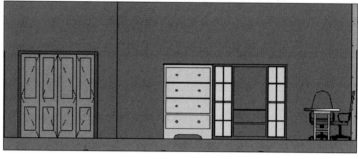

Figure 6–31

- Elevations markers must be placed in plan views.

- When you add an elevation or section to a sheet, the detail and sheet number are automatically added to the view title and elevation/section marker.

How To: Create an Elevation

1. In the *View* tab>Create panel, expand 🔼 (Elevation) and click 🔼 (Elevation).
2. In the Type Selector, select the elevation type. Two types come with the templates: **Building Elevation** and **Interior Elevation**.
3. Move the cursor near one of the walls that defines the elevation. The marker follows the angle of the wall.
4. Click to place the marker.

- The length, width, and height of an elevation are defined by the walls and ceiling/floor at which the elevation marker is pointing.

The software remembers the last elevation type used, so you can click the top button if you want to use the same elevation command.

• When creating interior elevations, ensure that the floor or ceiling above is in place before creating the elevation or you will need to modify the elevation crop region so that the elevation markers do not show on all floors.

Sections

Sections are slices through a model. You can create a section through an entire building or through one wall for a detail. Sections can be created in plan, elevation, and other section views. You can flip, resize, or split a section. Figure 6–32 shows all of the components of a section marker.

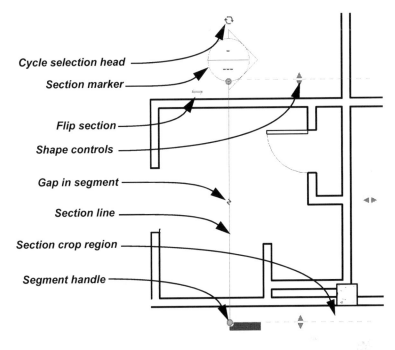

Cycle selection head

Section marker

Flip section

Shape controls

Gap in segment

Section line

Section crop region

Segment handle

Figure 6–32

How To: Create a Section

1. In the *View* tab>Create panel or in the Quick Access Toolbar, click (Section).

2. In the Type Selector, select **Section: Building Section** or **Section: Wall Section**. If you want a section in a Drafting view, select **Detail View: Detail**.

3. In the view, select a point where you want to locate the crop region and section marker.

4. Select the second or end point that defines the section.

5. The shape controls display. You can flip the arrow and change the size of the cutting plane, as well as the location of the bubble and flag.

• When placing a section, you can snap to other elements in the model as the start and end points of the section line. You can also use the **Align** command to reorient a section line to an element such as an angled wall.

• A section line can also be used as an alignment object and can be snapped to when placing other geometry.

Modifying Elevations and Sections

There are two parts to modifying elevations and sections:

• To modify the markers (as shown in Figure 6–33), use the controls to change the length and depth of elevations and sections. There are other specific type options as well.

• To modify the view (as shown in Figure 6–34), use the controls to modify the size or create view breaks.

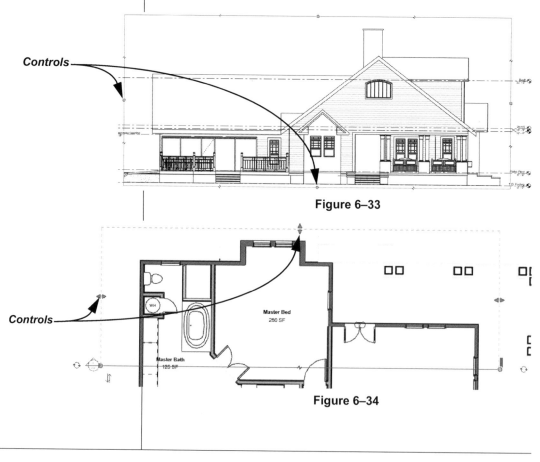

Figure 6–33

Figure 6–34

Modifying Elevation Markers

When you modify elevation markers, you can specify the length and depth of the clip plane, as shown in Figure 6–35.

- Select the arrowhead of the elevation marker (not the circle portion) to display the clip plane.

- Drag the round shape handles to lengthen or shorten the elevation.

- Adjust the ▲▼ (Drag) controls to modify the depth of the elevation.

To display additional interior elevations from one marker, select the circle portion (not the arrowhead) and place check marks in the Show Arrow boxes in the directions that you want to display, as shown in Figure 6–35.

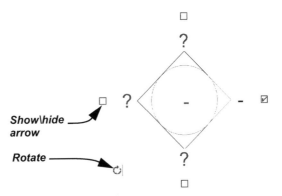

Figure 6–35

- Use the ↻ (Rotate) control to angle the marker (e.g., for a room with angled walls).

Modifying Section Markers

When you modify section markers, various shape handles and controls enable you to modify a section, as shown in Figure 6–36.

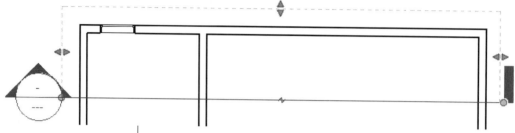

Figure 6–36

- Adjust the ⬍ (Drag) controls to change the length and depth of the cut plane.

- Drag the segment handle controls at either end of the section line to change the location of the arrow or flag without changing the cut boundary.

- Click ⇆ (Flip Section) to change the direction of the arrowhead, which also flips the entire section.

- Click ↻ (Cycle Section Head/Tail) to switch between an arrowhead, flag, or nothing on each end of the section.

- Click ↗ (Gaps in Segments) to create an opening in section lines, as shown in Figure 6–37. Select it again to restore the full section cut.

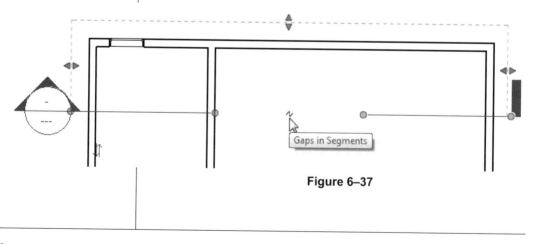

Figure 6–37

How To: Add a Jog to a Section Line

1. Select the section line you want to modify.

2. In the *Modify | Views* tab>Section panel, click 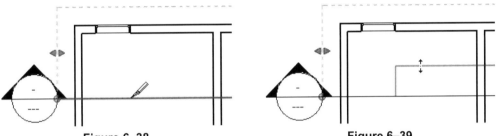 (Split Segment).

3. Select the point along the section line where you want to create the split, as shown in Figure 6–38.

4. Specify the location of the split line, as shown in Figure 6–39.

Figure 6–38   **Figure 6–39**

- If you need to adjust the location of any segment on the section line, modify it and drag the shape handles along each segment of the line, as shown in Figure 6–40.

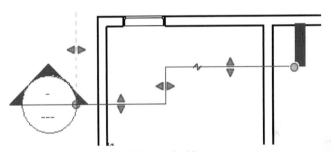

Figure 6–40

To bring a split section line back into place, use the shape handle to drag the jogged line until it is at the same level with the rest of the line.

Hint: Depth Clipping and Far Clipping

Depth Clipping (shown in Figure 6–41) is a viewing option that sets how sloped walls are displayed if the *View Range* of a plan is set to a limited view.

Far Clipping (shown in Figure 6–42) is available for section and elevation views.

Figure 6–41

Figure 6–42

- An additional graphic display option enables you to specify *Depth Cueing*, so that items that are in the distance will be made lighter.

3D Section Views

There are two ways you can create section views of your 3D model: creating a selection box (as shown in Figure 6–43) and orienting to a view. Both of these are very helpful as you are working and also can be used in construction documents and presentations.

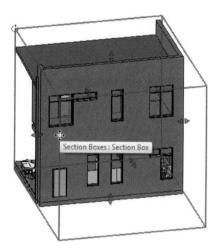

Figure 6–43

How To: Create a Selection Box

1. In a 3D view, select the elements you want to isolate. In the example shown in Figure 6–43, the front wall was selected.

2. In the *Modify* tab>View panel, click 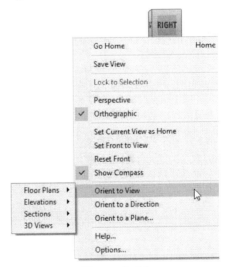 (Selection Box) or type **BX**.
3. The view is limited to a box around the selected item(s).
4. Use the controls of the section box to modify the size of the box to show exactly what you want.

- To toggle off a section box and restore the full model, in the view's Properties, in the *Extents* area, clear the check mark from **Section Box**.

How To: Orient a 3D View to a View

1. Open a 3D view.
2. Right-click on the ViewCube, select **Orient to View>Floor Plans**, **Elevations**, **Sections**, or **3D Views** (as shown in Figure 6–44), and select the view from the list.

Figure 6–44

3. The view displays similar to the partial floor plan view of a stair shown in Figure 6–45. Use the 3D view rotation tools to navigate around the 3D model, as shown in Figure 6–46.

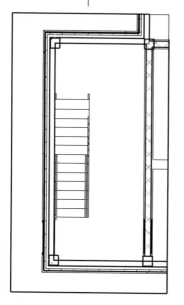

Figure 6–45

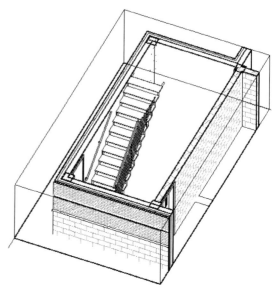

Figure 6–46

• **Orient to a Direction** (shown in Figure 6–47) allows you to rotate the view to a specific direction. This is similar to using the orientation planes of the ViewCube.

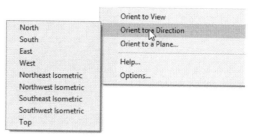

Figure 6–47

- **Orient to a Plane** opens the Select Orientation Plane dialog box and allows you to specify a level, grid, or named reference plane, pick a plane, or pick a line, as shown in Figure 6–48. The view is not cut at the plane but oriented in that direction.

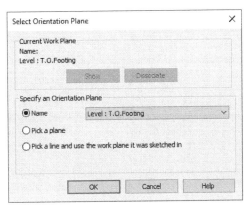

Figure 6–48

Practice 6b | Create Interior Elevations and Sections

Practice Objectives

- Create interior elevations.
- Add building sections and wall sections.

In this practice, you will create interior elevations of the kitchen. You will also add building sections, as shown in Figure 6–49, and a wall section to the project. (The DWG and tags have been hidden and the walls are set to halftone in the image for clarity.)

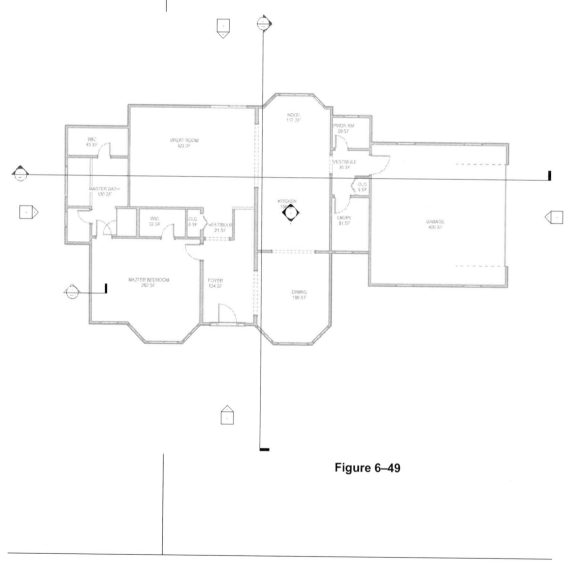

Figure 6–49

Task 1 - Add interior elevations.

1. Open the project **Residential-Elevations.rvt** from the practice files folder.

2. Open the **Floor Plans: First Floor** view.

3. In the *View* tab>Create panel, expand ⬆ (Elevation) and click ⬆ (Elevation). In the Type Selector, select **Elevation: Interior Elevation**.

4. Place an interior elevation marker in the kitchen, as shown in Figure 6–50.

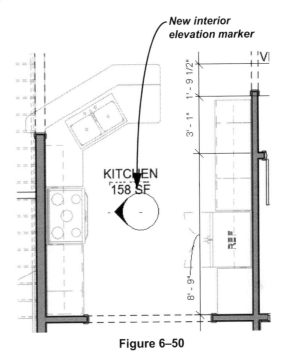

Figure 6–50

5. Click ⬆ (Modify).

In this project, North is considered the top of the project.

6. Zoom in to the interior elevation marker. Select the interior elevation marker that is pointing to the west wall in the kitchen and click the three boxes, as shown in Figure 6–51.

   - Hint: You can hide in view or set to halftone any elements needed to make adding interior elevation markers easier.

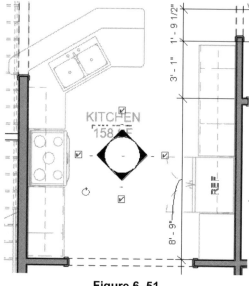

Figure 6–51

7. Click ⬚ (Modify).

8. Double-click on one of the arrowheads on the new interior elevation marker.

9. Change the length and depth of the crop region to show the walls in the kitchen up to the second floor, as shown in Figure 6–52.

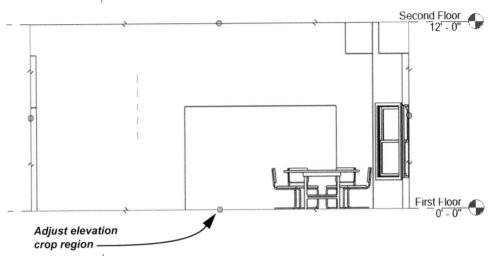

Adjust elevation crop region

Figure 6–52

10. In Project Browser, expand **Elevations (Interior Elevation)** and rename the *Elevation 1-a* view to **Kitchen-West**.

11. Click ▣ (Hide Crop Region).

12. Rename the other interior elevations accordingly.

13. Select all of the elevation marker arrows (not the circles) and, in Properties, set the *Hide at scales coarser than* to **1/4"=1'-0"**, as shown in Figure 6–53.

Doing this keeps these markers from showing up in other plans at larger scales.

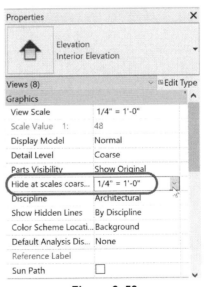

Figure 6–53

14. Save the project.

Task 2 - Modify the building elevations.

1. In the **First Floor** view, select the west elevation arrowhead.

2. In Properties, in the *Extents* area, select **Crop View**, as shown in Figure 6–54.

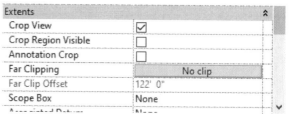

Figure 6–54

3. In the *Extents* area next to *Far Clipping,* click **No clip**.

4. In the Far Clipping dialog box, select **Clip with line**, as shown in Figure 6–55.

Figure 6–55

5. Click **OK**.

6. Use the grips to adjust the elevation crop region closer to the house.

7. Click in an empty area in the view to clear the selection.

8. Move the building elevation markers as needed.

9. Modify the other building elevation markers.

10. Save the project.

Task 3 - Add building sections.

1. In the **First Floor** view, type **ZA** (Zoom All to Fit) to zoom out to the extents of the view.

2. In the *View* tab>Create panel, click 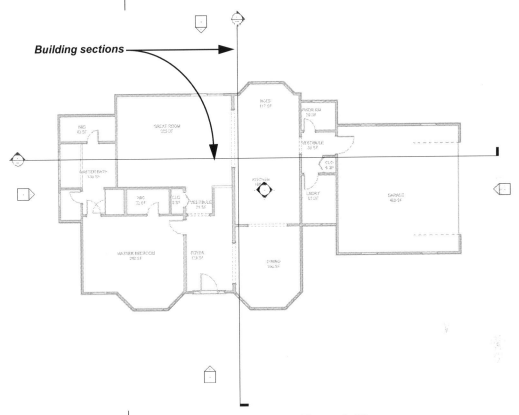 (Section).

3. In the Type Selector, select **Section: Building Section**.

4. Draw a vertical section and a horizontal section through the building, as shown in Figure 6–56.

Building sections

Figure 6–56

5. In the Project Browser, under *Sections (Building Section)*, rename the new sections to **N/S Building Section** and **E/W Building Section** respectively.

6. View the section and adjust the crop region to show up to the Roof Peak level.

7. Save the project.

Task 4 - Add a wall section.

1. Open the **Floor Plans: First Floor** view and close any other opened views.

2. Zoom in to the master bedroom area.

3. In the *View* tab>Create panel, click ⬙ (Section). In the Type Selector, select **Section: Wall Section**.

4. Draw a section in the master bedroom at the window, as shown in Figure 6–57.

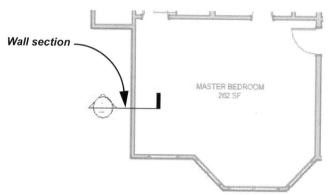

Figure 6–57

5. In the Project Browser, under *Section (Wall Elevation)*, rename the new section to **Typ. Wall Section**.

6. Open the view and modify the crop region.

7. Save and close the project.

6.4 Adding Callout Views

Callouts are enlarged details of plan, elevation, or section views. When you place a callout in a view, as shown in Figure 6–58, it automatically creates a new view clipped to the boundary of the callout, as shown in Figure 6–59. You can create rectangular or sketched callout boundaries.

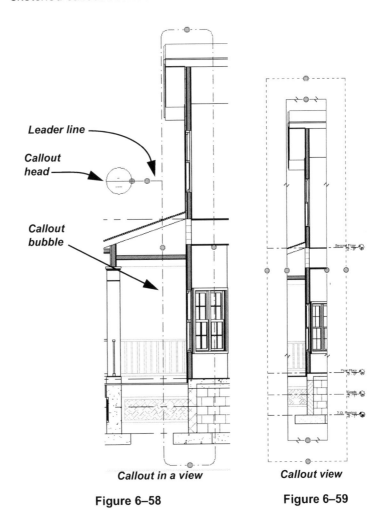

Leader line

Callout head

Callout bubble

Callout in a view

Callout view

Figure 6–58

Figure 6–59

- Callout views are saved in the same node in the Project Browser as the original view. For example, the callout view of a floor plan is placed within the Floor Plans node.

- To open the callout view, double-click on its name in the Project Browser or on the callout head (verify that the callout bubble is not selected before you double-click on it).

How To: Create a Rectangular Callout

1. In the *View* tab>Create panel, click 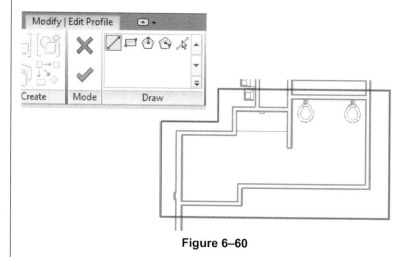 (Callout).
2. Select points for two opposite corners to define the callout bubble around the area you want to detail.
3. Select the callout bubble and use the shape handles to modify the location of the bubble and any other edges that might need changing.
4. In the Project Browser, you can rename the callout view.

How To: Create a Sketched Callout

1. In the *View* tab>Create panel, expand (Callout), and click (Sketch).
2. Sketch the shape of the callout bubble using the tools in the *Modify | Edit Profile* tab>Draw panel, as shown in Figure 6–60.

Figure 6–60

3. Click (Finish) to complete the boundary.
4. Select the callout bubble and use the shape handles to modify the location of the bubble and any other edges that might need to be changed.
5. In the Project Browser, rename the callout.

Modifying Callouts

Callouts are cropped and typically enlarged versions of the original view. When you modify them, you are changing the crop region of the view.

- If you change the size of the callout bubble in the original view, it automatically updates the callout view and vice-versa.

- Callouts can be reshaped. Select the callout bubble or crop region and, in the *Modify | Floor Plan* tab>Mode panel, click (Edit Crop) and use the Draw tools to modify the sketch.

- If you want to return a sketched or modified callout or crop region to a rectangular configuration, click (Reset Crop).

Working with Crop Regions

Plans, sections, elevations, and 3D views can all be modified by changing how much of the model is displayed in a view. One way to do this is to set the *model* crop region. If there are dimensions, tags, or text near the crop region, you can also use the *annotation* crop region to include these, as shown in Figure 6–61.

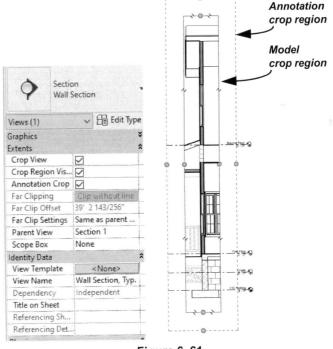

Figure 6–61

Zoom out if you do not see the crop region when you set it to be displayed.

- To display the crop region, in the View Control Bar, click (Show Crop Region). Alternatively, in Properties, in the *Extents* area, select **Crop Region Visible**. **Annotation Crop** is also available in this area.

- It is best practice to hide a crop region before placing a view on a sheet. In the View Control Bar, click (Hide Crop Region).

- Resize the crop region using the control on each side of the region.

Breaking the crop region is typically used with sections or details.

- Click the (Break Line) control to split the view into two regions, horizontally or vertically. Each part of the view can then be modified in size to display what is needed and be moved independently.

- The annotation crop region crops any annotation outside of the crop region and any annotations that it touches. If the model crop region crops an element that is tagged, the tag or annotation will automatically be cropped as well. You can turn on **Annotation Crop** and resize the crop region closer to the model crop region using the grip controls or by using the Crop Region Size dialog box, as shown in Figure 6–62. In the *Modify | Floor Plan* tab>Crop panel, click (Size Crop) to open the dialog box.

Model crop region

Annotation crop region

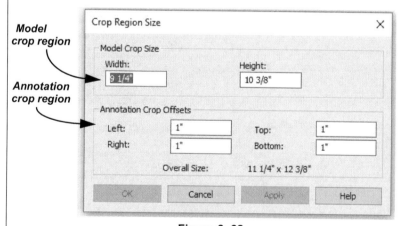

Figure 6–62

Plan Regions

When you have a plan view with multiple levels of floors or ceilings, you can create plan regions that enable you to set a different view range for part of a view, as shown in Figure 6–63 for a set of clerestory windows.

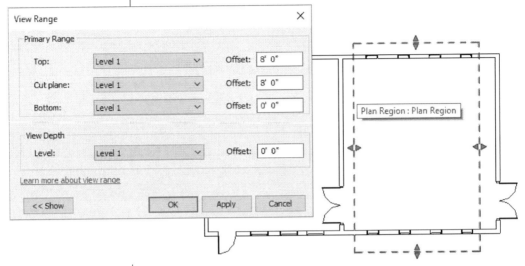

Figure 6–63

How To: Create Plan Regions

1. In a plan view, in the *View* tab>Create panel, expand (Plan Views) and select (Plan Region).
2. In the *Modify | Create Plan Region Boundary* tab>Draw panel, select a draw tool and create the boundary for the plan region.
    - The boundary must be closed and cannot overlap other plan region boundaries, but the boundaries can be side by side.

3. Click (Finish Edit Mode).
4. In the *Modify | Plan Region* tab>Region panel, click (View Range).
5. In the View Range dialog box, specify the offsets for the plan region and click **OK**. The plan region is applied to the selected area.

- Plan regions can be copied to the clipboard and then pasted into other plan views.

- You can use shape handles to resize plan region boundaries without having to edit the boundary.

- If a plan region is above a door, the door swing displays, but the door opening does not display, as shown in Figure 6–64.

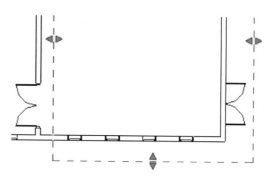

Figure 6–64

- Plan regions can be toggled on and off in the Visibility/Graphic Overrides dialog box on the *Annotation Categories* tab.

Practice 6c | Add Callout Views

Practice Objective

* Create callouts.

In this practice, you will create a callout view that displays a typical wall section, as shown in Figure 6–65.

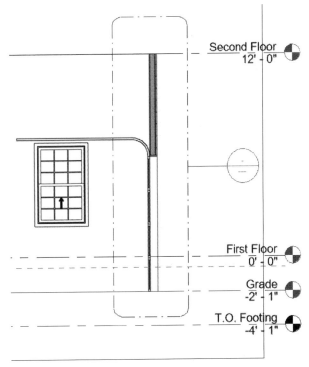

Figure 6–65

1. Open the project **Residential-Callouts.rvt** from the practice files folder.

2. Close any other projects you may have open.

3. Open the **Sections (Building Section): E/W Building Section** view.

4. Note that the *Scale* is set to **1/4"=1'-0"**.

5. In the *View* tab>Create panel, click (Callout).

6. In the Type Selector, select **Section: Wall Section**.

7. Place a callout around the exterior wall with the garage door, as shown in Figure 6–66.

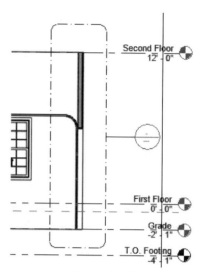

Figure 6–66

8. Click in an empty space in the view to release the selection.

9. Double-click on the callout view bubble to display the view. Note that the *Scale* is automatically set to **1/2"=1'-0"**.

10. In the Project Browser, expand *Sections (Wall Section)* and rename the new callout 1 to **Garage Wall Section**. Press <Enter>.

11. Ensure that the *Detail Level* is set to **Fine**.

12. Save and close the project.

Chapter Review Questions

1. Which of the following commands creates a view that results in an independent view displaying the same model geometry and containing a copy of the annotation?

   a. Duplicate

   b. Duplicate with Detailing

   c. Duplicate as a Dependent

2. Which of the following is true about the Visibility/Graphic Overrides dialog box?

   a. Changes made in the dialog box only affect the current view.

   b. It can only be used to toggle categories on and off.

   c. It can be used to toggle individual elements on and off.

   d. It can be used to change the color of individual elements.

3. If you want to hide just one of the elevation markers in a view, what do you have to do?

   a. Select the elevation marker, then right-click and select **Hide in View>By Filter**.

   b. Select the elevation marker, then right-click and select **Hide in View>Category**.

   c. Select the elevation marker, then right-click and select **Hide in View>Elements**.

   d. In the Visibility/Graphics Overrides dialog box, uncheck **Elevations**.

4. How do you create a jog in a building section, such as that shown in Figure 6–67?

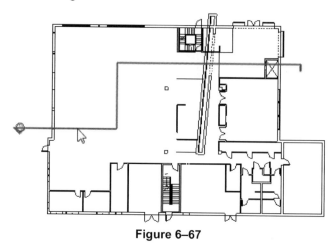

Figure 6–67

a. Use the **Split Element** tool in the *Modify* tab>Modify panel.

b. Select the building section and then click **Split Segment** in the contextual tab.

c. Select the building section and click the blue control in the middle of the section line.

d. Draw two separate sections and use the **Section Jog** tool to combine them into a jogged section.

5. How do you create multiple interior elevations in one room?

a. Using the **Interior Elevation** command, place the elevation marker.

b. Using the **Elevation** command, from the Properties Type Selector, change to **Interior Elevation** and place the first marker, select it, and select the appropriate Show Arrow boxes.

c. Using the **Interior Elevation** command, place an elevation marker for each wall of the room you want to display.

d. Using the **Elevation** command, select a Multiple Elevation marker type, and place the elevation marker.

6. What is the purpose of creating a callout?

    a. To create a boundary around part of the model that needs revising, similar to a revision cloud.

    b. To create a view of part of the model to export to the AutoCAD® software for further detailing.

    c. To create a view of part of the model that is linked to the main view from which it is taken.

    d. To create a 2D view of part of the model.

7. You placed dimensions in a view but only some of them display, as shown on the left in Figure 6–68. You were expecting the view to display as shown on the right in Figure 6–68. What do you need to modify to see the missing dimensions?

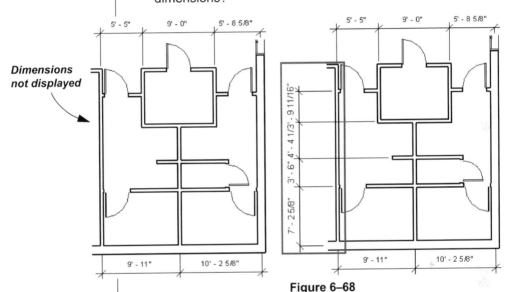

Figure 6–68

    a. Dimension Settings

    b. Dimension Type

    c. Visibility/Graphic Overrides

    d. Annotation Crop Region

Command Summary

Button	Command	Location
Views		
	Elevation	• **Ribbon:** *View* tab>Create panel> expand Elevation
	Callout: Rectangle	• **Ribbon:** *View* tab>Create panel> expand Callout
	Callout: Sketch	• **Ribbon:** *View* tab>Create panel> expand Callout
	Duplicate	• **Ribbon:** *View* tab>Create panel> expand Duplicate View • **Right-click:** (*on a view in the Project Browser*) expand Duplicate View
	Duplicate as Dependent	• **Ribbon:** *View* tab>Create panel> expand Duplicate View • **Right-click:** (*on a view in the Project Browser*) expand Duplicate View
	Duplicate with Detailing	• **Ribbon:** *View* tab>Create panel> expand Duplicate View • **Right-click:** (*on a view in the Project Browser*) Duplicate View
	Plan Region	• **Ribbon:** *View* tab>Create panel> expand Plan Views
	Section	• **Ribbon:** *View* tab>Create panel • **Quick Access Toolbar**
	Split Segment	• **Ribbon:** (*when the elevation or section marker is selected*) *Modify	Views* tab> Section panel
Crop Views		
	Crop View	• **View Control Bar** • **View Properties:** Crop View (*check*)
	Do Not Crop View	• **View Control Bar** • **View Properties:** Crop View (*clear*)
	Edit Crop	• **Ribbon:** (*when the crop region of a callout, elevation, or section view is selected*) *Modify	Views* tab>Mode panel
	Hide Crop Region	• **View Control Bar** • **View Properties:** Crop Region Visible (*clear*)
	Reset Crop	• **Ribbon:** (*when the crop region of a callout, elevation or section view is selected*) *Modify	Views* tab>Mode panel

	Show Crop Region	• **View Control Bar** • **View Properties:** Crop Region Visible (*check*)
	Size Crop	• **Ribbon:** (*when the crop region of a callout, elevation or section view is selected*) *Modify	Views* tab>Mode panel

View Display

	Hide in View	• **Ribbon:** *Modify* tab>View Graphics panel>Hide>Elements *or* By Category • **Right-click:** (*when an element is selected*) Hide in View>Elements *or* Category
	Override Graphics in View	• **Ribbon:** *Modify* tab>View Graphics panel>Hide>Elements *or* By Category • **Right-click:** (*when an element is selected*) Override Graphics in View>By Element *or* By Category • **Shortcut:** (*category only*) VV or VG
	Plan Region	• **Ribbon:** *View* tab>Create panel expand Plan Views.
	Selection Box	• **Ribbon:** *Modify* tab>View panel • **Shortcut: BX.**
	Reveal Hidden Elements	• **View Control Bar**
	Temporary Hide/Isolate	• **View Control Bar**
	Temporary View Properties	• **View Control Bar**

Modeling Floors

Floors in the Autodesk® Revit® software can be used as full-depth floors or as a thin veneer that shows floor material placed on an underlying structural pad. You can customize floors by creating slopes for drainage, cutting holes, or creating shafts that cut through multiple floors.

Learning Objectives in This Chapter

- Sketch and modify floor boundaries.
- Join geometry between floors and walls for a cleaner visual presentation.
- Slope a floor in one or more directions for drainage.

7.1 Modeling Floors

The **Floor** command can generate any flat or sloped surface, such as floors, decks, patios, and balconies, as shown in Figure 7–1. Typically created in a plan view, the floor can be based either on bounding walls or on a sketched outline.

Floors : Floor : Generic - 12"

Figure 7–1

- The floor type controls the thickness of a floor.

How To: Add a Floor

1. In the *Architecture* tab>Build panel, expand (Floor) and click (Floor: Architectural) or (Floor: Structural).
2. You are placed in sketch mode where other elements in the model are grayed out.
3. In the Type Selector, set the type of floor you want to use. In Properties, set any constraints as needed.
4. In the *Modify | Create Floor Boundary* tab>Draw panel, click (Boundary Line).

   - Click (Pick Walls) and select the walls, setting either the inside or outside edge. If you have selected a wall, you can click (Flip) to switch the inside/outside status of the boundary location, as shown in Figure 7–2.

   - Click (Line) or one of the other Draw tools and sketch the boundary edges.

   - Use the Modify tools to align, move, or trim the boundary lines.

The lines in the sketch must form a closed loop. Use tools in the Modify panel to adjust intersections.

5. Click 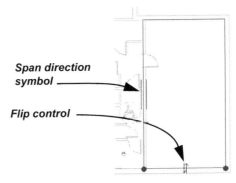 (Slope Arrow) to define a slope for the entire floor.

The span direction is automatically placed on the first sketch line.

6. Click (Span Direction), as shown in Figure 7–2, to modify the direction of the structural elements in the floor.

Span direction symbol

Flip control

Figure 7–2

7. Click (Finish Edit Mode) to create the floor.

- If you are using (Pick Walls), select the **Extend into wall (to core)** option in the Options Bar if you want the floor to cut into the wall. For example, the floor would cut through the gypsum wall board and the air space but stop at a core layer, such as CMU or stud.

- If you select one or more of the boundary sketch lines, you can also set *Cantilevers* for *Concrete* or *Steel*, as shown in Figure 7–3. (You will need to click (Modify) first before selecting a boundary sketch line to get Figure 7–3.)

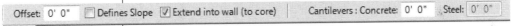
Offset: 0' 0"   ☐ Defines Slope ☑ Extend into wall (to core)   Cantilevers : Concrete: 0' 0"   Steel: 0' 0"

Figure 7–3

- To create an opening inside the floor, create a separate closed loop inside the first one, as shown in Figure 7–4.

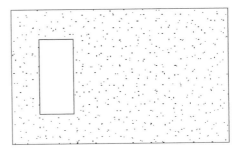

Figure 7–4

Hint: Sketched Arcs and Tangent Lock

If you are adding arcs or ellipses to a sketch that are tangent to other lines, you can lock the geometry in place by clicking on the tangency lock (Toggle Join Tangency), as shown in Figure 7–5.

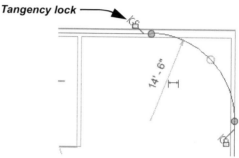

Figure 7–5

• This lock is available whenever you are in sketch mode.

• If you create a floor on an upper level, an alert box displays asking if you want the walls below to be attached to the underside of the floor and its level, as shown in Figure 7–6. If you have a variety of wall heights, it is better to click **Don't attach** and attach the walls separately.

• Another alert box might open, as shown in Figure 7–7. You can automatically join the geometry or can do so at a later time.

Figure 7–6

Figure 7–7

- Floors can be, and often are, placed on top of floors. For example, a structural floor can have a finish floor of tile or carpet placed on top of it, as shown in Figure 7–8. These floors can then be scheduled separately.

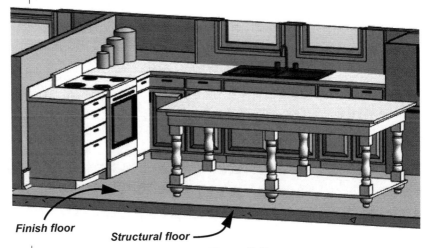

Finish floor   **Structural floor**

Figure 7–8

Modifying Floors

You can change a floor to a different type using the Type Selector. In Properties, you can modify parameters including the *Height Offset From Level*, as shown in Figure 7–9. When you have a floor selected, you can also edit the boundaries.

Many of the parameters in Properties are used in schedules, including Elevation at Top (Bottom) and Elevation at Top (Bottom) Core for multi-layered floors.

Properties		✕
	Floor Generic - 12"	▾
Floors (1)	▾	⊞ Edit Type
Constraints		
Level	Floor 1	
Height Offset From ...	0' 0"	
Room Bounding	☑	
Related to Mass	☐	
Structural		
Structural	☐	
Enable Analytical M...	☐	
Dimensions		
Slope		
Perimeter	40' 0"	
Area	99.00 SF	
Volume	99.00 CF	
Elevation at Top	0' 0"	
Elevation at Bottom	-1' 0"	
Properties help		Apply

Figure 7–9

How To: Modify the Floor Sketch

1. Select a floor. You might need to hover your cursor over an element near the floor and press <Tab> until the floor type displays in the Status Bar or in a tooltip, as shown in Figure 7–10.

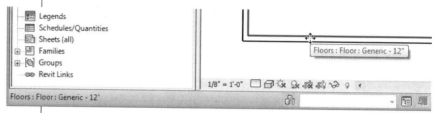

Figure 7–10

2. In the *Modify | Floors* tab>Mode panel, click (Edit Boundary). You are placed into Edit Boundary mode.
3. Modify the sketch lines using the Draw tools, controls, and the various Modify tools.

4. Click (Finish Edit Mode).

- Select a floor, then double-click on it to be placed directly into Edit Boundary mode.

- Floor sketches can be edited in plan and 3D views, but not in elevations. If you try to edit in an elevation view, you are prompted to select another view in which to edit.

Hint: Selecting Floor Faces

If it is difficult to select the floor edges, toggle on the selection option (Select Elements by Face) from the Status Bar. This will enable you to select the floor face and not just the edges.

Practice 7a

Model Floors

Practice Objective

- Add floors.

In this practice, you will create and modify floors in the first floor and second floor of a project, as shown in Figure 7–11. You will then clean up connections between the floors and walls. Tags, sections, callouts, and interior elevation markers are turned off in images in this section for clarity.

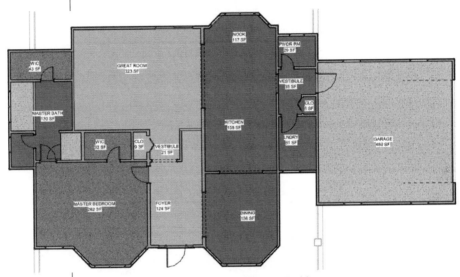

Figure 7–11

Task 1 - Add slab-on-grade flooring.

1. Open the project **Residential-Floors.rvt** from the practice files folder.

2. Open the **Floor Plans: First Floor** view.

3. To clean up the view, select one door tag, window tag, section marker, and interior elevation marker and type **VH** to hide those types in the view.

4. Type **ZA** to zoom all.

5. In the *Architecture* tab>Build panel, expand ⬜ (Floor) and select ⬜ (Floor: Structural).

6. In the Type Selector, select **Floor: Foundation Slab 4"**. In Properties, set the *Level* to **First Floor** and the *Height Offset From Level* to (negative) **-0'-0 3/4"**. This will ensure that a typical finish will be even with the level datum.

7. In the *Modify | Create Floor Boundary* tab>Draw panel, click

   (Pick Walls) and select the exterior face of core of the garage walls. Use the Modify tools to ensure that the boundary is a closed loop.

8. Draw the boundary around the first floor, as shown in Figure 7–12. Be sure that the boundary goes to the exterior face of core for the walls.

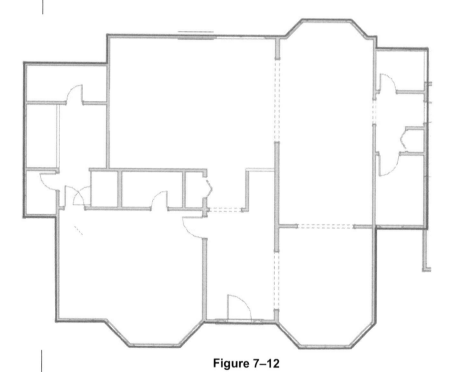

Figure 7–12

9. Click (Finish Edit Mode).

10. In the Attaching to floor dialog box, click **Don't attach**, as shown in Figure 7–13.

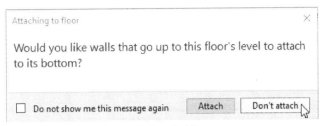

Figure 7–13

11. When prompted to join overlapping geometry, click **Yes**, as shown in Figure 7–14.

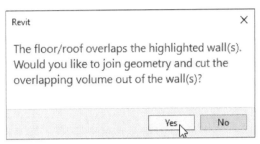

Figure 7–14

12. Click ⬦ (Modify).

13. Pan and zoom to the garage area.

14. In the *Architecture* tab>Build panel, expand 🗋 (Floor) and select 〰 (Floor: Structural).

15. In the Type Selector, select **Foundation Slab: 4"**.

16. In Properties, change the *Level* to **Grade** and set the *Height Offset From Level* to **0'-0"**.

17. In the *Modify | Create Floor Boundary* tab>Draw panel, click ▣ (Pick Walls) and select the exterior face of core of the garage walls. Use the Modify tools to ensure that the boundary is a closed loop.

18. Click ✔ (Finish Edit Mode).

19. When the alert box about joining geometry opens, click **Yes**. The floor pattern displays, as shown in Figure 7–15.

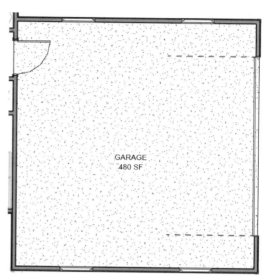

Figure 7–15

20. Click in an empty space in the view to release the floor selection.

Task 2 - Add finish flooring.

1. Zoom and pan over to the great room and foyer.

2. In the *Architecture* tab>Build panel, expand (Floor) and select (Floor: Architectural).

3. In the Type Selector, select **Floor: Wood Finish**.

4. In the Options Bar, ensure that **Extend into wall (to core)** is checked, as shown in Figure 7–16.

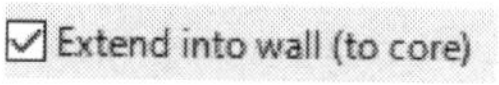

☑ Extend into wall (to core)

Figure 7–16

5. In Properties, set the *Height Offset From Level* to **0'-0 3/4"**.

6. In the *Modify | Create Floor Boundary* tab>Draw panel, click

    (Pick Walls) and select the inside face of the walls. Draw
   boundary lines around the great room and foyer, as shown in
   Figure 7–17.

GREAT ROOM
323 SF

WIC
32 SF

CLO
9 SF

VESTIBULE
21 SF

MASTER BEDROOM
262 SF

FOYER
124 SF

Figure 7–17

7. Use the Modify tools to ensure that the boundary is a closed
   loop. Use the Flip icon to flip the boundary lines, as needed.

8. Zoom in to the door going into the master bedroom. Use the
   ✎ (Line) draw tool to add boundary lines so the boundary
   ends at the door stop, as shown in Figure 7–18.

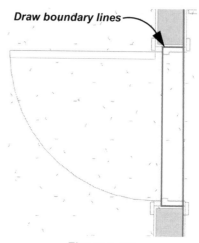

Draw boundary lines

Figure 7–18

9. In the *Modify | Create Floor Boundary* tab>Modify panel, click
   ⊏⊐ (Split).

10. In the Options Bar, select **Delete Inner Segment**.

11. Click on either side of the door, as shown in Figure 7–19. The
    inner boundary line deletes.

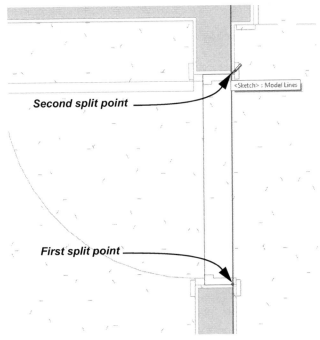

Figure 7–19

12. Pan up to the closet above this door. Modify the boundaries to include the closet.

13. Click ✔ (Finish Edit Mode).

   • If an Error dialog box displays, it will highlight the lines that are not trimmed correctly in orange. Click **Continue** and use the **Trim** tool to fix any lines that are not connected.

14. In the Attaching to floor dialog box, click **Don't attach**, as shown in Figure 7–20. You do not want to attach the walls to this floor. This will leave a cavity for a structural engineer to design joists.

Figure 7–20

15. When prompted to join overlapping geometry, click **Yes**, as shown in Figure 7–21.

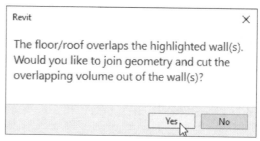

Figure 7–21

- Note: It is best to do each room separately to have better control over the floor and better quantity control for scheduling.

16. Start the **Floor** command again.

17. Add the **Floor: Wood Finish** to the closet off of the vestibule. Make sure to set the *Height Offset From Level* to **0'-0 3/4"**.

18. Click ✓ (Finish Edit Mode).

19. In the Attaching to floor dialog box, click **Don't attach**.

20. Pan and zoom to the master bedroom and bathroom.

21. Start the **Floor** command again.

22. In the Type Selector, select **Floor: Carpet Finish**. In Properties, ensure that the *Level* is set to **First Floor** and set the *Height Offset From Level* to **0'-0 1/8"**.

23. Draw the boundary shown in Figure 7–22.

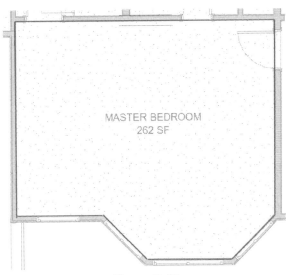

MASTER BEDROOM
262 SF

Figure 7–22

24. Modify the boundary line at the bathroom door and the door going into the hallway, as done previously.

25. Click (Finish Edit Mode).

26. In the Attaching to floor dialog box, click **Don't attach**. When prompted to join overlapping geometry, click **Yes**.

27. Start the **Floor** command again and add carpet to both walk-in closets.

28. Click (Finish Edit Mode).

29. Repeat the **Floor** command and create a tile finish in the master bathroom area, as shown in Figure 7–23. In Properties, set the *Height Offset From Level* to **0'-0"**.

30. Make sure not to add tile under where the tub will go.

31. Modify the boundary around the shower wall and door leading into the master bedroom, as shown in Figure 7–23.

Tub area

MASTER BATH
130 SF

Figure 7–23

32. Click  (Finish Edit Mode).

33. Pan over to the nook and kitchen area. Repeat the **Floor** command and create a tile finish (**25" Ceramic Tile**) in the common areas on the right side of the floor plan, as shown in Figure 7–24. In Properties, set the *Height Offset From Level* to **0'-0"**.

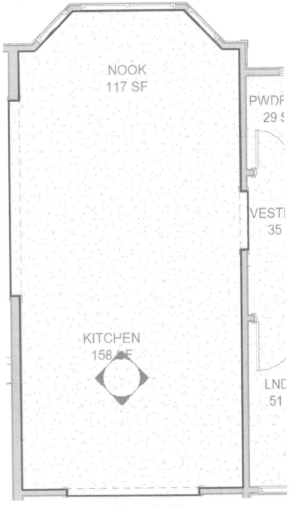

NOOK
117 SF

PWDF
29 S

VEST
35

KITCHEN
158 SF

LNC
51

Figure 7–24

34. Modify the boundary that borders the great room and vestibule.

35. Click (Finish Edit Mode).

36. In the Attaching to floor dialog box, click **Don't attach**. When prompted to join overlapping geometry, click **Yes**.

37. Repeat the process to create a tile floor in the dining area, powder room, vestibule, closet, and laundry room. Modify the boundaries as needed at the doors and openings.

38. Zoom out. In the View Control Bar, change the *Visual Style* to **Shaded** to display the different floor coverings.

39. Save the project.

Task 3 - Add a second floor.

1. Open the **Floor Plans: Second Floor** view.

2. Select one door tag and one window tag and type **VH**.

3. In the *Architecture* tab>Build panel, click 🔲 (Floor) and set the following options:

    - In the Type Selector, select **Floor: Wood Open Web Truss 22" - Wood Finish**.
    - In the Options Bar, select **Extend into wall (to core)**.

4. In Properties, set the *Height Offset From Level* to **0'-0"**.

5. In the *Modify | Create Floor Boundary* tab>Draw panel, click 🔍 (Pick Walls) and select the walls shown in Figure 7–25.

6. Change to 🔍 (Pick Lines) and select the lines of the balcony in the linked CAD file, as shown in Figure 7–25. Make sure to select the outline on the balcony and modify the boundary lines at each of the doors.

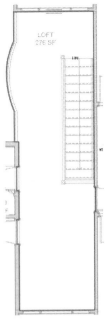

Figure 7–25

- Zoom in and make sure the balcony edge aligns with the wall where the windows are. Use the **Align** tool to align the boundary if necessary.

7. Click ✓ (Finish Edit Mode).

8. When the first alert box displays, click **Don't attach**.

9. When prompted to join overlapping geometry, click **Yes**.

10. Click in an empty space in the view to release the selection.

11. Repeat the process to place the **Wood Open Web Truss 22" - Wood Finish** in the vestibule, closet, and storage areas.

12. Click ✓ (Finish Edit Mode).

13. When the first alert box displays, click **Don't attach**.

14. When prompted to join overlapping geometry, click **Yes**.

15. Repeat the process to place carpet flooring in the bedrooms (use **Wood Open Web Truss 22" - Carpet Finish** with the *Height Offset From Level* at **0'-0"**) and tile flooring in the bathroom (use **25" Ceramic Tile over Wd Truss** with the *Height Offset From Level* at **0'-0"**).

16. Save the project.

Task 4 - (Optional) Add porch deck.

1. Open the **Floor Plans: First Floor** view.

2. In the *Architecture* tab>Build panel, expand 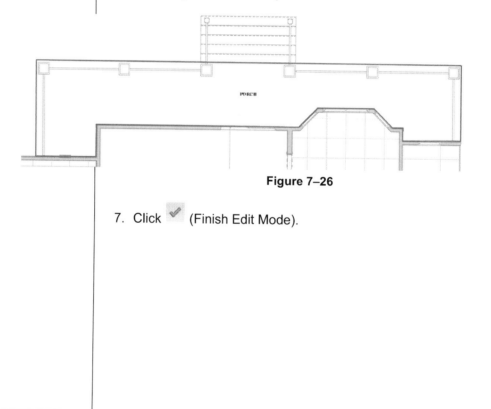 (Floor) and select (Floor: Architectural).

3. In the Type Selector, select **Floor: Wood Deck**.

4. In Properties, set the following:

   - *Level:* **First Floor**
   - *Height Offset From Level:* (negative) **-0'-4"**

5. In the Options Bar, ensure **Extend into wall (to core)** is not checked. This deck will only extend to the exterior finish of the wall.

6. Use (Pick Walls) and (Pick Lines) to select the exterior face of the walls and trace the deck, as shown in Figure 7–26. Use the Modify tools to ensure that the boundary is a closed loop.

PORCH

Figure 7–26

7. Click (Finish Edit Mode).

8. Open a 3D view to view the new floors and porch deck, as shown in Figure 7–27.

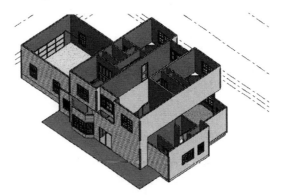

Figure 7–27

9. Use (Join Geometry) to clean up where floors meet wall geometry, as needed.

10. Repeat this process for the other porch on the other side of the floor plan.

11. Zoom out and orbit around the house to see all the changes.

12. Save and close the project.

7.2 Modeling Thickened Slab Edges

You can add elements to a foundation slab or structural floor for a haunched or thickened slab edge, as shown in Figure 7–28. Once the slab edge is in place, it needs to be joined to the slab or structural floor using **Join Geometry**.

Cutting a section through the objects you want to join helps to display them more clearly.

Figure 7–28

- Slab edges cannot be applied to roof elements.

How To: Place a Slab Edge

Note: Select the bottom edge of the slab, unless the slab edge profile includes the thickness of the slab.

1. Open a 3D view showing the slab.

2. In the *Architecture* tab>Build panel, expand ⬜ (Floor) and select ◁ (Floor: Slab Edge).

   - Alternatively, in the *Structure* tab>Structure panel, expand 〰 (Floor) and click ◁ (Floor: Slab Edge), or in the *Structure* tab>Foundation panel, expand ⬜ (Slab) and click ◁ (Floor: Slab Edge).

3. In the Type Selector, select the slab edge type.

4. Select the edges of the slab or floor where you want to apply the slab edge, as shown in Figure 7–29. You can press <Tab> to highlight and select all sides of the slab.

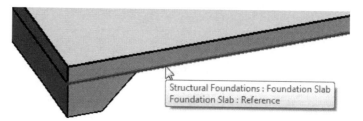

Figure 7–29

7.3 Adding Footings

Wall footings for bearing and retaining are hosted by the walls. Once a footing is in place, you can add reinforcement, as shown in Figure 7–30. With the advantages of having a true foundation in place, you can accurately tag and schedule the footings.

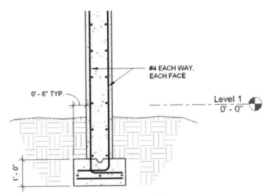

Figure 7–30

- You can apply two types of continuous footing systems, as shown in Figure 7–31. You must have walls in your model to add a footing system.

  - **Retaining footings:** A footing with one side offset to accommodate additional lateral loads and reinforcement

  - **Bearing footings:** A footing with an equal distance on either side of the bearing wall.

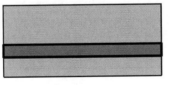
Retaining footing

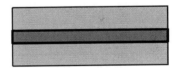
Bearing footing

Figure 7–31

How To: Place a Bearing or Retaining Footing

Wall foundations can also be placed in 3D, section, and elevation views.

1. Create walls or use existing ones. A wall must be in place for this command to work.
2. Open a foundation plan and set it up so that the walls are displayed and you can select them.

3. In the *Structure* tab>Foundation panel, click 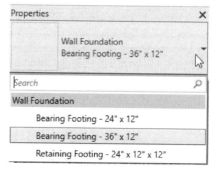 (Wall) to start the **Structural Foundations: Wall** command, or type **FT**.

4. In the Type Selector, select a type, as shown in Figure 7–32.

Figure 7–32

5. Select a wall. The footing is placed beneath the wall, as shown in Figure 7–33.

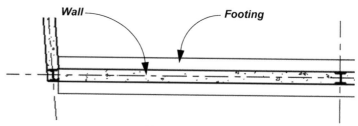

Figure 7–33

- To select multiple walls, hover over one wall and then press <Tab> to select all connected walls. Alternatively, in the *Modify | Place Wall Foundation* tab>Multiple panel, click

  (Select Multiple). Select the walls using any selection

  method and click (Finish) to place the footings.

- You can flip retaining footings, as shown in Figure 7–34.

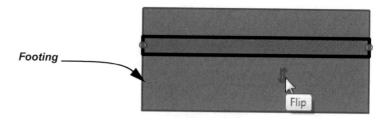

Figure 7–34

How To: Create a Footing Type

1. Select an existing foundation wall element or start the **Structural Foundation: Wall** command.
2. In the Type Selector, select a type similar to the type that you want to create and, in Properties, click 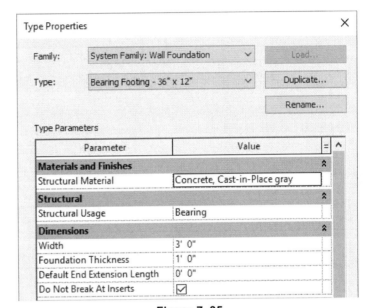 (Edit Type).
3. In the Type Properties dialog box, click **Duplicate**.
4. In the Name dialog box, type a new name for the element and click **OK**.
5. Make any changes to the type properties as needed, as shown in Figure 7–35.

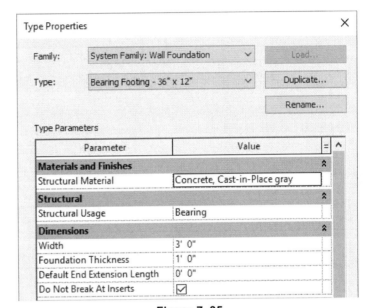

Figure 7–35

6. Click **OK** to close the dialog box.

Wall Profiles and Footings

Footings are appended to the bottom of a wall, which means that any change to the base of the host wall influences the footing. This occurs for lateral movement and horizontal movement. For the example shown in Figure 7–36, when the wall profile changes based on a sloped site (as shown on the left), the footing breaks and follows the modified profile (as shown on the right). This is accomplished by editing the profile of the foundation wall. After you adjust the sketch, you can add isolated footings to create the appropriate shape.

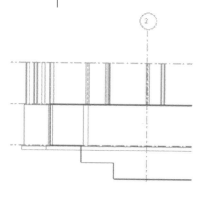

Wall profile in process

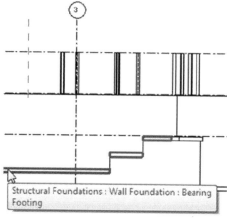

Completed wall with footing

Figure 7–36

Hint: Materials

When you are creating some types such as wall footings, one option is to set the *Structural Material*. In the Type Properties dialog box, in the *Materials and Finishes* area, click in the *Value* column and then click 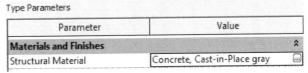 (Browse), as shown in Figure 7–37.

Figure 7–37

In the Material Browser (shown in Figure 7–38), specify the material you want to use and click **OK**.

Figure 7–38

7.4 Creating Columns, Piers, Pilasters, and Augers

The Autodesk Revit software does not have specific categories for piers and pilasters. If you need to create these elements, the best method is to use concrete columns, as shown in Figure 7–39. You can then analyze them as part of the foundation system and independently schedule them from the main column schedule. A concrete column also automatically embeds itself into a concrete wall.

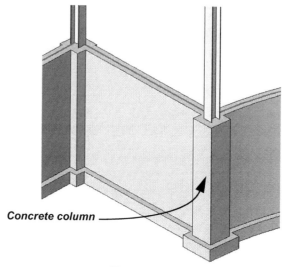

Concrete column

Figure 7–39

- Poured concrete columns can be created in many sizes. For typical rectangular, square, and round columns, it is easy to create custom sizes.

How To: Create a Custom Column Size

1. Open a plan view.

2. In the *Structure* tab>Structure panel, click (Column).

3. In the Type Selector, select an existing column family type similar to the one you want to create, such as **Concrete-Rectangular-Column**.

4. In Properties, click (Edit Type).

5. In the Type Properties dialog box, click **Duplicate**.

6. In the Name dialog box, type a name, as shown in Figure 7–40. Click **OK**.

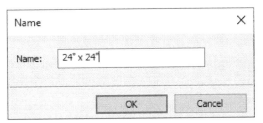

Figure 7–40

7. Modify the dimensions, as needed. Enter the required values for *b* (base) and *h* (height), as shown in Figure 7–41.

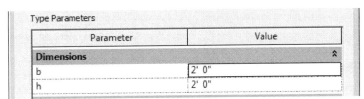

Figure 7–41

8. Click **OK**.
9. The new pier column can be placed at the base of the existing steel columns, as shown in Figure 7–42.

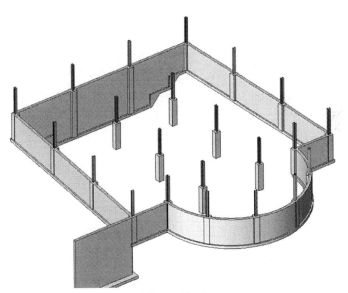

Figure 7–42

Adding Isolated Footings

Footings for columns (shown in Figure 7–43) are placed using the **Structural Foundation: Isolated** command. When you select a column, the footing automatically attaches to the bottom of the column. This is true even when the bottom of the column is on a lower level than the view you are working in.

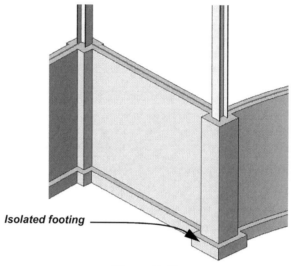

Isolated footing

Figure 7–43

How To: Place an Isolated Footing

1. Open a plan view, such as a **T.O. Footing** structural floor plan.

2. In the *Structure* tab>Foundation panel, click (Isolated) to start the **Structural Foundation: Isolated** command.
3. In the Type Selector, select a footing type.
4. In the view, click to place the individual footing, as shown in Figure 7–44.

   - If needed, press <Spacebar> to rotate the isolated footings after they are placed.

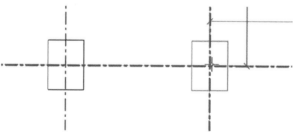

Figure 7–44

See A.3 Creating
Structural Grids for
more information on
grids.

- To add more than one footing at a time, in the *Modify | Place Isolated Foundation* tab>Multiple panel, select 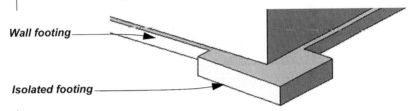 (At Grids) or (At Columns) and select the grids or columns.
  - If needed, press <Spacebar> to rotate the isolated footings after they are placed.
- If the material of the wall footing and the material of the isolated footing are the same, they automatically join, as shown in Figure 7–45.

Wall footing

Isolated footing

Figure 7–45

Hint: Foundation Element Properties

Some of the element properties are automatically generated from the location and size of the element in the model and are grayed out, for example the *Host*, *Elevation at Top*, and *Elevation at Bottom* properties shown in Figure 7–46. These can be used in tags and schedules.

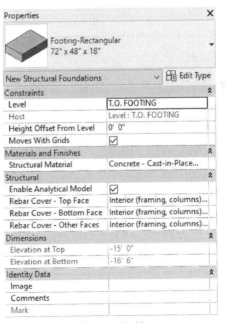

Figure 7–46

Working with Custom Families

Sometimes you need to work with a custom family that has parameters that you can manipulate to fit a specific situation. For example, to add the step footings shown in Figure 7–47, you need to insert an angled isolated footing and modify it to fit the exact size and location.

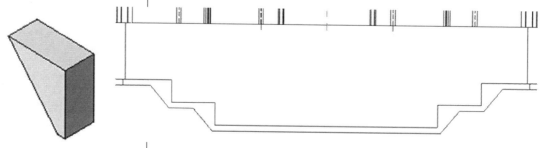

Figure 7–47

How To: Load, Insert, and Modify a Custom Footing

1. Open a plan view.

2. In the *Structure* tab>Foundation panel, click ![icon] (Isolated) and in the *Modify | Place Isolated Foundation* tab>Mode panel, click ![icon] (Load Family).

3. In the Load Family dialog box, find the structural foundation family that you want to use and click **Open**.

4. Place the footing in the plan view. It might not be in the right place, but you can modify it in a section or elevation view.

5. Open an elevation or section view.

6. Move the footing to the correct location. As long as it is in line with another footing, it automatically cleans up, as shown in Figure 7–48.

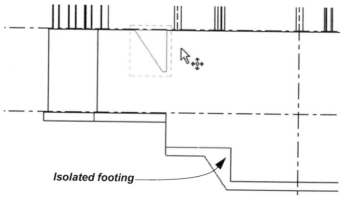

Isolated footing

Figure 7–48

- Use 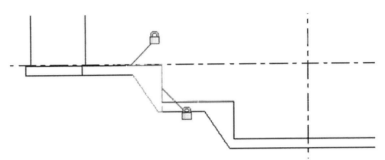 (Align) to align the isolated footing with the footing already in the model. When it is aligned, select the lock, as shown in Figure 7–49. This ensures that if the elevation of the footing wall changes, the step footing will also adjust appropriately.

Figure 7–49

- Some custom families have sizing options in either Properties (per instance) or in the Type Properties (as shown in Figure 7–50) so that you can create additional types in various sizes as needed in the project.

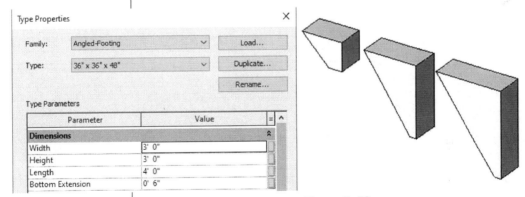

Figure 7–50

Practice 7b

Creating Slab Edges and Footings

Practice Objectives

- Add thickened slab edges.
- Add wall footings.
- Create piers and isolated footings.

In this practice, you will create thickened slabs common to slab-on-grade construction. You will also create thickened edges that resemble header blocks, which will allow for stem walls and footings. Lastly, you will create piers for the porch areas with isolated footings, as shown in Figure 7–51.

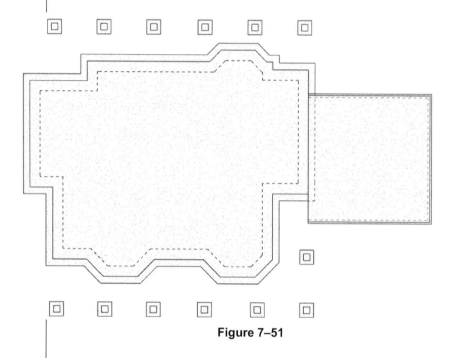

Figure 7–51

Task 1 - Create a slab edge.

1. Open the project **Residential-Foundations.rvt** from the practice files folder.

2. Verify that you are in the **3D Views: {3D}** view.

3. Use the ViewCube to rotate the model so that you are viewing the bottom of the slab, as shown in Figure 7–52.

Hint: In the ViewCube, click the corner at the intersection of the Front, Right, and Bottom planes.

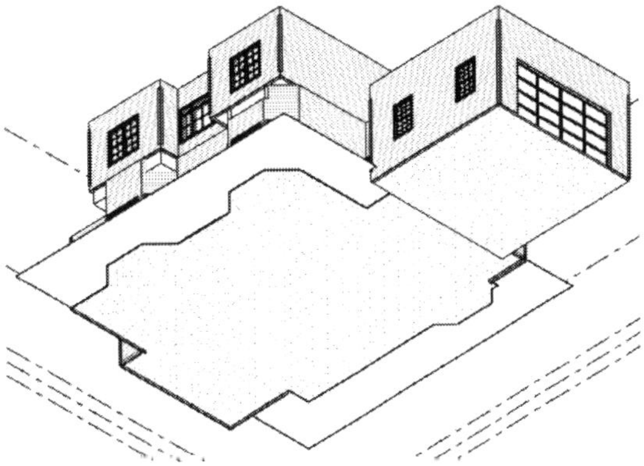

Figure 7–52

4. Zoom in under the garage slab.
5. In the View Control Bar, set the *Visual Style* to **Consistent Colors**.
6. Select the garage foundation. In the View Control Bar, expand (Temporary Hide/Isolate) and select **Isolate Element**.
7. In the *Architecture* tab>Build panel, expand (Floor) and select (Floor: Slab Edge).
8. In the Type Selector, select **Slab Edge: Thickened Edge 8x8**.
9. Select the three bottom edges of the slab, as shown in Figure 7–53. The slab edges and the foundation will automatically join because they have the same material.

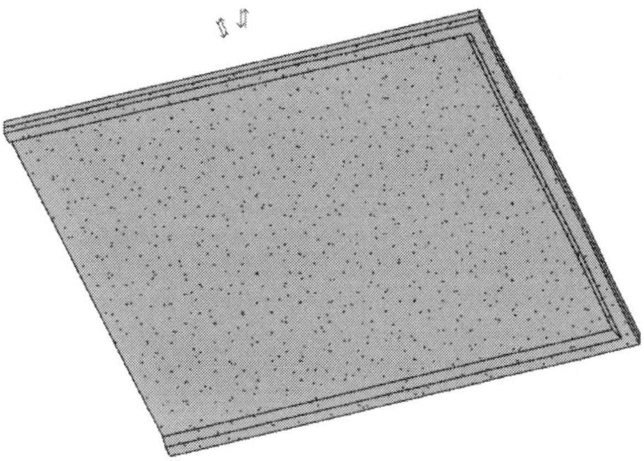

Figure 7–53

10. In the View Control Bar, select *Isolate* and choose **Reset Temporary Hide/Isolate**.

Task 2 - Create a structural plan view.

1. In the *View* tab>Create panel, expand 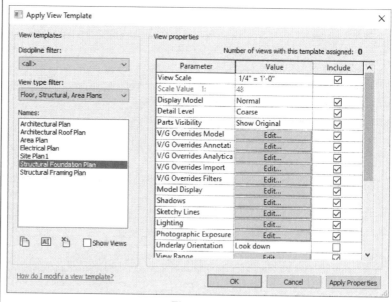 (Plan Views) and select (Structural Plan).

2. In the New Structural Plan dialog box, select **First Floor** and click **OK**.

3. In the Project Browser, under *Structural Plans*, select First Floor and rename it to **Foundation Plan**.

4. Click **No** when prompted to rename corresponding levels and views.

5. In the *View* tab>Graphics panel, expand (View Templates) and click (Apply Template Properties to Current View).

6. In the Apply View Template dialog box, in the *Name* area, select **Structural Foundation Plan** (as shown in Figure 7–54) and click **OK**.

Figure 7–54

7. In the View Control Bar, set the *Visual Style* to **Hidden Lines**. The geometry should look similar to Figure 7–55.

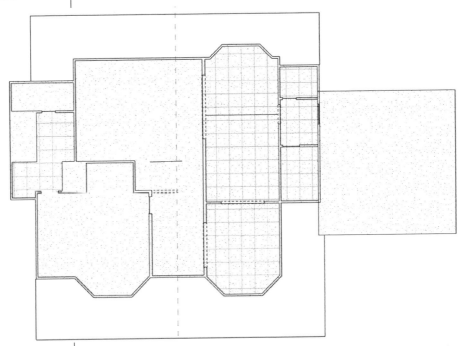

Figure 7–55

8. To clean up the view, select the tile floor, right-click, and select **Select All Instances>Visible in View**. Then, right-click again and select **Hide in View>Element**. Do this for the carpet, wood floors, porches, door openings, reference planes, and separation lines. The final view should look similar to Figure 7–56.

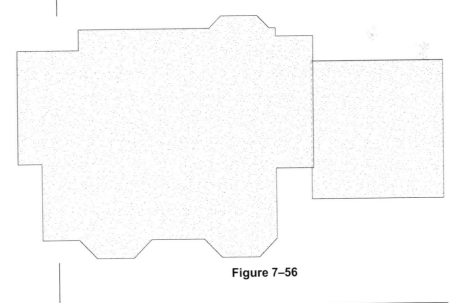

Figure 7–56

9. Save the project.

Task 3 - Add a slab edge.

1. Make sure only the default **{3D}** view and **Foundation Plan** views are open. Press **WT** on your keyboard to show both views side by side.

2. In the **{3D}** view, pan and orbit until you can see the concrete slab for the main floor plan.

3. In the *Architecture* tab>Build panel, expand (Floor) and select (Floor: Slab Edge).

4. In the Type Selector, select **Slab Edge: Header Block 8x8**.

5. Select the bottom edges of the concrete slab of the main floor plan, as shown in Figure 7–57. Make sure to go all the way around the main floor foundation slab.

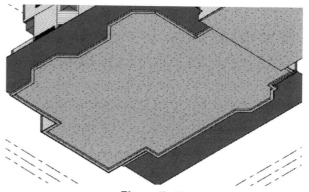

Figure 7–57

6. Save the project.

Task 4 - Add stem walls for continuous footings.

1. Activate the **Foundation Plan** view.

2. In the *Architecture* tab>Build panel, expand (Wall) and select (Wall: Structural).

3. From the *Modify | Place Structural Wall* tab>Draw panel, select (Pick Lines).

4. Create stem walls with the following properties:

- *Wall Type:* **Basic Wall 8x8x16 CMU**
- *Location Line:* **Core Face: Exterior**
- *Base Constraint:* **T.O. Footing**
- *Base Offset:* **0'-0"**
- *Top Constraint:* **Up to level: First Floor**
- *Top Offset:* (negative) **-0'-8 3/4"**

5. Hover your cursor over the edge of the slab and make sure the wall is created on the inside, as shown in Figure 7–58. Create stem walls wherever the header block edge exists.

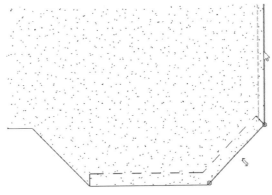

Figure 7–58

6. Click (Modify).

7. In the {3D} view, pan and orbit until you can see the bottom of the stem walls.

8. In the *Structure* tab>Foundation panel, click (Wall).

9. In the Type Selector, select **Wall Foundation: Bearing Footing - 36" x 10"**.

10. Select each of the stem walls. Alternatively, hover your mouse over one stem wall and press <Tab> until all the stem walls highlight. Click to place the bearing footing.

11. A continuous footing will automatically be placed at the bottom of each stem wall, as shown in Figure 7–59.

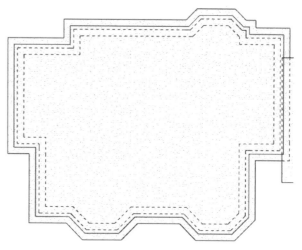

Figure 7–59

12. Save the project.

Task 5 - Add columns and isolated footings.

1. Open the **Floor Plans: First Floor** view and close all other views.

2. Set the *Visual Style* to **Hidden Lines**.

3. In the View Control Bar, click 💡 (Reveal Hidden Elements). Select the DWG, right-click, and select **Unhide in View>Category**.

4. Select the DWG and, in Properties, verify that the *Draw Layer* is set to **Foreground**.

   • This will allow you to see the porch deck to know where to place the columns.

5. In the *Architecture* tab>Build panel, expand 🗍 (Column) and select 🗍 (Architectural: Column).

6. In the Options Bar, set the *Height* to **Second Floor**.

7. In Properties, verify that **Square Column 12 x 12** is selected.

8. Place a column on both porches, as shown in Figure 7–60. Use the Modify tools to place and/or align the columns to the DWG.

   - The columns in the DWG are a different size than what we are using, but we want to use the 12 x 12 column. Place the 12 x 12 columns as centered as possible over the DWG columns.

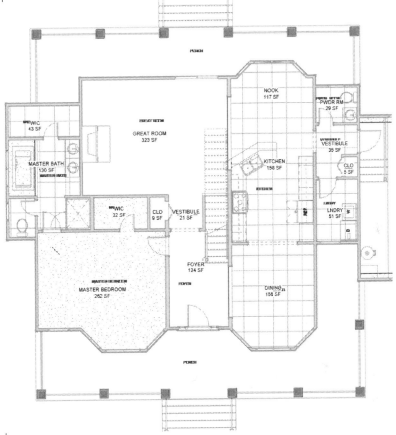

Figure 7–60

9. Select one column, right-click, and select **Select All Instances>Visible in View**. This selects all the columns.

10. In Properties, set the following:

   - *Base Level:* **First Floor**
   - *Base Offset:* (negative) **-0'-4"**
   - *Top Level:* **First Floor**
   - *Top Offset:* **8'-6"**

11. Click in an empty area in the view to clear the selection.

12. In the *Architecture* tab>Build panel, expand ⬜ (Column) and select ⬜ (Structural Column).

13. In the Type Selector, select **Concrete-Square-Column: 14 x 14**.

14. Place a structural column in a blank area off to the side of the porch, as shown in Figure 7–61.

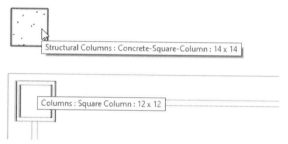

Figure 7–61

15. Select the structural column. In Properties, set the following:

- *Base Level:* **T.O. Footing**
- *Base Offset:* **0'-0"**
- *Top Level:* **First Floor**
- *Top Offset:* (negative) **-0'-4 3/4"**

16. Use the Modify commands to move and copy (with **Multiple** selected) this column to be in line under the square architectural columns on both porches, as shown in Figure 7–62.

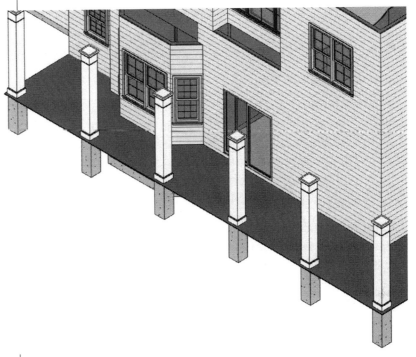

Figure 7–62

17. In the Project Browser, open **Structural Plans: Foundation Plan**.

   • Note that the columns are now shown.

18. In the *Structure* tab>Foundation panel, select 🔲 (Structural Foundation: Isolated).

19. In the Type Selector, choose **Footing-Rectangular: 30" x 30" x 10"**.

20. In the *Modify | Place Isolated Foundation* tab>Multiple panel, select 🔲 (At Columns).

21. You can window select all of the structural columns in this view, as shown in Figure 7–63.

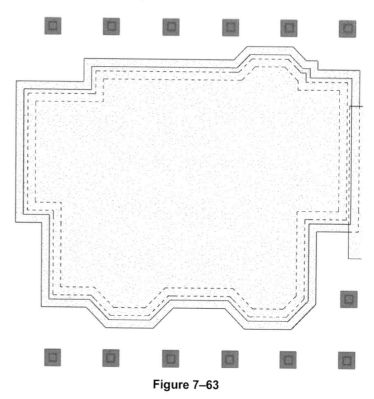

Figure 7–63

22. Click ✔ (Finish).

23. Save and close the project.

7.5 Creating Sloped Floors

Floors can have slopes applied to them. To make a floor slope in one direction, you place a *slope arrow* in the sketch of the floor, as shown in Figure 7–64.

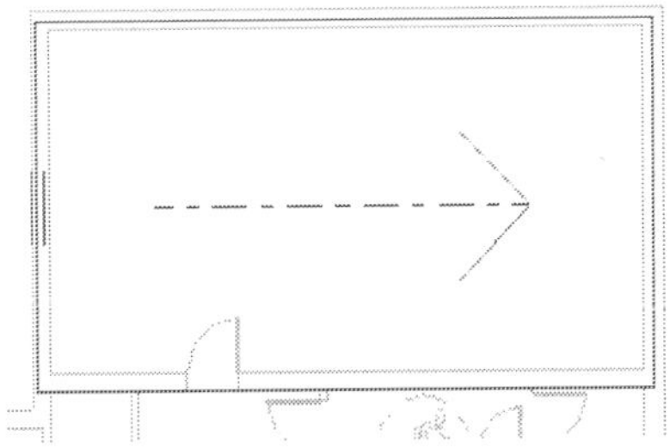

The slope arrow only displays while Sketch mode is active.

Figure 7–64

- Once the floor is created, you can add multiple drainage points and cause the floor to warp toward them.

- A floor can only have a slope arrow or be edited to have multiple drainage points; it cannot have both.

- These tools also work with roofs.

How To: Slope a Floor in One Direction

1. Select the floor you want to slope. In the *Modify | Floors* tab> Mode panel, click (Edit Boundary).
2. In the *Modify | Floors>Edit Boundary* tab>Draw panel, click (Slope Arrow).
3. Select two points to define the arrow. The first point is the tail and the second is the head. The tail and head locations are points at which you can specify heights. The direction of the arrow determines the orientation of the slope.
4. In Properties, you can choose to define the slope arrow by setting the *Specify* value to **Height at Tail** or **Slope**, as shown in Figure 7–65.

Figure 7–65

- If *Specify* is set to **Height at Tail**, you can modify the *Level at Tail*, *Height Offset at Tail*, *Level at Head,* and *Height Offset at Head*, as shown in Figure 7–66.

Figure 7–66

- If *Specify* is set to **Slope**, you can modify the *Level at Tail*, *Height Offset at Tail,* and *Slope,* as shown in Figure 7–67.

Figure 7–67

Creating Multiple Slopes for Drainage

Custom shower enclosures, garages, and other rooms often need to have floors that slope towards drains, as shown in Figure 7–68. Several tools provide ways of creating points for the drain locations, as well as creating lines to define how the slope is going to drain.

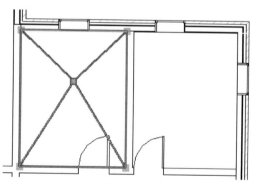

Figure 7–68

- These tools work with floors, roofs, and structural floors.

- These tools cannot be combined with the slope arrow. If a floor or roof has a slope arrow, these tools will not be available.

How To: Create Multiple Slopes for Drainage

1. Select the flat floor, roof, or slab you want to add a slope to.
2. In the *Modify | Floors* tab>Shape Editing panel (shown in Figure 7–69), select the tools that you want to use to define the slopes (as described in the following table).

Figure 7–69

	Add Point: Specify the location of the low or high points on the surface. In the Options Bar, set the *Elevation*. • By default, the elevation is relative to the top of the surface. Clear the **Relative** option if you want to use the project elevation. 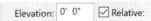 • displays when you place the point. Slope lines are automatically added from the corners of the surface to the point.
	Add Split Line: Define smaller areas on the surface when you place more than one drain. Depending on the size of the area you are working with, you might want to create these before you add the drains. Select the **Chain** option if you want to add more than one connected segment.
	Pick Supports: Select structural beams that define the split lines.
	Modify Sub-Elements: Change the elevation of edges and points and change the location of points. You can also move points using shape handles without clicking (Modify Sub-Elements), as shown in the figure below. Press <Tab> to cycle through the options to reach the element you want to modify.

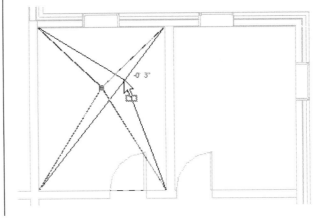

- If you want to remove the slopes from a surface, click 🗲 (Reset Shape).

- Floors, roofs, and slabs use material layers set to a constant thickness (where the entire element slopes) or to a variable thickness (where only that layer and layers above it slopes), as shown in Figure 7–70.

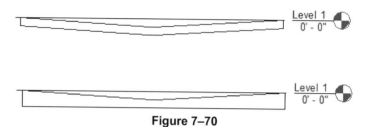

Figure 7–70

Practice 7c

Create Sloped Floors

Practice Objective

- Slope floors.

In this practice, you will slope the garage floor using the Shape Editing tools, as shown in Figure 7–71.

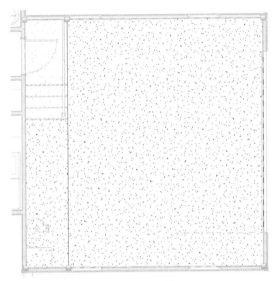

Figure 7–71

1. Open the project **Residential-Slope Floor.rvt** from the practice files folder.

2. Verify that you are in the **Floor Plans: First Floor** view and pan over to the garage area.

3. In the *Architecture* tab>Build panel, expand (Floor) and select (Floor: Architectural).

4. In the Type Selector, select **Floor: 1" Concrete Topping**.

5. In Properties, change the *Level* to **Grade** and the *Height Offset From Level* to **0'-1"**.

6. In the *Modify | Create Floor Boundary* tab>Draw panel, click (Pick Walls) and select the exterior face of core for the exterior garage walls. Use the Modify tools to ensure that the boundary is a closed loop.

7. Click (Finish Edit Mode).

8. When the alert box about joining geometry opens, click **Yes**, as shown in Figure 7–72.

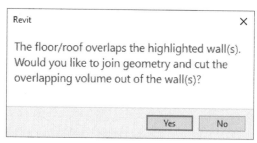

Figure 7–72

9. Click in an empty space in the view to release the floor selection.

10. Select the 1" concrete topping.

  - If the edge of the floor does not highlight in this view, you cannot select the floor using the standard method. In the Status Bar, click ▣ (Select Elements by Face), then click on the face of the floor to select it.

11. In the *Modify | Floors* tab>Shape Editing panel, click ⬭ (Add Split Line). Draw the line **4'-0"** off from the inside finish of the wall.

12. Hover your cursor over the upper-left corner and slowly drag your cursor to the right. Use temporary dimensions to find 4' away from the edge, as shown in Figure 7–73.

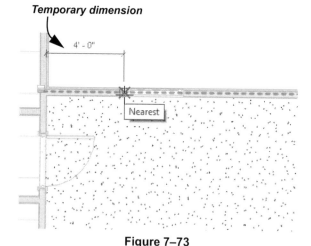

Figure 7–73

13. When you see **4'-0"**, click to place the split's starting point and then click to place the end point straight down to the other side of the garage, as shown in Figure 7–74.

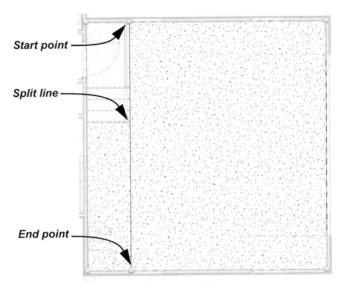

Start point

Split line

End point

Figure 7–74

14. In the *Modify | Floors* tab>Shape Editing panel, click  (Modify Sub Elements).

15. Move your cursor over one of the points near the garage door, as shown in Figure 7–75.

Figure 7–75

16. Click on the dimension given and change it to (negative) **-0'-1"**.

17. Do the same to the point on the opposite side of the garage door.

18. Press <Esc> to end the command.

19. Use a section cut to view the slope in the garage slab.

20. Use **Join Geometry** to join the concrete topping to the structural slab.

21. Save and close the project.

Chapter Review Questions

1. When creating a floor, the boundary sketch must be a closed loop to finish the sketch.

   a. True

   b. False

2. How do you change the thickness of a floor, such as those shown in Figure 7–76?

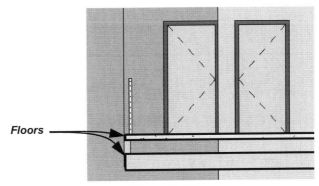

Figure 7–76

   a. In the Type Selector, change the *Floor Type*.

   b. In the Options Bar, change the *Floor Thickness*.

   c. In Properties, change the *Floor Thickness*.

   d. In the contextual ribbon, change the *Offset*.

3. Which of the following Opening commands cuts an opening in multiple floors at the same time?

   a. **By Face**

   b. **Shaft**

   c. **Wall**

   d. **Vertical**

4. When creating a sloped floor, the (Add Points) command places a point where?

   a. The end of the floor where you want the slope to end.

   b. The end of the floor where you want the slope to begin.

   c. The high or low points of a floor.

   d. A point where two slopes converge.

Command Summary

Button	Command	Location
	Floor: Architectural	• **Ribbon:** *Architecture* tab>Build panel>expand Floor
	Floor: Structural	• **Ribbon:** *Architecture* tab>Build panel>expand Floor
	Shaft	• **Ribbon:** *Architecture* tab>Opening panel
Shape Editing Tools		
	Add Point	• **Ribbon:** *Modify	Floors* tab>Shape Editing panel
	Add Split Line	• **Ribbon:** *Modify	Floors* tab>Shape Editing panel
	Modify Sub Elements	• **Ribbon:** *Modify	Floors* tab>Shape Editing panel
	Pick Supports	• **Ribbon:** *Modify	Floors* tab>Shape Editing panel
	Reset Shape	• **Ribbon:** *Modify	Floors* tab>Shape Editing panel

Modeling Ceilings

In the Autodesk® Revit® software, ceilings are modeled using reflected ceiling plans. You can add ceilings by selecting a room boundary or by sketching ceilings that do not fill an entire room. You can create basic flat ceilings, or you can create custom ceilings of different heights with a soffit wall added between. In addition to creating a ceiling, you can also place ceiling fixtures, such as fans and lights, directly onto ceiling elements.

Learning Objectives in This Chapter

- Add automatic ceilings that fill an entire room boundary and sketched ceilings that are customized to suit a design.
- Add ceiling components, including lighting fixtures.
- Add soffit walls in the gap between ceilings of different heights.

8.1 Modeling Ceilings

Adding ceilings to Autodesk Revit models is a straightforward process. To place a ceiling, click inside areas that are bounded by walls and, if the walls extend above the height of the proposed ceiling, the ceiling is created (as shown in the room on the right in Figure 8–1). You can also sketch custom ceilings when required. Any fixtures you attach to a ceiling display in reflected ceiling plans, as well as in sections and 3D views.

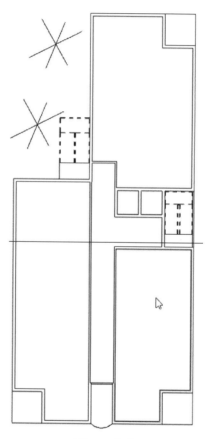

Figure 8–1

- Ceiling plans are typically created by default when you add a level with a view. If you do not want a level to have a ceiling plan, you can right-click on its name in the Project Browser and select **Delete**, as shown in Figure 8–2.

Figure 8–2

How To: Create an Automatic Boundary Ceiling

1. Switch to a ceiling plan view.
2. In the *Architecture* tab>Build panel, click 📁 (Ceiling).
3. In the Type Selector, select the ceiling type. In Properties, set the *Height Offset From Level*.
4. In the *Modify | Place Ceiling* tab>Ceiling panel, verify that

   📁 (Automatic Ceiling) is selected. Click inside a room to create a ceiling, as shown in Figure 8–3.

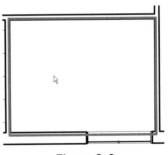

Figure 8–3

5. Continue adding ceilings to other rooms, as needed, or click ↳ (Modify) to end the command.

Hint: Room Bounding Status

Elements such as walls, floors, ceilings, and roofs have a *Room Bounding* property set in Properties. In most cases, this is toggled on by default as these elements typically define areas and volumes.

The **Automatic Ceiling** tool uses this property to identify walls that set the outline of a ceiling. If you toggle off this property for a wall (such as a partial height wall), the **Automatic Ceiling** tool ignores the wall.

Ceilings can also be used as a *Room Bounding* for volume calculations.

- To modify a ceiling boundary, select a ceiling and either:
  - In the *Modify |Ceilings* tab>Mode panel, click [icon] (Edit Boundary), or
  - Double-click on the ceiling to enter Edit Boundary mode.

Sketching Ceilings

To add a ceiling to part of a room, as shown in Figure 8–4, or to have two different ceiling types at separate levels, you need to sketch a ceiling.

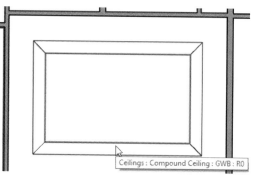

Ceilings : Compound Ceiling : GWB : R0

Figure 8–4

How To: Sketch a Ceiling

1. In the *Architecture* tab>Build panel, click ▱ (Ceiling).
2. In the *Modify | Place Ceiling* tab>Ceiling panel, click

    ▱ (Sketch Ceiling).

3. In the Draw panel, click ╱ (Line) or ▨ (Pick Walls) and define a closed loop for the ceiling boundary, similar to sketching a floor boundary.

4. Click ✔ (Finish Edit Mode) to create the ceiling.

• To include a hole in a ceiling, include the hole as part of the sketch. The hole must be a closed loop completely inside the ceiling boundary.

• In the *Architecture* tab>Opening panel, you can also use

    ⟊ (Opening By Face), ⊞ (Shaft Opening), or ⟊ (Vertical Opening) to cut a hole in a ceiling that is separate from the sketch. These can often be used for fireplaces or skylights.

8.2 Adding Ceiling Fixtures

Several groups of components are commonly used with ceilings, such as:

- Lighting fixtures (shown in Figure 8–5)

- HVAC equipment (for registers and diffusers)

- Specialty equipment (such as speakers and ceiling fans)

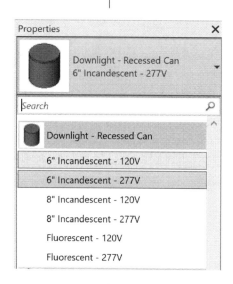

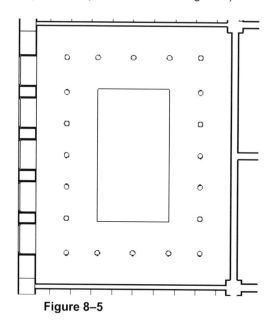

Figure 8–5

After placing a component, press <Spacebar> to rotate it in 90-degree increments.

- Use 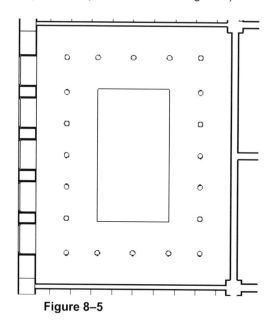 (Component) to place ceiling fixtures in the ceiling view.

- The Autodesk Revit Library contains a variety of light fixtures and HVAC ceiling fixtures.

- Many light fixtures include types that specify the voltage of the lamp, as shown in Figure 8–5.

- Some light fixtures are wall-based, instead of ceiling-based, and need to be placed on a wall in a floor plan view. These include items such as sconces.

- When you delete a ceiling, the associated components (such as light fixtures) are also deleted.

- Components come in based on their center point and respond to the nearby walls. Place an instance of the component and use **Move** or **Align** to get it to the correct location. Use **Copy** to place additional instances on the ceiling.

- Some light fixtures can display the light source, as shown in the section in Figure 8–6. To display the light source, in the Visibility/Graphic Overrides dialog box, in the *Model Categories* tab, expand **Lighting Fixtures** and select **Light Source,** as shown on the left in Figure 8–6.

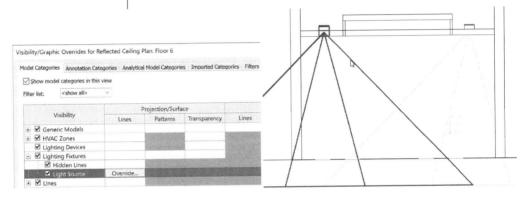

Figure 8–6

- The light sources display their true strength in renderings.

Hint: Placing Components in Rooms Without a Ceiling

If you need to place components in a room that does not have a ceiling, you can create a reference plane at the height where you want them and place workplane-based families on it. You can also place workplane-based components on the underside of a floor.

1. In a section or elevation view, sketch a reference plane at the required height.
2. Click on the *<Click to name>* field, type a name, and press <Enter>.
3. Open the ceiling plan where you want to work.
4. Start the **Component** command and select a workplane-based component.
5. In the *Modify | Place Component* tab>Placement panel, click ◇ (Place on Workplane), as shown in Figure 8–7.

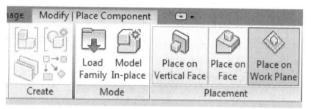

Figure 8–7

6. In the Options Bar, specify the named reference plane from the Placement Plane drop-down list, as shown in Figure 8–8.

Figure 8–8

7. Place the component.

• These options are only available if you have selected a workplane-based or face-based component.

Practice 8a

Model Ceilings and Add Ceiling Fixtures

Practice Objectives

- Create automatic ceilings.
- Add ceiling components.

In this practice, while working in a reflected ceiling plan, you will add gypsum ceilings to several rooms. You will then add light fixtures, as shown in Figure 8–9 (the DWG has been hidden for clarity).

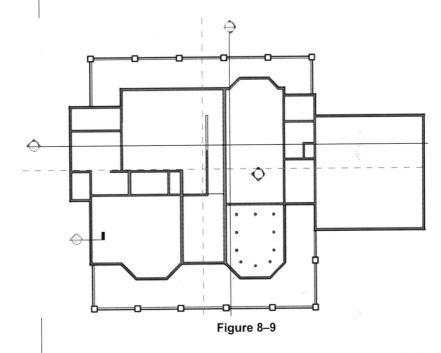

Figure 8–9

Task 1 - Create automatic ceilings.

1. Open the project **Residential-Ceilings.rvt** from the practice files folder.

2. Verify that you are in the **Ceiling Plans: First Floor** view.

3. In the *Architecture* tab>Build panel, click 🖾 (Ceiling).

4. In the *Modify | Place Ceiling* tab>Ceiling panel, click 🖾 (Sketch Ceiling).

5. In the *Modify | Create Ceiling Boundary* tab>Draw panel, click (Pick Walls).

6. In the Type Selector, verify that **Compound Ceiling: GWB** is selected.

7. In Properties, set the *Height Offset From Level* to **10'-0"**.

8. Create a ceiling in each of the highlighted rooms shown in Figure 8–10 by selecting the inside of the walls. In the foyer, select the vestibule wall as the boundary.

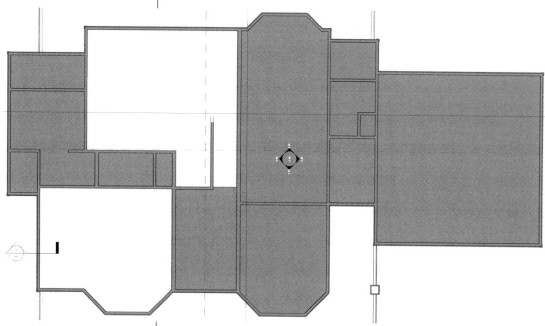

Figure 8–10

9. Save the project.

Task 2 - Add ceiling components.

1. In the *Architecture* tab>Build panel, click (Component).

2. In the *Modify | Place Component* tab>Mode panel, click (Load Family) and load the **Recessed Lamp - Round - LED.rfa** component from the Revit Library's *Lighting> Architectural>Internal* folder.

3. When prompted, select **4" Trimmed Downlight**.

4. In the *Modify | Place Component* tab>Placement panel, choose 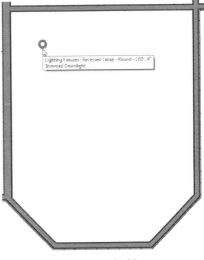 (Place on Face).

5. Place one recessed lamp **2'-0"** away from the corner of the dining room, as shown in Figure 8–11.

Figure 8–11

6. Use **Copy** to copy the light to other locations on the ceiling.

7. Use reference planes, detail lines, dimensions set to equal, or the **Array** command to space the lights equally around the room, as shown in Figure 8–12.

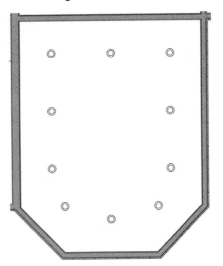

Figure 8–12

8. Save the project.

Task 3 - (Optional) Add second floor ceilings.

1. If time permits, open the **Ceiling Plans: Second Floor** view.

2. Start the **Ceiling** command. Use 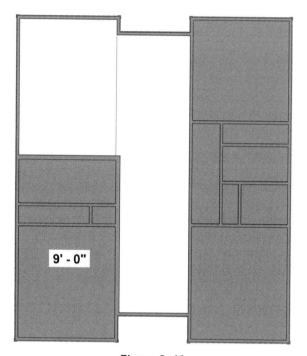 (Sketch Ceiling) and ▨ (Pick Walls) to create ceilings for the second floor rooms. Use the **Compound Ceiling: GWB** type and the following offsets:

   • For the rooms highlighted in Figure 8–13, set the *Height Offset From Level* to **9'-0"**.

9' - 0"

Figure 8–13

- For the rooms highlighted in Figure 8–14, set the *Height Offset From Level* to **8'-7 1/2"**.

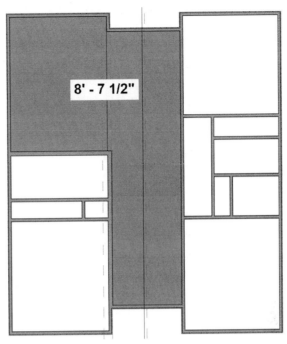

8' - 7 1/2"

Figure 8–14

3. Save and close the project.

8.3 Creating Ceiling Soffits and Raised Ceilings

Ceiling soffits are parts of a ceiling that have been lowered, as shown in Figure 8–15, or that connect two ceilings of different heights. Creating a ceiling soffit takes two steps. First, you create a ceiling, and then you model walls using a soffit wall type. This is how you would create waffle and raised ceilings.

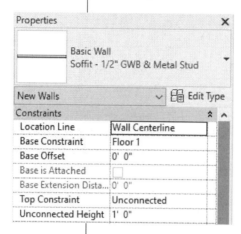

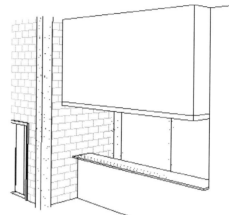

Figure 8–15

How To: Create a Ceiling with a Soffit

1. Open a ceiling plan.
2. In the *Architecture* tab>Build panel, click ▱ (Ceiling).
3. In the Type Selector, select the ceiling type. In Properties, set the *Height Offset From Level*.
4. In the *Modify | Place Ceiling* tab>Ceiling panel, click

   ▱ (Sketch Ceiling).
5. Draw the ceiling outline, such as the example shown in Figure 8–16.

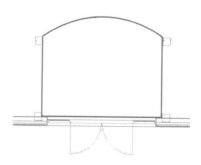

Figure 8–16

6. Click ![checkmark](Finish Edit Mode).

7. In *Architecture* tab>Build panel, click ![wall icon] (Wall) to create the soffit wall.

8. In the Type Selector, select a soffit wall type. In Properties, set the *Base Offset* from the floor and set the *Top Constraint/Unconnected Height* as required to establish the height of the soffit.

   • Sometimes it is easier to set the height of the soffit walls by extending or trimming elements in a section view.

9. In the *Modify | Place Wall* tab>Draw panel, click

   ![pick lines icon] (Pick Lines). Select the edges of the ceiling to create the walls, as shown in Figure 8–17.

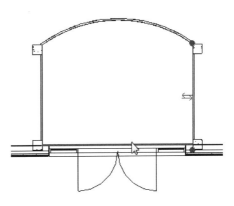

*If the wall is on the outside of the ceiling, flip it using the Flip control and create the rest of the walls using the opposite **Location Line** option.*

Figure 8–17

10. Display the ceiling in 3D or a section to verify that it is displayed correctly.

Hint: Joining Geometry

When you are working with elements that are next to each other, they might need additional modification so that they display as expected. For example, one way to fix connections between walls and ceilings is to join the geometry.

In the *Modify* tab>Geometry panel, click ![join geometry icon] (Join Geometry) and then select the elements to join.

Practice 8b

Create Ceiling Soffits

Practice Objective

- Create ceiling soffits.

In this practice, you will sketch a ceiling and create a soffit, as shown in Figure 8–18. Optionally, you will also add a recessed ceiling and soffit to the master bedroom.

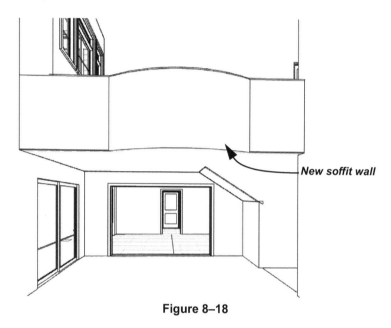

New soffit wall

Figure 8–18

Task 1 - Sketch a ceiling.

1. Open the project **Residential-Ceiling Soffit.rvt** from the practice files folder.

2. Verify that you are in the **Ceiling Plans: First Floor** view.

3. In the *Architecture* tab>Build panel, click ❐ (Ceiling).

4. In the Type Selector, verify that **Compound Ceiling: GWB** is selected. In Properties, set the *Height Offset From Level* to **8'-0"**.

5. In the *Modify | Place Ceiling* tab>Ceiling panel, click ❐ (Sketch Ceiling) and sketch the outline of the ceiling in the loft area, as shown in Figure 8–19.

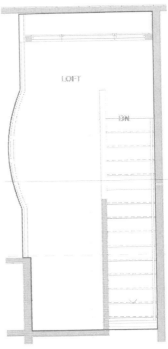

Figure 8–19

6. Click ![checkmark](Finish Edit Mode).

7. Save the project.

Task 2 - Add a soffit.

1. Open the **E/W Building Section** view and zoom in on the edge of the lower ceiling, as shown in Figure 8–20.

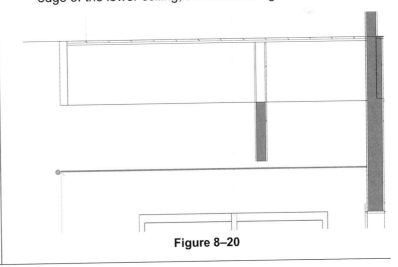

Figure 8–20

2. Return to the **Ceiling Plans: First Floor** view. Close all views except the E/W Building Section and Ceiling Plan views, and type **WT** to tile the two views.

3. Click ⬚ (Wall). In the Type Selector, select **Basic Wall: Interior – 4" Chase**.

4. In Properties, set the following:

    *   *Location Line:* **Finish Face: Interior**
    *   *Base Constraint:* **First Floor**
    *   *Base Offset:* **8'-0"**
    *   *Top Constraint:* **Up to level: Second Floor**
    *   *Top Offset:* (negative) **-0'-0 3/4"**

5. Use the different draw tools to draw a wall across the face of the ceiling, as shown in Figure 8–21. The image on the right shows the building section view and the wall edge meeting the ceiling edge.

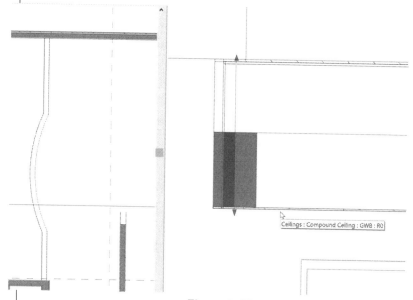

Ceilings : Compound Ceiling : GWB : RO

Figure 8–21

6. Activate the section view.

7. In the *Modify* tab>Geometry panel, click ⬚ (Join).

8. Select the soffit wall above the ceiling and then select the ceiling, as shown in Figure 8–22.

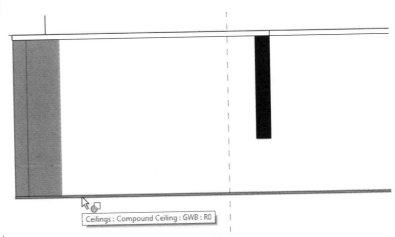

Ceilings : Compound Ceiling : GWB : R0

Figure 8–22

9. Do this for the two other wall segments. Hint: Create a camera view on the First Floor view in the great room and stretch the crop region so you can see the ceiling and the chase wall. The elements clean up as shown in Figure 8–23.

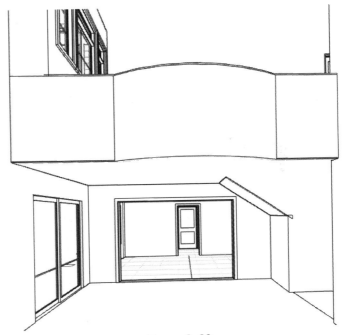

Figure 8–23

10. Save the project.

Task 3 - (Optional) Add a raised ceiling.

1. In the **Ceiling Plans: First Floor** view, pan over to the master bedroom.

2. Select the DWG file and the wall section, and type **VH** to hide them in the view.

3. Start the **Ceiling** command and select 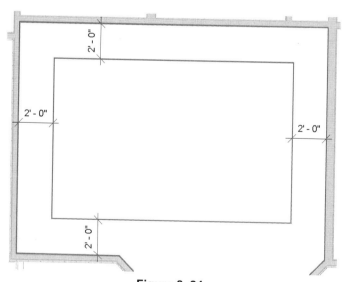 (Automatic Ceiling).

4. In the Type Selector, select **Compound Ceiling: GWB**. In Properties, set the *Height Offset From Level* to **9'-0"**.

5. Select inside the master bedroom to create a ceiling.

6. Click (Modify).

7. Double-click on the ceiling that was just created. This puts you in Edit mode.

8. Click (Pick Lines) and, in the Options Bar, set the *Offset* to **2'-0"**.

9. Create a ceiling, similar to the one shown in Figure 8–24, that has an opening in the center with two feet of soffit on either side.

2' - 0"

2' - 0"

2' - 0"

2' - 0"

Figure 8–24

10. Click ✔ (Finish Edit Mode). The ceiling is still selected.

11. Create another ceiling of the same type using the **Sketch Ceiling** command, but with the *Height Offset From Level* at **10'-0"**.

12. Click ✎ (Pick Lines). In the Options Bar, set the *Offset* to **1'-0"**.

13. Select the interior linework of the lower ceiling. Use ⬒ (Trim/Extend to Corner) to clean up the corners, as needed, as shown in Figure 8–25.

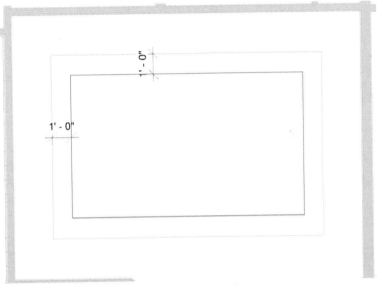

Figure 8–25

14. Click ✔ (Finish Edit Mode).

15. Create another ceiling using the same type and height offset on the left side between the two previously created ceilings, as shown in Figure 8–26.

16. In the *Modify | Ceilings>Edit Boundary* tab>*Draw* panel, select 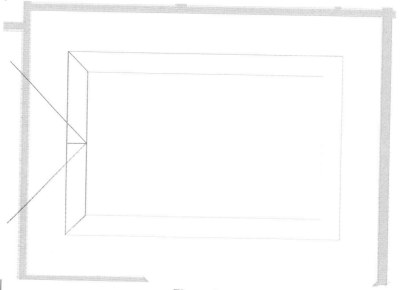 (Slope Arrow).

17. Create an arrow, as shown in Figure 8–26.

Figure 8–26

18. Select the arrow. In Properties, set the following:

- *Specify:* **Height at Tail**
- *Level at Tail:* **First Floor**
- *Height Offset at Tail:* **9'-0"**
- *Level at Head:* **First Floor**
- *Height Offset at Head:* **10'-0"**

19. Click ✔ (Finish Edit Mode). The ceiling is still selected.

20. Mirror this sloped ceiling to the other side of the raised ceiling.

21. Create a similar ceiling on the longer side of the opening.

22. Mirror this new longer sloped ceiling to the other side of the opening, as shown in Figure 8–27.

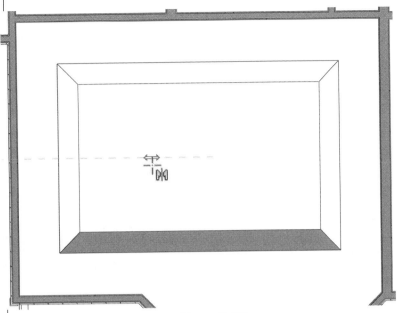

Figure 8–27

23. Save the project.

Task 4 - (Optional) Carry the raised ceiling linework to a floor plan.

---

1. Ensure that the **Ceiling Plans: First Floor** view is the only view open.

2. In the Project Browser, open the **Floor Plans: First Floor** view.

3. Press **WT** to tile the two views.

4. Activate the **Floor Plans: First Floor** view.

5. In Properties, set the following parameters in the *Underlay* group:

   - *Range Base Level:* **First Floor**
   - *Range Top Level:* **Second Floor**
   - *Underlay Orientation:* **Look Up**

6. In the *Annotate* tab>Detail panel, select ⬚ (Detail Line). Set the *Line Style* to **<Overhead>**. Use ⬚ (Pick Lines) to select the ceiling linework, as shown in Figure 8–28.

- Be sure to lock the alignment constraint when prompted on the lines. This will ensure that the detail lines adjust if the ceiling adjusts.

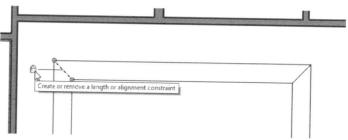

Create or remove a length or alignment constraint

Figure 8–28

7. In Properties, in the *Underlay* area, set the *Range: Base Level* to **None**.

8. Zoom out to view the whole floor plan.

9. Save and close the project file.

Chapter Review Questions

1. Ceiling plans are typically created by default when you add a level with a view.

   a. True

   b. False

2. Which of the following component types can be hosted by ceiling elements? (Select all that apply.)

   a. Mechanical diffusers and returns

   b. Lighting fixtures

   c. Curtain grids

   d. Columns

3. What can you use to place components in a room that does not have a ceiling? (Select all that apply.)

   a. Reference plane

   b. Bottom of the roof

   c. Bottom of the floor

   d. You cannot place components in a room without a ceiling

4. Which of the following commands would you use to create a ceiling with a soffit around the edges? (Select all that apply.)

   a. (Automatic Ceiling)

   b. (Sketch Ceiling)

   c. (Wall)

   d. (Component)

Command Summary

Button	Command	Location
	Automatic Ceiling	• **Ribbon:** *Modify | Place Ceiling* tab>Ceiling panel
	Ceiling	• **Ribbon:** *Architecture* tab>Build panel
	Component	• **Ribbon:** *Architecture* tab>Build panel
	Join	• **Ribbon:** *Modify* tab>Geometry panel
	Sketch Ceiling	• **Ribbon:** *Modify | Place Ceiling* tab>Ceiling panel

Modeling Roofs

Roofs, in the Autodesk® Revit® software, are building components that represent different types of actual roofs on a building. You can create roofs from footprint outlines, as extrusions, or from mass instances. You can also modify the properties of a roof, including its outline, structural composition, and slope. Roofs will also include elements like soffits, fascias, and gutters.

Learning Objectives in This Chapter

- Sketch roofs using the footprint method for flat, shed, gable, or hip roofs.
- Set work planes to help you create extruded roof profiles.
- Sketch a profile for the roof that can then be extruded.

9.1 Modeling Roofs

The Autodesk Revit software provides two main ways of creating roofs:

- **By Footprint:** The roof is created in a floor plan view by defining the area to be covered.

- **By Extrusion:** The roof is created in an elevation or section view by defining a profile sketch.

The footprint method can generate most common roof types, including shed, gable, mansard, and hip roofs. The extrusion method is required for an odd-shaped roof or a roof with two slopes on the same face, such as gambrel, barrel vault, and eyebrow roofs, as shown in Figure 9–1.

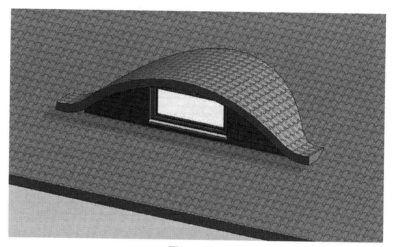

Figure 9–1

- Other roof options, found in the Roof drop-down list, include Roof by Face, Roof Soffit, Fascia, and Gutter. **Roof by Face** can be used with massing elements to create irregular shapes. **Roof Soffit** connects the edge of the roof to the wall with a flat footprint. **Fascia** places a profile, whether flat or built-up board, on the outside edge of the roof and can be used for friezes. **Gutter** adds a gutter on the edge of the roof, but does not include downspouts.

Roof Types

The following are examples of roof types that would typically be created using **Roof by Footprint** or **Roof by Extrusion**.

Flat Roof

A flat roof is simply a roof in which none of the edges define a slope. Specify an overhang distance to extend the roof beyond the walls or define the profile along the inside of the wall to create a roof behind a parapet, as shown in Figure 9–2.

Figure 9–2

Shed Roof

For shed roofs, only the edge at the low eave line is slope defining, as shown in Figure 9–3.

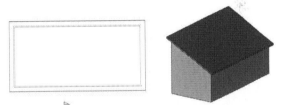

Figure 9–3

Hipped Roof

With hipped roofs, all four edges are the roof are slope defining. Vary the slope to create different types of hips, as shown in Figure 9–4. Half-hip (or jerkinhead) roof types are also created this way.

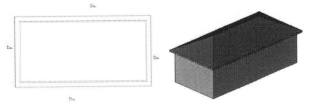

Figure 9–4

Mansard Roof

A mansard roof is generally constructed as two roofs, the first steeply sloped and the second either flat or sloping at a much shallower angle, as shown in Figure 9–5. This type of roof can be created using two separate roofs, the first ending at a cutoff level and the second filling the opening in the first. Before starting this process, create a level at the elevation corresponding to where the roof slopes change.

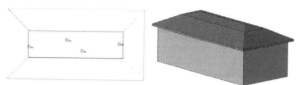

Figure 9–5

- Remember to cut a section through the roof and then use the **Move** tool to adjust the starting height of the upper roof so that it matches the ending height of the lower roof.

Hip Gable/Dutch Gable/Bonnet Roof

This type of roof is also created by constructing two roofs: a hip and a gable. In this case, rather than using a cutoff level, create the roof by sketching the perimeter of the first roof (the hip roof) and then sketch another closed perimeter inside the first. This second perimeter will form a hole in the hip roof and will then be used to draw the sketch for the gable roof, as shown in Figure 9–6.

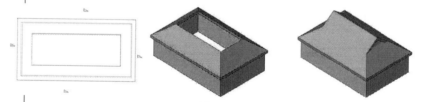

Figure 9–6

- When creating this type of roof, add walls to fill in the open end of the gable and attach the wall to the upper gable and lower hip roof.

Gambrel Roof

A gambrel roof consists of two roofs: a lower portion with a steep slope angle and an upper portion with a shallower slope angle, but with gable ends. Creating it as an extrusion works better because the roof maintains a consistent fascia along the gable end, as shown in Figure 9–7.

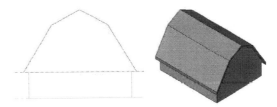

Figure 9–7

Barrel Vault Roof

A barrel vault roof, by definition, is a roof that is an extrusion of a curve, whether cylindrical or elliptical, along a given distance (as shown in Figure 9–8). This is also true for bow roofs.

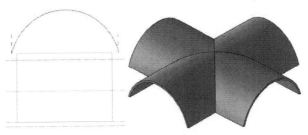

Figure 9–8

Complex Roofs

Revit will automatically create complex roofs that follow the shape of the roof footprint. For example, Revit will automatically create valleys for roofs that follow L-shaped footprints or create conical roofs when following an arc footprint, as shown in Figure 9–9.

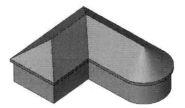

Figure 9–9

9.2 Creating Roofs by Footprint

To create any basic single-sloped roofs (hip, shed, or gable), start with a plan view and define a sketch or "footprint" around the area that you want the roof to cover, as shown in Figure 9–10.

Because footprint roof elements are sloped by default, even with a zero-degree slope, the slope arrow option can be drawn on a roof boundary line. This is often used to create dormers, as shown in Figure 9–10, though sometimes dormers are created using a custom family.

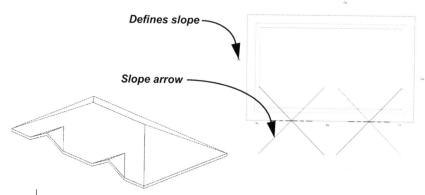

Figure 9–10

You control the type of roof by specifying which edge(s) define the slope:

- No edges sloped = flat roof

- One edge sloped = shed roof

- Two opposing edges sloped = gable roof

- All edges sloped = hip roof

How To: Add a Roof by Footprint

1. Open a plan view at the roof level of the building.

2. In the *Architecture* tab>Build panel, expand ⬚ (Roof) and click ⬚ (Roof by Footprint).

3. In the Options Bar (shown in Figure 9–11), you can set the following options:

- **Defines slope:** This check box toggles the slope-defining property of the sketch line on and off. When selected (on), the sketch line you create will display an adjacent angle symbol and a value specifying the slope. You can change the slope by editing this value. When not selected (off), the perimeter line you sketch will not define a slope. Note that lines representing gable ends do not define a slope.

- **Overhang:** When picking walls to define the perimeter, this value lets you specify how far the roof extends beyond the face of the wall.

- **Extend to wall core:** When selected, the overhang dimension is measured from the roof edge to the exterior core of the wall. When not selected, the overhang is measured from the exterior finish face of the wall.

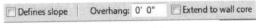

Figure 9–11

4. In the *Modify | Create Roof Footprint* tab>Draw panel, ensure that **Boundary Line** is selected. Click 🏷 (Pick Walls), ✏ (Line), or any other Draw tool to create the roof footprint.

- The lines must form a closed boundary with no overlapping lines. If they do not, use 🗝 (Trim) to modify the lines, as needed.

5. As you are drawing your footprint, you can select and modify each segment of the sketch (as shown in Figure 9–12) using the Options Bar, Properties, or controls to create different roof types.

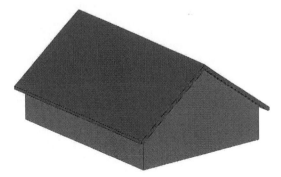

Figure 9–12

6. Click ✅ (Finish Edit Mode).

7. An alert box might open, as shown in Figure 9–13. You can attach the highlighted walls to the roof now or later.

- You have the option to check the box for **Do not show me this message again**. Revit will remember your last selection and do this for every instance this occurs.

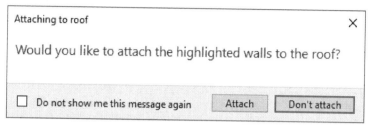

Figure 9–13

Attaching Walls to Roofs

Attaching walls to the roof extends the walls up to the roof, as shown in Figure 9–14. Attach walls while still in the **Roof** command, or you can use the **Attach Top/Base** command later in the design process.

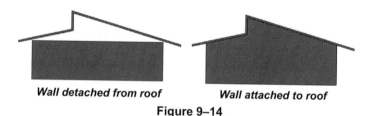

Wall detached from roof   *Wall attached to roof*

Figure 9–14

- **Attach Top/Base** can also be used with walls that are against sloping floors or topographic site features.

How To: Attach Walls to Roofs

1. Select the wall or walls that you want to attach to the roof.

2. In the *Modify | Walls* tab>Modify Wall panel, click ⬚ (Attach Top/Base). Verify that *Attach Wall* is set to **Top**, as shown in Figure 9–15.

Figure 9–15

3. Select the roof. The walls are trimmed or extended to the roof line.

Note: Walls will typically need to be attached to the roof in order to match the elevation profile of the roof element. If the walls you previously created extend above the roof, Revit will ask you if you want to attach the highlighted walls to the roof. If you say **Yes**, the profile of the walls will be changed to follow the slope of the roof. If the walls end below the roof, you can select the walls and then attach them to the roof.

9.3 Creating Roofs by Extrusion

Extruded roofs enable you to create complex roof forms, such as the curved roof shown in Figure 9–16. Extruded roofs are based on a sketch of the roof profile in an elevation or section view and do not need to be a closed sketch. The profile is extruded between a start and end point. From there you can modify the roof by adding openings or joining it to other roofs. Only the top-most line of the profile needs to be created and does not require a closed loop like a footprint roof does.

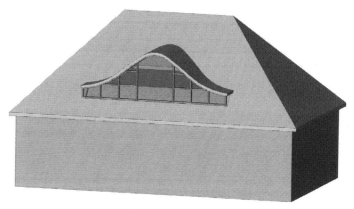

Figure 9–16

Establishing Work Planes

When creating a roof by extrusion, you are prompted to specify a work plane. A work plane is the surface you sketch on or extrude from.

- In a plan view, the work plane is automatically parallel to the level.

- In an elevation or 3D view, you need to specify the work plane before you start sketching.

To see the active work plane, in the *Architecture* tab>Work Plane panel, click ⊞ (Show Work Plane).

Alternatively, you can click 🔲 (Viewer). This opens the Workplane Viewer, a separate window showing the current work plane, as shown in Figure 9–17.

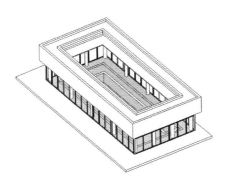

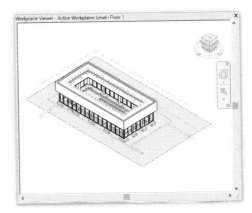

Figure 9–17

- Named reference planes can be used to specify a work plane that would otherwise not be displayed in a view. This is especially helpful when creating extruded roofs.

How To: Set a Work Plane

1. Start a command that requires a work plane or, in the

   Architecture tab>Work Plane panel, click 🗔 (Set).
2. In the Work Plane dialog box, select one of the options.
   - **Name:** Select an existing level, grid, or named reference plane, as shown in Figure 9–18, and click **OK**.

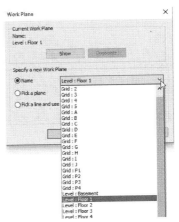

Figure 9–18

- **Pick a plane:** Click **OK** and select a plane in the view, such as a wall face. Ensure the entire plane is highlighted before you select it.
- **Pick a line and use the work plane it was sketched in:** Click **OK** and select a model line, such as a room separation line.

- If you are in a view in which the sketch cannot be created, the Go To View dialog box opens, as shown in Figure 9–19. Select one of the views and click **Open View**.

Figure 9–19

How To: Create an Extruded Roof

1. Open an elevation or section view.

2. In the *Architecture* tab>Build panel, expand (Roof) and click (Roof by Extrusion).

3. In the Work Plane dialog box, select the work plane on which you want to sketch the roof profile and click **OK.**

4. In the Roof Reference Level and Offset dialog box, specify the base *Level* and *Offset* (if any), as shown in Figure 9–20.

By default, this level is set to the highest one in the project. The offset creates a reference plane at that distance.

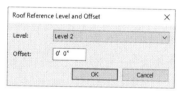

Figure 9–20

- Use reference planes to help you create the roof profile. Reference planes created in Sketch mode do not display once the roof is finished.

5. Use the Draw tools to create the profile, as shown in Figure 9–21.

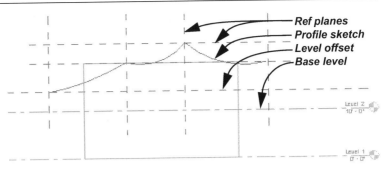

Figure 9–21

6. In Properties, set the *Extrusion Start* and *End*.

- The direction in which the roof profile extrudes is known as the extrusion direction. The extrusion of a roof can extend in either direction along a line perpendicular to the plane in which the profile is created. To adjust the extrusion distance, click the **Roof Properties** button to display the Instance Properties dialog box and then use the *Extrusion Start* and *Extrusion End* values to adjust the length of the extrusion. You can extend the extrusion towards or away from the view.

  - Extrusion directions that are up or towards the view are positive, and extrusion directions that are down or away from the view are negative.

7. Click ✓ (Finish Edit Mode).
8. In the Type Selector, select the roof type.
   - The thickness, which is determined by the roof type, is added below the profile sketch line.

9. View the roof in 3D and make any other needed modifications. For example, you can use the controls on the ends of the roof to extend the overhang (as shown in Figure 9–22), as well as modify the roof using temporary dimensions and Properties.

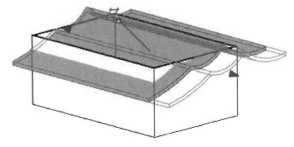

Figure 9–22

10. Attach the walls to the roof.

9.4 Modify Roofs

Once your roof is created, you can modify it by selecting the roof and changing its parameters in Properties. You can also modify the roof footprint sketch or extruded profile of a roof.

Roof by Footprint Properties

Base Level	Sets the level for the roof.
Base Offset From Level	Sets the height of the roof above or below the level where it is being sketched (allows for raised heel truss designs).
Cutoff Level	Specifies the level at which the roof should be cut off. Typically, another roof will be created to fill the hole created by cutting off the first roof. This property and the *Cutoff Offset* apply to the first roof, not the second roof.
Cutoff Offset	Specifies the height of the cutoff above or below the level specified by the *Cutoff Level*.
Rafter Cut	Defines the rafter cut on an eave by selecting from a drop-down list: • **Plumb Cut:** Cuts the roof fascia at a 90-degree vertical. • **Two Cut - Plumb:** Cuts the roof fascia 90 degrees vertically and horizontally at the *Fascia Depth*. • **Two Cut - Square:** Cuts the roof fascia at 90 degrees relative to the face of the roof and horizontally at the *Fascia Depth*.
Fascia Depth	Sets the length of the lines defining the fascia. Does not affect the size of additionally applied fascia profiles.

Rafter or Truss	Select either **Rafter** or **Truss** for the roof construction method to control how the roof sits on the walls. If **Rafter** is selected, the *Plate Offset From Base* is measured from the inside of the wall. If **Truss** is selected, the *Plate Offset From Base* is measured from the outside of the wall, as shown in Figure 9–23.

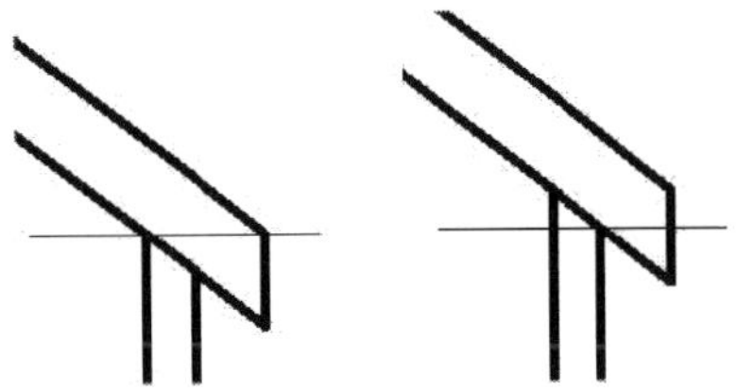

Figure 9–23

Maximum Ridge Height	A read-only value that displays the maximum height of the top of the roof above the base level of the building.
Slope	Controls the value of the slope-defining line.

Roof by Extrusion Properties

Extrusion Start	Sets the extrusion start point for the roof.
Extrusion End	Sets the extrusion end point for the roof.
Reference Level	Specifies the reference level for the roof.
Level Offset	Specifies the offset from the reference level for the roof.
Rafter Cut	Defines the rafter cut on an eave by selecting from a drop-down list: • **Plumb Cut:** Cuts the roof fascia at a 90-degree vertical. • **Two Cut - Plumb:** Cuts the roof fascia 90 degrees vertically and horizontally at the *Fascia Depth*. • **Two Cut - Square:** Cuts the roof fascia at 90 degrees relative to the face of the roof and horizontally at the *Fascia Depth*.

How To: Modify the Footprint of a Roof

1. To edit a roof sketch, double-click on the edge of the roof. Alternatively, with the roof selected, in the *Modify | Roofs* tab>Mode panel, click 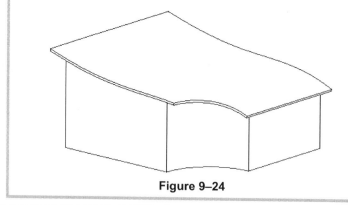 (Edit Footprint).
2. In the *Modify | Roofs* tab>Mode panel, use the tools to edit the roof's sketch lines.
3. To finish editing the roof, click ✓ (Finish Edit Mode).

How To: Modify the Profile of an Extruded Roof

1. Double-click on the edge of the roof. Alternatively, select the roof and in the *Modify | Roofs* tab>Mode panel, click ✎ (Edit Profile).
2. In the *Modify | Create Extrusion Roof Profile* tab>Draw panel, use the tools to create a closed boundary. The boundary can be entirely inside the roof or touching the roof boundaries.
3. Click ✓ (Finish Edit Mode).

Hint: Creating an Opening

You can create an opening in the roof using the **Vertical** opening tool.

1. Open a plan view where the entire roof displays.
2. In the *Modify | Roofs* tab>Opening panel, click ▨ (Vertical).
3. In the *Modify | Create Extrusion Roof Profile* tab>Draw panel, use the tools to create a closed boundary.
4. Click ✓ (Finish Edit Mode).
5. The extruded roof now has a cutout, as shown in Figure 9–24.

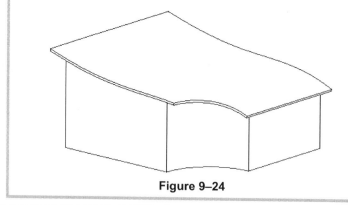

Figure 9–24

Join Roofs

When you want to join an extruded roof to another roof or a wall face that is taller than the roof, you can use the **Join/Unjoin Roof** command, as shown in Figure 9–25.

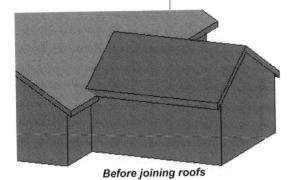
Before joining roofs

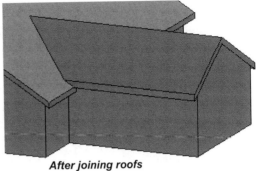
After joining roofs

Figure 9–25

How To: Use Join/Unjoin Roof

1. In the *Modify* tab>Geometry panel, click (Join/Unjoin Roof).
2. Select one of the roof edges.
3. Select the other roof or the wall.

Hint: Join Geometry

Where roofs overlap walls or other roofs, use **Join Geometry** to clean up the intersections. The elements remain separate, but the intersections are cleaned up, as shown in Figure 9–26.

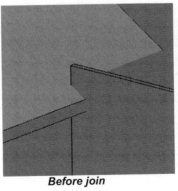
Before join

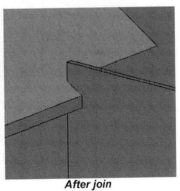
After join

Figure 9–26

9.5 Creating Dormers

You can add two types of dormers to a project. One type of dormer cuts through the roof, as shown in Figure 9–27. This dormer type has walls supporting a separate roof. You create the supporting walls and dormer roof, and then cut a hole in the roof.

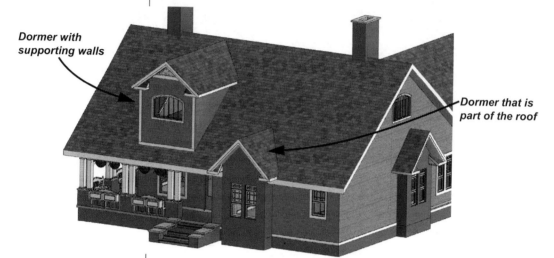

Dormer with supporting walls

Dormer that is part of the roof

Figure 9–27

The other type of dormer is part of the roof, as shown above in Figure 9–27. It is created by sketching the roof, modifying it, and adding slope arrows to define the additional peak.

- The dormer must be added to a plane that defines a slope.

How To: Add a Dormer with Supporting Walls to a Roof

1. Draw the main roof. When it is placed correctly, create a secondary dormer roof and supporting walls, as shown in Figure 9–28.

Figure 9–28

2. Move the new dormer (walls and roof) into position.

3. In the *Modify* tab>Geometry panel, use  (Join Geometry) and (Join/Unjoin Roof) to connect the dormer walls/roof to the existing roof.

4. In the *Architecture* tab>Opening panel, click (Dormer).

5. In a roof plan view, select the main roof (the one to be cut).

6. In the *Modify | Edit Sketch* tab>Pick panel, click (Pick Roof/Wall Edges) and select the opening to be cut.

- The dormer opening sketch does not need to be closed.

- Clean up the roofs and roof edges, as needed, using tools such as **Join**, **Attach Top/Base**, etc.

How To: Add a Dormer Using Slope Arrows to a Roof

1. Draw a roof. When it is placed, select the roof. In the *Modify | Roofs* tab>Mode panel, click (Edit Footprint) to edit the roof sketch.

2. In the *Modify | Roofs>Edit Footprint* tab>Modify panel, click (Split Element) to split the edge of the roof between the two points where you want the dormer to be located. Do not delete the inner segment. You can use dynamic dimensions to help locate the points to split.

3. In the Selection panel, click (Modify) and select the new segment between the split points. In the Options Bar, clear the **Defines slope** option for this segment.

4. In the Draw panel, click (Slope Arrow).

5. Draw a slope arrow from one end of the segment to the midpoint, then sketch a second slope arrow from the other end to the midpoint, as shown in Figure 9–29.

Figure 9–29

6. Select the slope arrows. In Properties, specify the *Height at the Tail* or *Slope* and type the required properties.

7. In the Mode panel, click  (Finish Edit Mode).
8. View the roof in a 3D view to verify the results, as shown in Figure 9–30.

Figure 9–30

Practice 9a | Create Roofs by Footprint

Practice Objectives

- Create roofs using **Roof by Footprint**.
- Modify roofs.
- Join a complex roof.

In this practice, you will create several roofs using the footprint method and then join them together to create a more complex overall roof, as shown in Figure 9–31.

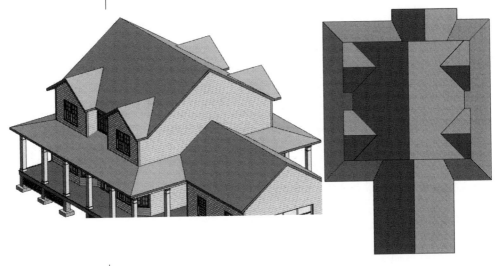

Figure 9–31

Task 1 - Create the main roof.

1. Open the project **Residential-Roof.rvt** from the practice files folder.

2. Open the **Floor Plans: Roof Plan** view.

3. In the *Architecture* tab>Build panel, expand (Roof) and click (Roof by Footprint).

4. In the *Modify | Edit Roof Footprint* tab>Draw panel, click (Pick Walls).

5. In the Options Bar, do the following:

   • Verify that the **Defines slope** option is selected.
   • Set the *Overhang* to **1'-6"**.
   • Ensure that **Extend to wall core** is selected.

6. In Properties, set the following:

   • *Type Selector:* **Basic Roof: Wood Rafter 6" - Asphalt Shingle**
   • *Base Level:* **Second Floor**
   • *Base Offset From Level:* **8'-8"**
   • *Rafter Cut:* **Two Cut - Plumb**

7. Select the exterior walls on the floor plan. **Do not** select the parts that extend out at the top and bottom of the plan.

8. Use 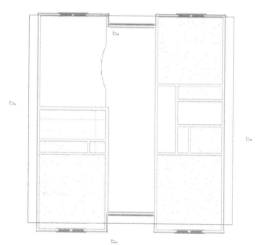 (Trim/Extend to Corner) to clean up the rectangle border, as shown in Figure 9–32.

Figure 9–32

9. Select the two vertical borders and in Properties, clear the check box for **Defines Roof Slope**, as shown in Figure 9–33.

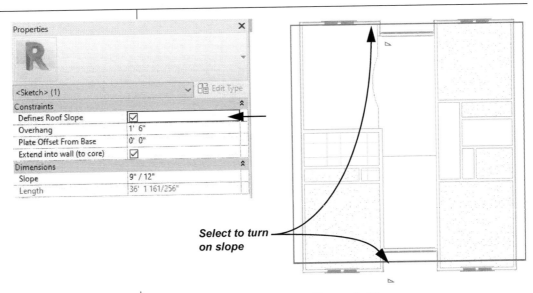

Select to turn on slope

Figure 9–33

10. Click ⌖ (Modify).

11. In Properties, set the following in the *Construction* area:

- *Rafter or Truss:* **Rafter**
- *Slope:* **8" / 12"**

12. Click ✓ (Finish Edit Mode).

13. In the Attaching to roof dialog box, select **Don't attach**.

14. The second floor roof should look like the one shown in Figure 9–34.

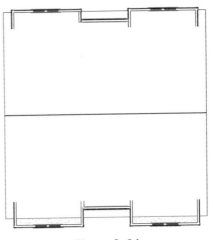

Figure 9–34

15. In the View Control Bar, set the *Visual Style* to **Wireframe** to see the walls below the roof.

16. Save the project.

Task 2 - Create dormers for the roof.

You will now create four separate roofs for the parts that extend out past the main roof you just created.

1. Start the **Roof by Footprint** command again.

2. In the *Modify | Create Roof Footprint* tab>Draw panel, click (Pick Walls).

3. In the Options Bar, do the following:

   - Verify that the **Defines slope** option is selected.
   - Set the *Overhang* to **1'-6"**.
   - Ensure that **Extend to wall core** is selected.

4. In Properties, set the following:

   - *Type Selector:* **Basic Roof: Wood Rafter 6" - Asphalt Shingle**
   - *Base Level:* **Second Floor**
   - *Base Offset From Level:* **8'-8"**
   - *Rafter Cut:* **Two Cut - Plumb**

5. Select the three exterior walls shown in Figure 9–35.

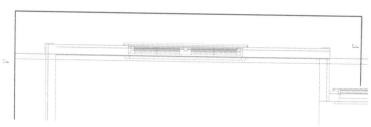

Figure 9–35

6. There is no wall for the most interior portion of this roof to select. In the *Modify | Create Roof Footprint* tab>Draw panel, click (Pick Lines). In the Options Bar, uncheck **Defines slope** and set the *Offset* to **3'-0"**.

7. Hover your cursor over the horizontal roof sketch line. When the reference line shows on the correct side (as shown Figure 9–36), click to place the boundary line.

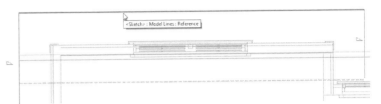

Figure 9–36

8. In the *Modify | Create Roof Footprint* tab>Modify panel, click (Trim/Extend to Corner) to clean up the corners.

9. Select the horizontal boundary and clear the box for **Defines slope** in the Options Bar. (This option could also be cleared in Properties).

10. Click (Modify).

11. In Properties, set the following in the *Construction* area:

- *Rafter or Truss:* **Rafter**
- *Slope:* **8" / 12"**

12. Click (Finish Edit Mode).

13. In the Attaching to roof dialog box, select **Don't attach**.

14. Repeat the process to create similar roofs for the three other areas where the second floor extends out.

- Take extra care to make sure you set all the settings correctly; otherwise, the roof lines (fascias) will not align properly.

Task 3 - Join roofs.

1. In the Project Browser, open the **3D Views: {3D}** view. Note that this shows a series of gable roofs.

2. Close all views except for the 3D view and the **Roof Plan** view.

3. Press **WT** to tile the two views, then ensure you are in the 3D view.

4. Zoom out and orbit to observe the gable orientation between different roof components.

5. Orbit and zoom until you can see both a sloped roof face and a gable roof edge in the same view, as shown in Figure 9–37.

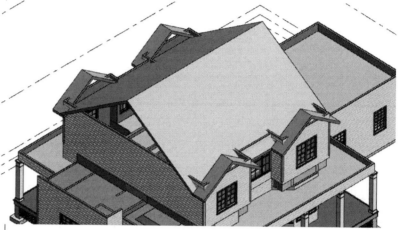

Figure 9–37

6. In the *Modify* tab>Geometry panel, click (Join/Unjoin Roof).

7. Select a roof edge on one of the smaller gable roofs, then select a roof surface that the edge will extend to, as shown in Figure 9–38.

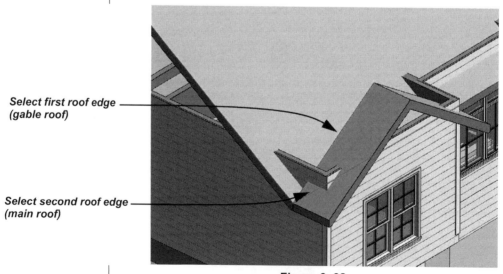

Select first roof edge (gable roof)

Select second roof edge (main roof)

Figure 9–38

8. Note that the two roofs are now joined. However, the larger roof still has a portion of it that extends under the smaller gable. Join the rest of the gable roofs to the main roof, as shown in Figure 9–39.

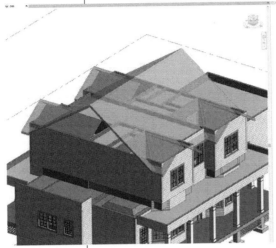 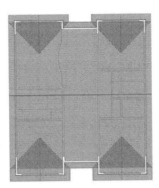

Figure 9–39

Task 4 - Create dormer roofs.

1. Activate the **Floor Plans: Roof Plan** view.

2. In the *Architecture* tab>Opening panel, click ✎ (Dormer).

3. Select the larger roof.

   • Note in the ribbon that the **Pick Roof/Wall Edges** command is selected by default.

4. Select one of the smaller gables, as shown in Figure 9–40.

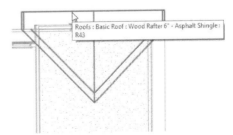

Figure 9–40

• This creates two border lines where the underside of the small gable meets the larger main roof slope.

5. Select the horizontal edge of the main roof, as shown in Figure 9–41.

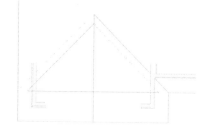

Figure 9–41

6. Use the **Trim** command to close the border.

7. Click (Finish Edit Mode).

8. Repeat this process with the other small gable roofs to create dormers.

Task 5 - Clean up walls.

---

1. Activate the **{3D}** view and type **TW** to tab the views again and enlarge the 3D view.

2. Orbit and zoom in to the second floor wall on the side by the garage.

3. Select the wall along the open end of the larger main roof, as shown in Figure 9–42. Note how the wall does not extend up to close the open end of the roof and how the wall extends above the roof on the ends.

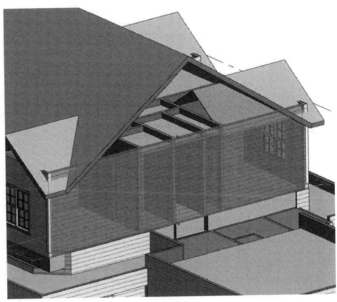

Figure 9–42

4. In the *Modify | Walls* tab>Modify Wall panel, select

   ☐ (Attach Top/Base).

5. In the Options Bar, verify *Attached Wall* is set to **Top**.

6. Select the large main roof.

7. The wall extends to match the profile of the larger main roof gable. Use the same process to clean up the wall at the small gables on both ends.

8. The wall profile now matches both the larger main roof gable and the smaller gable roofs, as shown in Figure 9–43.

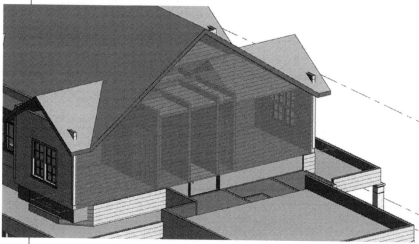

Figure 9–43

9. Orbit and zoom in to the second floor wall on the left side of the plan (opposite the garage).

- When attaching the walls that touch multiple roofs, sometimes the order of attaching affects how the wall responds to the attachment. If attaching to one roof creates an error or it does not attach correctly, try attaching to the other roof first.

10. Repeat the process to attach the front and back walls (walls with windows) to the small gables and the larger main roof that they intersect. Figure 9–44 shows Back and Front views of the final result.

Back

Front

Figure 9–44

11. Orbit and zoom as needed to get a clear view to work.

12. Save the project.

Task 6 - Create the garage, porch, and master bathroom roofs.

1. Close the Roof Plan view and open the **Floor Plans: First Floor** view.

2. With the 3D view and First Floor view open, press **WT** to tile the views. Close any other views that are currently open.

3. Activate the **First Floor** view.

4. In Properties, in the *Underlay* area, set the *Range: Base Level* to **Second Floor.**

5. Zoom in on the garage area. Ensure that the garage can be seen in the other view.

6. In the *Architecture* tab>Build panel, expand [icon] (Roof) and click [icon] (Roof by Footprint).

7. Select the **Pick Walls** tool from the Draw panel.

8. In the Options Bar, do the following:

    • Verify that **Defines slope** is selected.
    • Set the *Overhang* to **1'-6"**.
    • Ensure that **Extend into wall core** is selected.

9. In Properties, set the following:

    • *Type Selector:* **Basic Roof: Wood Rafter 6" - Asphalt Shingle**
    • *Base Level:* **Second Floor**
    • *Base Offset From Level:* (negative) **-1'-5 27/128"**
    • *Rafter Cut:* **Two Cut - Plumb**
    • *Fascia Depth:* **0'-6"**

The base offset is important to set as indicated so the roof fascia in the next practice lines up correctly.

10. Create three sides of the roof over the garage, as shown in Figure 9–45.

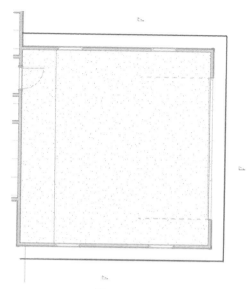

Figure 9–45

11. Use the **Pick Lines** draw tool to create the fourth side of the roof. In the Options Bar, set the *Offset* to **30'-4"**.

12. Hover over the vertical roof sketch line to place a line as shown in Figure 9–46. Use the **Trim** tool to clean up and create the outline.

13. Select the two vertical borders shown in Figure 9–46 and deselect **Defines slope**.

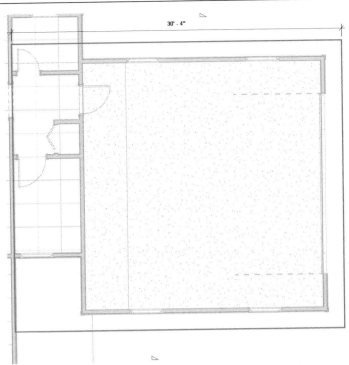

Figure 9–46

14. Click 🔓 (Modify).

15. In Properties, set the following:

    - *Rafter or Truss:* **Rafter**
    - *Slope:* **8" / 12"**

16. Click ✔️ (Finish Edit Mode).

17. In the Attaching to roof dialog box, select **Don't attach**.

18. Using the same Options Bar and Properties settings used to draw the gable roof over the garage, follow a similar process to create a gable roof over the master bathroom area that extends out past the left most exterior wall of the master bedroom, as shown in Figure 9–47.

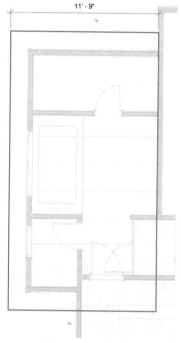

Figure 9–47

19. Click ✓ (Finish Edit Mode).

20. In the Attaching to roof dialog box, select **Don't attach**.

21. Pan and zoom over to the porch (bottom porch).

22. Start the **Roof** command. Select the **Pick Lines** draw tool.

23. In the Options Bar, select **Defines slope** and set the *Offset* to **1'-4"**.

24. Select the lines of the porch to create the three sides of the roof, as shown in Figure 9–48.

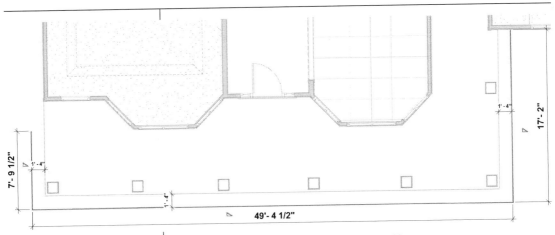

Figure 9–48

25. Select the **Pick Lines** draw tool. In the Options Bar, set the *Offset* to **7'-9 1/2"**.

26. Hover your mouse over the horizontal roof sketch line and click to place the boundary line when you see the dashed line run along the front of the house, as shown Figure 9–49.

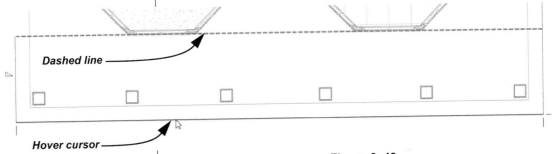

Dashed line ——

Hover cursor——

Figure 9–49

27. Select **Pick Lines** again and set the *Offset* to **8'-3"**. Hover over the right horizontal roof sketch line, as shown in Figure 9–50.

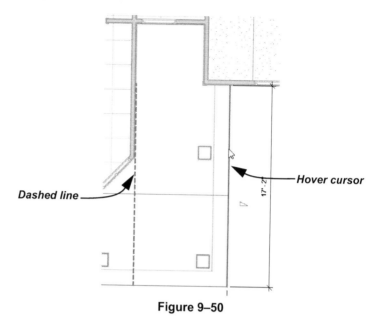

Figure 9–50

28. Draw a line and use the **Trim** tool to clean up the corners, as shown in Figure 9–51.

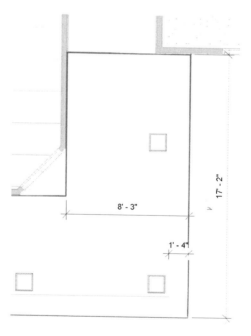

Figure 9–51

29. Clear **Defines slope** for the three interior edge sketch lines.

30. Click (Modify).

31. In Properties, set the following:

- *Type Selector:* **Basic Roof: Wood Rafter 6" - Asphalt Shingle**
- *Base Level:* **Second Floor**
- *Base Offset From Level:* (negative) **-2'-6 1/2"**
- *Rafter Cut:* **Two Cut - Plumb**
- *Fascia Depth:* **0'-6"**
- *Slope:* **4" / 12"**

32. Click (Finish Edit Mode).

33. In the Attaching to roof dialog box, select **Don't attach**.

34. Use the same settings and process used to create the front porch roof to create the top porch roof. See Figure 9–52 for the outline.

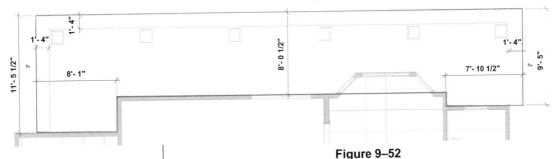

Figure 9–52

35. Save the project.

Task 7 - Join porch roofs.

1. Activate the **{3D}** view and type **TW** to tab the views.

2. Rotate the 3D view so you can see the southwest corner of the house.

3. In the *Modify* tab>Geometry panel, click (Join/Unjoin Roof). You have to restart the **Join/Unjoin Roof** command each time you want to join a roof.

4. Select the roof edge on the front porch roof that is closest to the master bathroom roof, as shown in Figure 9–53.

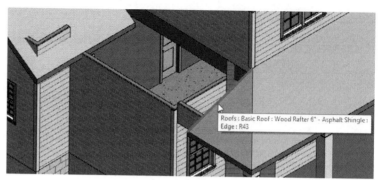

Figure 9–53

5. Select the roof face on the master bathroom roof that is adjacent to the selected edge. This will extend the front porch roof over to the master bathroom.

6. Rotate or pan the 3D view so you are viewing the center of the porch roof.

7. Using the **Join/Unjoin Roof** tool, select the edge of the front porch roof that is under the windows on the second floor, then select the exterior wall with the large window, as shown in Figure 9–54. This will extend the roof to this wall.

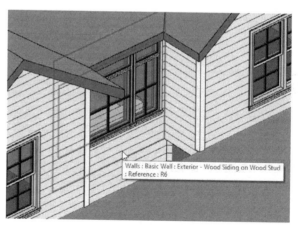

Figure 9–54

8. Rotate to a southeast isometric view. Repeat the joining process on the porch with the garage roof.

9. Rotate to a northeast isometric view. Continue using the **Join/Unjoin Roof** tool to join the porch roof to the garage and master bathroom roofs and to the wall under the large window in the middle on the second floor.

10. Save the project.

Task 8 - Clean up walls.

To clean up the walls extending above the roof or that do not touch the roof, you will use the **Attach Top/Base** tool.

1. In the 3D view, rotate to the garage.

2. Select the wall with the overhead garage door in it.

3. In the *Modify | Wall* tab>Modify Wall panel, select (Attach Top/Base). In the Options Bar, set *Attach Wall:* to **Top**, then select the garage roof. Continue on the rest of the garage walls.

4. Repeat this process to attach the walls in the master bathroom area to the roof above the master bathroom. Figure 9–55 shows the completed roof joins and wall joins.

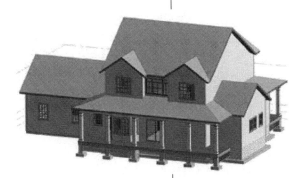 

Figure 9–55

Task 9 - Modify the garage and master bathroom roof valleys.

Now that roofs have been joined, there are areas where the two roofs extend beyond each other in the roof valleys by the garage and master bathroom. To clean these up, you will use the **Dormer** tool; you could also use the **Vertical** opening tool.

1. Still in the 3D view, rotate to a northeast isometric view.

2. In the *Architecture* tab>Opening panel, select  (Dormer).

3. Select the garage roof, the select the porch.

4. A small sketch line is added to the corner near the valley, as shown in Figure 9–56. Since this sketch line touches both the lower part of the roof and the gable end, it does not need any other edges to create the opening.

Figure 9–56

5. Select ✔ (Finish Edit Mode).

6. Repeat this process for the other roof valley by the front porch.

7. Hover your cursor over the roof over the garage and note how the roof corners are cut off under the valleys. Figure 9–57 shows the before and after of the garage roof.

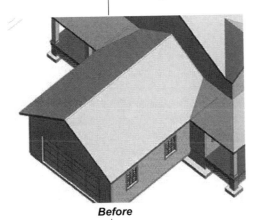
Before

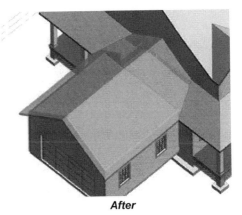
After

Figure 9–57

8. If time permits, repeat the process for the roof over the master bathroom.

9. Save and close the project.

9.6 Creating Fascias, Soffits, and Gutters

Autodesk Revit provides specific tools for adding fascias, soffits, and gutters to your model, as shown in Figure 9–58.

Figure 9–58

Fascias

You can add fascia boards to the edge of a roof as one continuous piece or as individual segments. You can also use the **Fascia** tool to create fascia-bands, frieze boards, and bird boxes.

How To: Apply a Fascia

1. In the *Architecture* tab>Build panel, expand ⬛ (Roof) and click ⬿ (Roof: Fascia).
2. Select the desired fascia profile from the Type Selector. (Note that you will need to load the profile from the *Profile>Roofs* folder in the Revit Library using the **Load Family** tool on the *Insert* tab before starting the command.)
3. Highlight the edges of roofs, soffits, other fascias, or model lines and click to place the fascia.
4. Click ⬚ (Modify) or press <Esc>.

- As you click edges, Revit treats them as one continuous fascia. If the fascia segments meet at corners, they miter. To start another fascia, in the ribbon, click **Restart Fascia** and then click on a new edge. This creates a different fascia, which does not miter with other existing fascias even if they meet at the corners.

- **Hint:** Offset the fascia from the edge of the roof by setting the *Vertical Profile Offset* in Properties to the thickness of the roof deck finish, then use the Flip control to flip the profile so that it will cut into the roof. Use the **Join Geometry** command to cut the profile from the roof in order to create a drip edge with the deck and finish.

Soffits

There are many different styles of soffits, so the method you use can vary widely. However, in general, the soffit is created as a roof object and is bounded by a closed loop. You can then use the **Join Geometry** tool to join the soffit and the roof, as shown in Figure 9–59. Depending on the construction of the roof and soffit, you may also need to add trim to close spaces at the ends of soffits.

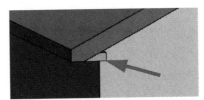

Figure 9–59

How To: Add a Soffit

1. In the *Architecture* tab>Build panel, expand (Roof) and select (Roof: Soffit).
2. Select the desired soffit type from the Type Selector.
3. In the *Modify | Create Roof Soffit Boundary* tab>Draw panel, select a Draw tool to draw the soffit's boundary.

4. Click (Finish Edit Mode).

Gutters

You can add gutters to the edges of roofs, soffits, and fascias, as shown in Figure 9–60. You can also add gutters to model lines.

Figure 9–60

How To: Add a Roof Gutter

1. In the *Architecture* tab>Build panel, expand   (Roof) and click   (Roof: Gutter).
2. Select the desired gutter profile from the Type Selector. (Note that you will need to load the profile from the *Profile>Roofs* folder in the Revit Library using the **Load Family** tool on the *Insert* tab before starting the command.)
3. Highlight the edges of roofs, soffits, fascias, or model lines and click to place the gutter.

4. Click   (Modify).

- As you click edges, Revit treats this as one continuous gutter. To start a new gutter, click **Restart Gutter** and click on a new edge.

- After creating a gutter, you can use other tools to resize it, flip the gutter, add or remove segments, and change the horizontal and vertical offsets.

Practice 9b

Add Fascias and Soffits

Practice Objectives

- Add roof fascias and soffits.
- Create bird box on roof trim.

In this practice, you will create roof trim, including fascias, soffits, and frieze boards. You will also create bird boxes for trim cornices, as shown in Figure 9–61.

Figure 9–61

Task 1 - Add roof fascias.

1. Open the project **Residential-Roof Trim.rvt** from the practice files folder.

2. Open the **Elevations (Building Elevation): South** view and the default **3D** view. Close any other projects or views.

    -   You will use the Elevation South view to verify that the fascia and soffits are created in the correct location. If they are not, this view is where you can use the Modify tools to move or align the element into place.

3. Press **WT** to tile the views.

4. Activate the **3D** view.

5. Zoom and pan in to the gable over one of the second floor extended areas, as shown in Figure 9–62.

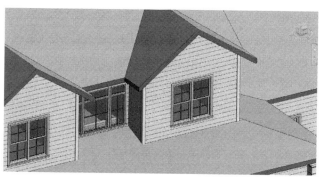

Figure 9–62

6. In the *Architecture* tab>Build panel, expand (Roof) and click (Roof: Fascia).

7. In the Type Selector, select **Fascia: Fascia-Band**.

8. In Properties, set the *Vertical Profile Offset* to (negative) **-0'-1"**.

9. Pick one of the top edges of the gable roof, as shown in Figure 9–63.

Figure 9–63

10. Continue picking the top edges of the roof on the second floor, all the way around until you get back to where you started.

11. Click (Modify).

12. Repeat this process to add fascia trim to all the roof edges on the first floor as well, as shown in Figure 9–64.

Figure 9–64

13. Save the project.

Task 2 - Add a sloped roof above the garage door.

In this task, you will add a small sloped roof over the garage door and modify the fascia-band board to it.

1. Open the **First Floor** view.

2. Close the South Elevation view and type **WT** to tile the **First Floor** and **3D** views. Rotate the views so you can see the garage.

3. Activate the **First Floor** view.

4. Start the **Roof by Footprint** command and select the **Pick Walls** draw tool.

5. In the Options Bar, do the following:

   - Select **Defines slope**.
   - Set the *Overhang* to **1'-6"**.
   - Select **Extend to wall core**.

6. In Properties, set the following:

- *Type Selector:* **Basic Roof: Wood Rafter 6" - Asphalt Shingle**
- *Base Level:* **Second Floor**
- *Base Offset From Level:* (negative) **-1'-5 33/256"**
- *Rafter Cut:* **Two Cut - Plumb**
- *Fascia Depth:* **0'-6"**

7. Select the three exterior walls of the garage, as shown in Figure 9–65.

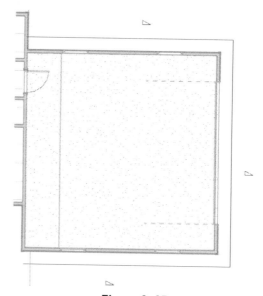

Figure 9–65

8. Using the **Pick Lines** draw tool, select the exterior finish face of the right vertical wall of the garage.

9. Use the **Trim** tool to clean up sketch lines to create a complete loop.

10. Click (Modify).

11. Select the vertical roof sketch line that is along the garage wall with the garage door and, in Properties, uncheck **Defines Roof Slope**. Your sketch lines should look like those shown in Figure 9–66.

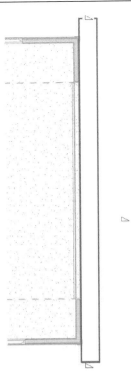

Figure 9–66

12. Click ▷ (Modify).

13. In Properties, set the following:

   - *Rafter or Truss:* **Rafter**
   - *Slope:* **8" / 12"**

14. Click ✓ (Finish Edit Mode).

15. Activate the default **{3D}** view.

16. In the *Modify* tab>Geometry panel, click ⟳ (Join).

17. Select the garage gable roof and then the new roof over the garage. This cleans up the roofs and joins their geometry.

18. In the *Architecture* tab>Build panel, expand ⬀ (Roof) and click ▽ (Roof: Fascia).

19. Set the type to **Fascia: Fascia-Band** and the *Vertical Profile Offset* to **-1"**.

20. Select the top edge of the new roof's fascia to add the fascia-band to it.

21. Use the **Join** tool and select the two fascia-band geometries to clean up their ends, as shown in Figure 9–67.

Figure 9–67

22. Select the Fascia-Band family. If you look in the valley areas by the garage and master bathroom, the fascia extends beyond the face of the intersecting roof line. These can be cleaned up by dragging the control end of the fascia until the corners miter correctly, as shown in Figure 9–68. Do this until all four areas are cleaned up.

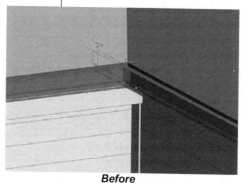
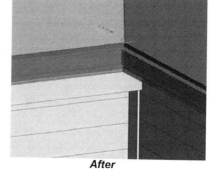

Before   *After*

Figure 9–68

23. Save the project.

Task 3 - Add roof soffits to the first floor.

1. Activate the **First Floor** view and type **TW**.

2. In Properties, in the *Underlay* area, set the *Range: Base Level* to **Second Floor** and the *Underlay Orientation* to **Look Up**.

3. In the *Architecture* tab>Build panel, expand 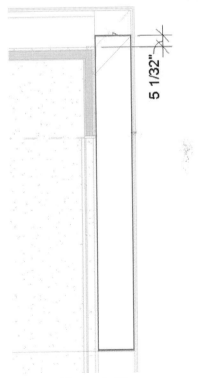 (Roof) and select (Roof: Soffit).

4. In the *Modify | Create Roof Soffit Boundary* tab>Draw panel, use (Rectangle).

5. In Properties, set the following:
   - *Type Selector:* **Porous Vinyl Soffit**
   - *Level:* **Second Floor**

6. Draw a rectangle, as shown in Figure 9–69.
   - The top line should be **5 1/32"** above the exterior face of the garage, the right edge should line up with the roof edge (not the outside line of the fascia-band), the bottom line should line up with the peak (roof center line), and the left line should line up with the exterior finish face of the wall, as shown in Figure 9–69.

Figure 9–69

7. Click 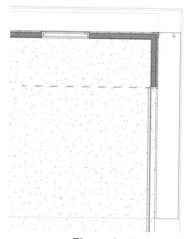 (Modify).

8. Select the top horizontal line. In Properties, set the following:

   - Select **Defines Constant Height**
   - Select **Defines Slope**
   - *Slope:* **8" / 12"**
   - *Level:* **Second Floor**
   - *Offset From Base:* (negative) **-2'-0 1/4"**

9. Click (Finish Edit Mode).

- The soffit will appear light gray as it is being viewed as part of the underlay. Hovering over the top edge, the soffit should highlight. If the soffit does not highlight as in Figure 9–70, turn on **Select Underlay Elements** in your Selection Options.

Figure 9–70

10. Select the soffit.

11. In the *Modify | Roof Soffits* tab>Modify panel, select
    (Mirror - Pick Axis), or type **MM**. Make sure **Copy** is checked in the Options Bar.

12. Select the bottom edge of the soffit (center of the roof) to mirror the soffit to the other side.

Use the Building Elevation views to help position the soffit into the correct location.

13. Repeat the process for the gable end by the master bathroom, using the same settings and slopes. Align the sketch lines similar to how the garage was done, except that the edge that defines the slope should align with the exterior wall face, not extend above it.

You will use a similar process to create the flat soffits for the front and back. This will be one large outline.

14. Start the **Soffit** command.

15. In Properties, set the following:

- *Type Selector:* **1/2" Plywood w 2x4 Stud**
- *Level:* **Second Floor**
- *Height Offset From Level:* (negative) **-2'-5 83/128"**

16. Draw the boundary shown in Figure 9–71. Use any of the Draw and Modify tools you prefer.

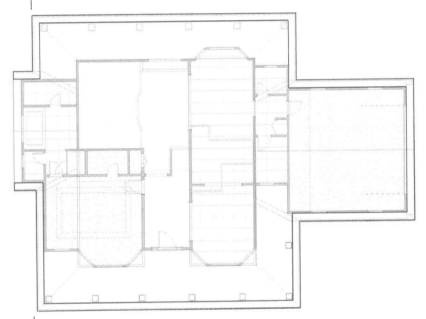

Figure 9–71

17. Click (Finish Edit Mode).

18. Use the default **{3D}** view to look at the soffits created for the first floor.

Task 4 - Add frieze boards.

1. Verify that you are in or activate the default **{3D}** view.

2. Rotate the view so it shows the roof gable over the garage door, similar to Figure 9–72.

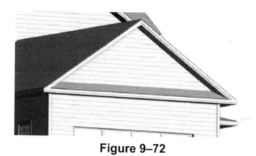

Figure 9–72

3. In the *Architecture* tab>Build panel, expand (Roof) and click (Roof: Fascia).

4. In the Type Selector, select **Fascia: Fascia-Freeze 1x12**.

5. Click on the edge of the sloped soffit, closest to the wall. If needed, use the Flip controls to flip the orientation of the frieze as it may appear inside the wall (similar to Figure 9–73).

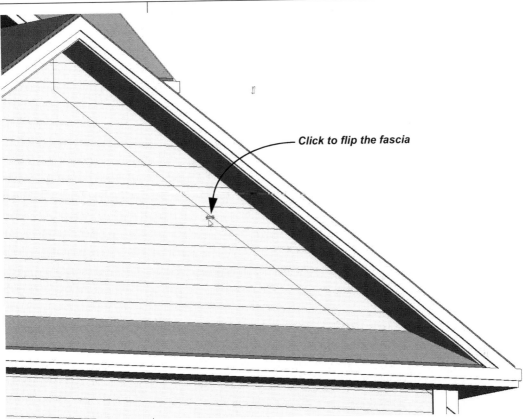

Click to flip the fascia

Figure 9–73

6. Select the frieze board and in the *Modify | Fascia* tab>Roof Fascia panel, click (Add/Remove Segments).

7. Select the same edge on the opposite soffit.

    *   Hint: It may be helpful to orbit, pan, and/or zoom to find the correct edge of the soffit.

8. Click (Modify).

9. Note that the boards extend past the exterior wall and below the lower soffit. Select the frieze board and in the *Modify |*

Fascia tab>Roof Fascia panel, click 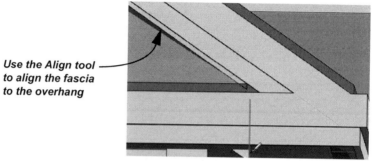 (Modify Mitering). Hover over the edge of the board. When you see that the edge you want mitered highlights (as shown in Figure 9–74), click to cut it back.

Use the Align tool to align the fascia to the overhang

Figure 9–74

10. Use the Drag End controls to pull the ends of the frieze boards back to where the board intersects the overhang roof, as shown in Figure 9–75.

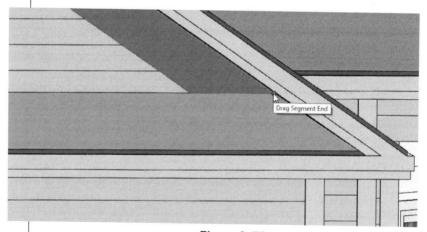

Figure 9–75

11. Use the **Join** command to clean up the frieze board and overhang roof.

12. Use the **Align** tool to align the frieze board with the overhang so the frieze board is flush with the overhang edge.

13. Add another frieze board to the other side of the garage.

14. Zoom out and review the fascia-band, soffits, and frieze boards, then save the project.

Task 5 - Create a bird box.

1. Verify that the default {3D} view is active.

2. Use zoom, pan, and orbit to view the gable overhang over the master bathroom.

3. Start the **Fascia** command.

4. In the Type Selector, select **Fascia: Fascia-Frieze 1x12**.

5. In Properties, set the *Vertical Profile Offset* to **0'-6 3/4"**.

6. Select the top edge of the flat soffit, as shown in Figure 9–76.

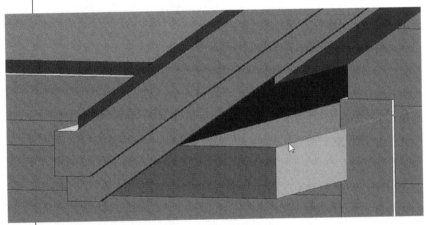

Figure 9–76

7. Click (Modify) and then select the piece of fascia just created.

8. Note how the board extends into the house. Use the Drag End control to pull the end of the board back to be flush with the exterior finish face of the adjacent wall.

9. Adjust the other end of the board to be flush with the fascia-band board, as shown in Figure 9–77.

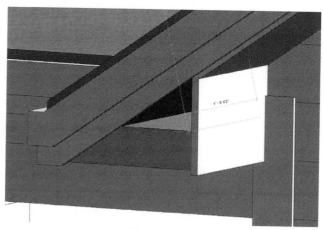

Figure 9–77

10. Start the **Fascia** command again. In the Type Selector, select **Fascia: Fascia-Flat 1x6**.

11. In Properties, set the *Vertical Profile Offset* to **0'-1"**.

12. Select the top edge of the soffit perpendicular to the previously selected edge, as shown in Figure 9–78.

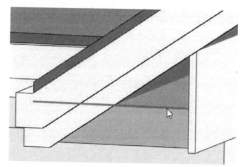

Figure 9–78

13. In the *Modify | Place Fascia* tab>Placement panel, click **Restart Fascia**.

14. In Properties, set the *Vertical Profile Offset* to **0'-5 1/2"** and select the outside top edge of the lower 1x6 fascia board.

15. If needed, use the Flip control and Drag End controls, as shown in Figure 9–79, to adjust the top fascia board to match.

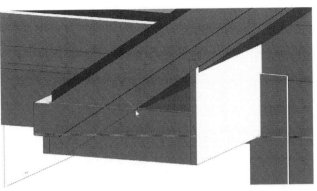

Figure 9–79

16. Use the **Join** tool to clean up the fascia boards so they appear as shown in Figure 9–80.

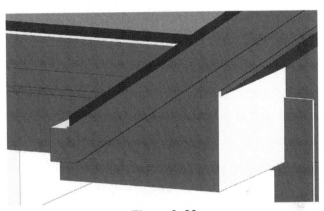

Figure 9–80

- Note that the board lines disappear and create clean joints.

17. Repeat these steps and settings for the other side of this gable.

18. Zoom out and review the bird boxes, then save the project.

Task 6 - (Optional) Add the second floor soffits and bird boxes.

If time permits, create the soffits and bird boxes on the second floor, as shown in Figure 9–81. This task has limited instruction, and it is intended for you to use the knowledge you gained in the previous task to complete this task. **Hint:** Use your elevation views when drawing soffits to verify that they are in the correct location. If not, use your **Move** tool to move them into place.

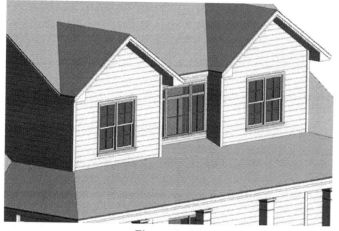

Figure 9–81

1. In the Project Browser, open the **Second Floor** view.

2. In the Visibility/Graphic Overrides dialog box (type **VV**), turn on the **Roofs** category.

3. In Properties, set the following:

    - *Range:* **Base Level: Second Floor**
    - *Underlay Orientation:* **Look up**

4. Use the **Roof: Soffit** tool to create sloped and flat soffits.

5. Use the following properties for the front and back gables' sloped soffits:

    - *Type Selector:* **Porous Vinyl Soffit**
    - *Level:* **Second Floor**
    - *Height Offset From Level:* **8'-4 59/256"**
    - *Slope:* **8" / 12"**

6. Use the following properties for the front and back flat soffits:

   - *Type Selector:* **1/2" Plywood w 2x4 Stud**
   - *Level:* **Second Floor**
   - *Height Offset From Level:* **7'-6 251/256"**

7. Use the following properties for the side end of the main gable roof's sloped soffits:

   - *Type Selector:* **Porous Vinyl Soffit**
   - *Level:* **Second Floor**
   - *Height Offset From Level:* **7'-6 251/256"**
   - *Slope:* **8" / 12"**

8. Use the **Roof: Fascia** tool to create the bird boxes on the front and rear gables. Use similar types and offsets to create the appropriate shapes.

9. Save and close the project.

Chapter Review Questions

1. How would you create a roof sloping in one direction only?

   a. By extrusion and rotate the roof to the correct angle.

   b. By footprint and specify the slope along one side.

   c. By extrusion and use the Slope Arrow to define the overall slope of the roof.

   d. By footprint and use the Shape Editing tools to create the slope.

2. To create a gambrel roof, which of the following commands would you use to sketch the boundary of the roof and to set its thickness?

   a. **Roof by Extrusion** with the thickness set by the roof type.

   b. **Roof by Footprint** with the thickness set by the roof type.

3. How would you create a mansard roof (as shown in Figure 9–82)?

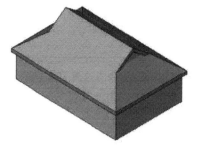

Figure 9–82

   a. By extrusion and cut openings to the correct height.

   b. By footprint using two separate roofs, the first ending at a cutoff level and the second filling the opening in the first.

   c. By extrusion and use the Slope Arrow to adjust the pitches.

   d. By footprint and use Shape Editing tools to edit the pitches for both.

4. How would you create a frieze board?

   a. Create a second wall with the appropriate thickness and use **Join Geometry** to the existing wall.

   b. Use the **Soffit** command with the appropriate type on a roof edge adjacent to the wall.

   c. Use the **Fascia** command with the appropriate type on a roof edge adjacent to the wall.

   d. Use the **Fascia** command with the appropriate type on a wall face adjacent to the roof.

5. To create a flat roof, which of the following commands would you use to sketch the boundary of the roof and to set its thickness?

   a. **Roof by Footprint** with the thickness set by the roof type.

   b. **Roof by Extrusion** with the thickness extruded from the sketch.

6. Which of the following methods makes a wall touch the underside of a roof?

   a. Select the wall and use ⬒ (Attach Top/Base).

   b. Select the roof and use ⬒ (Attach Top/Base).

   c. Select the wall and edit the profile.

   d. Select the roof and use **By Face**.

7. Which roof type and view should you use to create a curved roof, as shown in Figure 9–83?

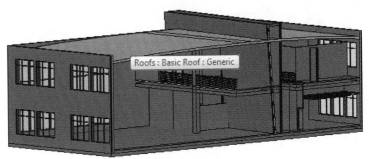

Figure 9–83

   a. Roof by Footprint, Plan view

   b. Roof by Footprint, Elevation or Section view

   c. Roof by Extrusion, Plan view

   d. Roof by Extrusion, Elevation or Section view

8. A work plane can be assigned using a named reference plane.

   a. True

   b. False

Command Summary

Button	Command	Location
	Add/Remove Segments	• **Ribbon:** *Modify	Fascia* tab> Roof Fascia panel
	Attach Top/Base	• **Ribbon:** *Modify	Walls* tab> Modify Wall panel
	Dormer	• **Ribbon:** *Architecture* tab> Opening panel
	Edit Footprint	• **Ribbon:** *Modify	Roofs* tab> Mode panel
	Edit Profile	• **Ribbon:** *Modify	Roofs* tab> Mode panel
	Join Geometry	• **Ribbon:** *Modify* tab>Geometry panel, expand Join
	Join/Unjoin Roof	• **Ribbon:** *Modify* tab>Geometry panel
	Mirror - Pick Axis	• **Ribbon:** *Modify	Roof Soffits* tab> Modify panel
	Modify Mitering	• **Ribbon:** *Modify	Fascia* tab> Roof Fascia panel
	Pick Roof/Wall Edges	• **Ribbon:** *Modify	Edit Sketch* tab> Pick panel
	Rectangle	• **Ribbon:** *Modify	Create Roof Soffit Boundary* tab>Draw panel
	Ref Plane	• **Ribbon:** *Architecture* tab>Work Plane panel
	Roof by Extrusion	• **Ribbon:** *Architecture* tab>Build panel, expand Roof
	Roof by Footprint	• **Ribbon:** *Architecture* tab>Build panel, expand Roof
	Roof: Fascia	• **Ribbon:** *Architecture* tab>Build panel, expand Roof
	Roof: Gutter	• **Ribbon:** *Architecture* tab>Build panel, expand Roof
	Roof: Soffit	• **Ribbon:** *Architecture* tab>Build panel, expand Roof
	Set Work Plane	• **Ribbon:** *Architecture* tab>Work Plane panel
	Show Work Plane	• **Ribbon:** *Architecture* tab>Work Plane panel

	Slope Arrow	• **Ribbon:** *Modify	Roofs>Edit Footprint* tab>Draw panel
	Split Element	• **Ribbon:** *Modify	Roofs>Edit Footprint* tab>Modify panel
	Trim/Extend to Corner	• **Ribbon:** *Modify	Create Roof Footprint* tab>Modify panel
	Unjoin Geometry	• **Ribbon:** *Modify* tab>Geometry panel expand Join
	Vertical (Opening)	• **Ribbon:** *Modify	Roofs> Opening* tab
	Viewer	• **Ribbon:** *Architecture* tab>Work Plane panel

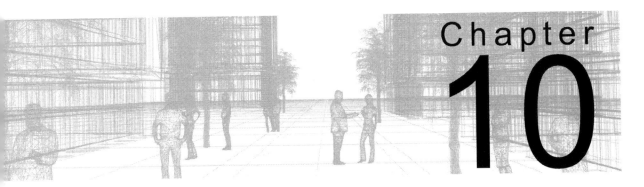

Chapter 10

Modeling Stairs and Railings

When modeling in the Autodesk® Revit® software, you can easily create basic stairs in straight, U-shaped, and multi-landing configurations. To create more complex shapes, you can convert runs and landings to sketches. Railings can be added automatically with the Stair command, or you can sketch railings on stairs and add them to balconies and decks. Railings are also sometimes used for fence lines.

Learning Objectives in This Chapter

- Create and modify component-based stairs made of runs, landings, supports, and railings.
- Convert runs and landings to sketches.
- Add and modify railings that are connected to stairs, as well as freestanding railings for balconies.

10.1 Creating Component Stairs

As with other Autodesk Revit elements, stairs are *smart* parametric elements. With just a few clicks, you can create stairs of varying heights and designs, complete with railings. Stairs can be created by assembling stair components (as shown in Figure 10–1) or by sketching a custom layout.

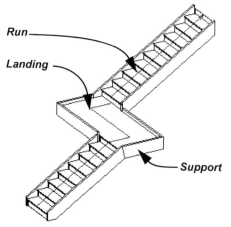

Run

Landing

Support

Figure 10–1

When creating component-based stairs, there are three parts of a stair that can be assembled, as shown in Figure 10–1:

- **Runs:** The actual stair tread and riser elements. These include straight runs that can be combined for multi-landing stairs, spiral stairs, and L-shaped and U-shaped winders.

- **Landings:** The platform between runs. These are typically created automatically and then modified if needed. They can also be created independently of the assembly for grand staircases.

- **Supports:** The stringer or carriage that structurally holds the stair elements. These can be created automatically or you can pick the edges where you want the different types to go. These can be placed on either side of the stairs or in the center of the stairs.

- Railings are typically added in the **Stair** command. They display after you complete the stair. Railings can also be created for independent use, such as fencing.

- You can select and edit each of the components while you are in Stair Edit mode or after the stair has been created.

- Each component of the stair is independent, but also has a relationship to the other components. For example, if steps are removed from one run, they are added to connected runs to maintain the overall height, as shown in Figure 10–2.

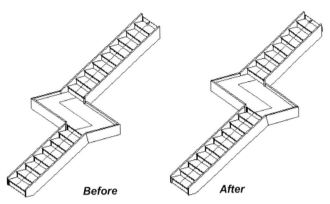

Before   **After**

Figure 10–2

Creating Runs

Component stairs can include a mix of the different types of runs.

To create a component stair, you must first place the run elements. There are six different options available in the Components panel, as shown in Figure 10–3 and described in the following table.

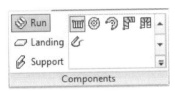

Figure 10–3

📏	**Straight**	Draws a straight run by selecting the start and end points of the run.
⊚	**Full-Step Spiral**	Draws a spiral run based on a start point and radius.
⌐	**Center-Ends Spiral**	Draws a spiral run based on a center point, start point, and end point.
⌐	**L-Shape Winder**	Draws an L-shaped winder based on the lower end.
⊞	**U-Shape Winder**	Draws a U-shaped winder based on the lower end.
↶	**Create Sketch**	Opens additional tools where you can sketch the stair boundary and risers individually.

> **Hint: Stairs and Views**
>
> When creating stairs, you can work in either plan or 3D views. It can help to have the plan view and a 3D view open and tiled side by side. Only open the views in which you want to work and type **WT** to tile the views.

How To: Create a Component-Based Stair

The stair type can impact all of the other settings. Therefore, it is important to select it first.

1. In the *Architecture* tab>Circulation panel, click ⬡ (Stair).
2. In the Type Selector, select the stair type, as shown in Figure 10–4.
3. In Properties (shown in Figure 10–5), set the *Base Level, Top Level*, and any other information that is needed.

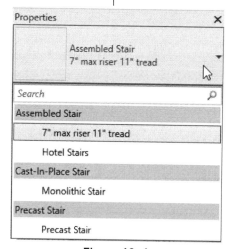

Figure 10–4

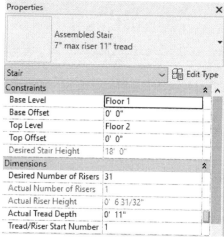

Figure 10–5

4. In the *Modify | Create Stairs* tab>Tools panel, click

   (Railing), select a railing type in the Railings dialog box (as shown in Figure 10–6), and specify whether the *Position* is on the **Treads** or **Stringer**. Click **OK**.

Railings can also be added and modified after the stair has been placed.

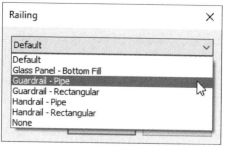

Figure 10–6

5. In the *Modify | Create Stair* tab>Components panel, click
    (Run) and then click   (Straight).
6. In the Options Bar (shown in Figure 10–7), specify the
    following options:
    - *Location Line:* Select **Exterior Support: Left**, **Run: Left**,
      Run: Center, **Run: Right**, or **Exterior Support: Right**.
    - *Offset:* Specify a distance from the location line. This is
      typically used if you are following an existing wall but do
      not need to have the stairs directly against it.
    - *Actual Run Width:* Specify the width of the stair run (not
      including the supports).
    - *Automatic Landing:* When selected, creates landings
      between stair runs (recommended).

| Location Line: Run: Center | Offset: 0' 0" | Actual Run Width: 3' 0" | ☑ Automatic Landing |

Figure 10–7

7. Click on the screen to select a start point for the run. A box
    displays, indicating the stair orientation and the number of
    risers created and remaining, as shown in Figure 10–8.

*If you are creating a complex stair pattern, sketch reference planes in the **Stair** command to help you select the start and end points of each run.*

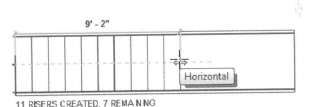

9' - 2"

Horizontal

11 RISERS CREATED, 7 REMAINING

Figure 10–8

- For straight stairs of a single run, select a second point
  anywhere outside the box to create the run.
- For multi-landing or U-shaped stairs, select a second
  point inside the box for the length of the first run, move the
  cursor in the direction of the turn, then select a start point
  and an end point for the next run.
- If the stair is going in the wrong direction, click   (Flip)
  in the *Modify | Create Stair* tab>Tools panel.

8. Click   (Finish Edit Mode) to create the stairs, complete
    with railings.

Creating Other Types of Runs

While most stairs are created using straight runs, there are times when you need to create specialty runs, such as spirals and winders, or when you need to sketch a stair such as the one shown in Figure 10–9.

Figure 10–9

How To: Create a Full-Step Spiral Run

1. Start the **Stair** command and set up the properties as needed.
2. In the Components panel, click ⊚ (Full-Step Spiral).
3. Select the center point of the spiral.
4. Select (or type) the radius of the spiral. The run is created, as shown in Figure 10–10.

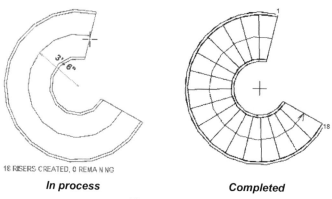

18 RISERS CREATED, 0 REMA N NG

In process   *Completed*

Figure 10–10

How To: Create a Center-Ends Spiral Run

1. Start the **Stair** command and set up the properties as needed.
2. In the Components panel, click ⟳ (Center-Ends Spiral).
3. Select the center of the spiral.
4. Select (or type) the radius of the spiral, as shown on the left in Figure 10–11.
5. Drag the cursor to display the number of risers, as shown on the right in Figure 10–11.

You can create spiral stairs with landings with this option.

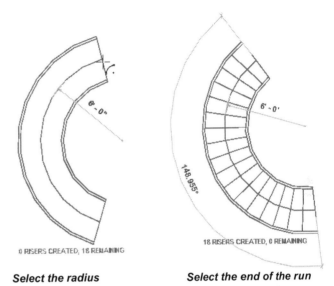

Select the radius   **Select the end of the run**

Figure 10–11

How To: Create Winder-Based Stairs

1. Start the **Stair** command and set up the properties as needed.

2. In the Components panel, click ◪ (L-Shape Winder) or

   ▦ (U-Shape Winder).

3. Click a start point to place the overall stair.

4. Select the stair and use the arrow controls to modify the length, as shown in Figure 10–12.

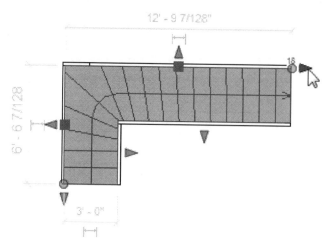

Figure 10–12

How To: Sketch a Stair

1. Start the **Stair** command and set up the properties as needed.

   - In many cases, a custom stair is shorter and should be set using a base and top offset from the same level, as shown in Figure 10–13. By default, a stair height is from level to level.

Change the level offsets before starting to sketch the stair.

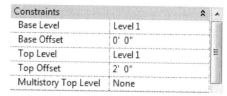

Figure 10–13

2. In the *Modify | Create Stair* tab>Components panel, click (Run) and then click (Sketch).

3. In the *Modify | Create Stair>Sketch Run* tab, use

   ⌐ (Boundary), ⌐ (Riser), and ⌐ (Stair Path) to draw the parts of the stair, as shown in Figure 10–14.

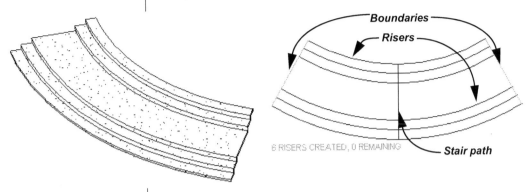

6 RISERS CREATED, 0 REMAINING

Figure 10–14

4. Click ✓ (Finish Edit Mode).
5. If you want to add a landing, you can sketch one.

6. Click ✓ (Finish Edit Mode) to complete the final assembly.

Creating Landings

Landings are typically created automatically between any breaks in runs. Once finishing the stair, you can easily modify the landings to create custom designs. There are two additional options to create landings, as shown in Figure 10–15:

- **Pick Two Runs:** Places the landing at the correct height between the runs.

- **Create Sketch:** Enables you to sketch the shape of the landing, but you must place it at the correct height.

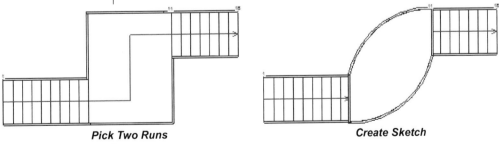

Pick Two Runs   *Create Sketch*

Figure 10–15

- You can connect runs with a landing as long as the start level and end level of the runs are at the same height.

Adding Supports

Stair supports are included in the stair type, if needed. However, you might want to delete them and add them later. Note that this only works if the stair type has supports that are specified in the Type Properties.

How To: Add Stair Support Components

1. If there are no supports, double-click on the stair and in the *Modify | Create Stair* tab>Components panel, click

   (Support) and then click (Pick Edges).
2. Select the edge on which you want to place the support. Hover your cursor over the first support and press <Tab> if you have more than one connected edge on which you want to place the supports.
3. Finish the stair as needed.

Hint: Troubleshooting

When working with stairs and other elements, Warnings (such as the one shown in Figure 10–16) display when something is wrong, but you can keep on working. In many cases, you can close the dialog box and fix the issue or wait and do it later.

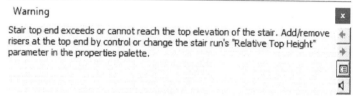

Warning

Stair top end exceeds or cannot reach the top elevation of the stair. Add/remove risers at the top end by control or change the stair run's "Relative Top Height" parameter in the properties palette.

Figure 10–16

Sometimes Errors display where you must take action. These force you to stop and fix the situation.

When you select an element that has a related warning,

(Show Related Warnings) displays in the ribbon. When selected, it opens a dialog box in which you can review the warning(s) related to the selected element. You can also display a list of all of the warnings in the project by clicking

(Review Warnings) in the *Manage* tab>Inquiry panel.

Practice 10a	# Create Component Stairs

Practice Objectives

- Create a component stair.
- Modify a component stair.

In this practice, you will create stairs and railings for the porches, as shown in Figure 10–17.

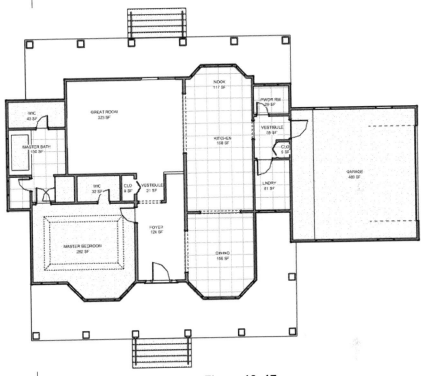

Figure 10–17

1. Open the project **Residential-Stairs.rvt** from the practice files folder.

2. Close any other projects you may have open.

3. Open the **Floor Plans: First Floor** view.

4. Select the DWG. In Properties, set it to **Foreground** so you can see the stairs and railings.

5. In the *Architecture* tab>Circulation panel, click (Stair).

6. In Properties, set or verify the following:

   • *Stair Type:* **Precast Stair**
   • *Base Level:* **Grade**
   • *Base Offset:* (negative) **-1'-2"**
   • *Top Level:* **First Floor**
   • *Top Offset:* (negative) **-0'-7 3/4"**
   • *Desired Number of Risers:* **5**

7. In the *Modify | Create Stair* tab>Tools panel, click

   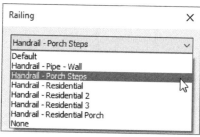 (Railing). In the Railings dialog box, select **Handrail - Porch Steps**, as shown in Figure 10–18. Verify that the *Position* is set to **Treads** and click **OK**.

Figure 10–18

8. Select the midpoint of the porch as the start point. Pick the second point past the ghost image of the completed number of stairs going down your view.

9. Select the newly created stair. Use the arrow shape handles on the sides to adjust the width to match the DWG's stair width, as shown in Figure 10–19. Use the control grip at the bottom of the stairs, not the arrow grip, to drag the stairs down to create six risers. The overall width of the stair should be **10'-5"**.

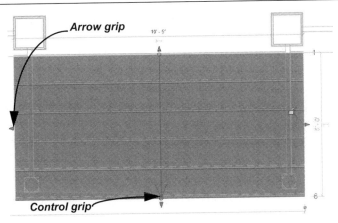

Figure 10–19

10. Click ✓ (Finish Edit Mode).

11. Ignore the warning message that displays.

- Note that in this case, the bottom of the stair may need to be flipped using the control. The rails may also be in the wrong direction, but they will be adjusted in a later task.

12. To verify if the stairs needs to be flipped, open the default **{3D}** view and rotate the model as needed to view the stairs.

13. Activate the **First Floor** view. Select the stairs and click on the Flip Stairs Up Direction icon, as shown in Figure 10–20. Activate the **3D** view to see that the stairs are now correct.

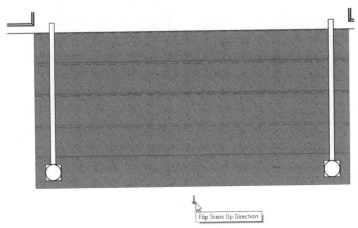

Figure 10–20

14. Copy or create these stairs on the back porch. They should be identical.

15. Save and close the project.

10.2 Modifying Component Stairs

Stairs can be modified in a variety of ways. For example, in Figure 10–21, a straight stair with a landing has been modified to make one run wider than the other and the landing wider than both runs, creating a balcony. The landing has been further customized by sketching a curved feature.

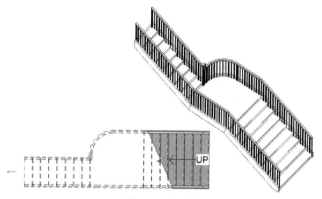

Figure 10–21

- Modifying stair components can be done when you first create the stair or later when you edit a stair.

- When working with a finished stair, you can change the type and properties and flip the stair direction, as shown in Figure 10–22. You can select a stair run and use temporary dimensions to modify the length and width, as shown in Figure 10–23.

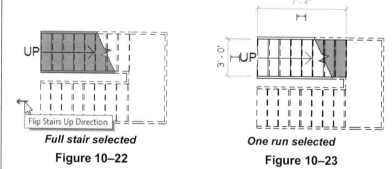

Full stair selected

Figure 10–22

One run selected

Figure 10–23

- To select a stair run, hover your cursor over the stair and press <Tab> to cycle through until the one you want highlights.

Editing Individual Stair Components

Within Stair Edit mode, you can make more significant modifications to individual components using temporary dimensions and shape handles, as shown in Figure 10–24. Numerous snaps and alignment lines are also available as you modify the components.

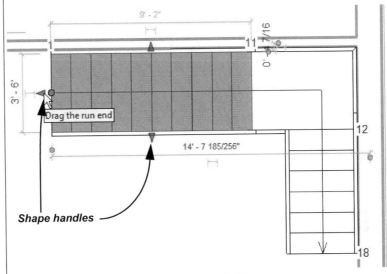

Figure 10–24

- To edit stairs, double-click on the stairs or, in the *Modify |*

  Stairs tab>Edit panel, click  (Edit Stairs).

  - The arrow shape handle at the end of a run lengthens or shortens the run and modifies the other run so that the overall number of steps stays consistent and retains the start and end level.
  - The circle shape handle at the end of a run lengthens or shortens the run without modifying any other runs, but changes the start and end level.
  - The arrow shape handle on the sides of the runs or landings can be used to modify the width.
  - You can use temporary dimensions for the run width and connections to other elements, but not for run lengths. Use the shape handles instead.
  - When you have finished modifying the stair, click

    (Finish Edit Mode).

Converting Components to Sketches

To customize a run or landing with more options, convert it into a sketch and modify the outline of the sketch, as shown for a curved landing in Figure 10–25.

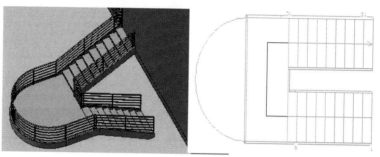

Figure 10–25

How To: Turn Stair Components into a Sketch

1. Select a stair.
2. In the *Modify | Stairs* tab>Edit panel, click 🐢 (Edit Stairs).
3. Select the run or landing that you want to customize.

4. In the Tools panel, click ▦ (Convert to sketch-based). Doing so turns the component into a custom sketched element.

5. In the Mode panel, click ✏️ (Edit Sketch).
6. Use the options in the *Modify | Create Stair>Sketch Landing* (or *Run*) tab>Draw panel to modify the boundary, riser, or stair path, as needed. The boundary of a landing is shown in Figure 10–26.

Editing an existing landing is the easiest way to create a custom landing.

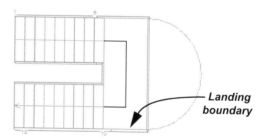

Landing boundary

Figure 10–26

7. Click ✔️ (Finish Edit Mode) to complete the sketch. Click again to return to the stair.

Practice 10b | Create and Modify Stairs

Practice Objective

- Create and modify a component stair.

In this practice, you will modify stairs, as shown in Figure 10–27.

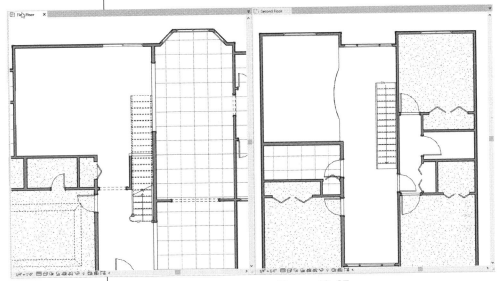

Figure 10–27

Task 1 - Create multi-story stairs.

1. Open the project **Residential-Stairs Modify.rvt** from the practice files folder.

2. Open the **Floor Plans: First Floor** view.

3. Select the vertical section and type **VH** to hide it in the view.

4. Zoom or pan as required to show the main entry of the house as well as the great room.

5. In the *Architecture* tab>Circulation panel, click 📎 (Stair).

6. In the Options Bar, set the following, as shown in Figure 10–28:

   • *Location Line:* **Run: Right**
   • *Offset:* **0'-0"**
   • *Actual Run Width:* **3'-2"**
   • Select **Automatic Landing**

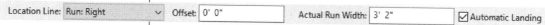

Location Line:	Run: Right	∨	Offset:	0' 0"	Actual Run Width:	3' 2"	☑ Automatic Landing

Figure 10–28

7. In Properties, verify and set the following:

   • *Stair Type:* **Assembled Stair Residential – Open 2 sides**
   • *Base Level:* **First Floor**
   • *Base Offset:* **0'-0"**
   • *Top Level:* **Second Floor**
   • *Top Offset:* **0'-0"**
   • *Desired Number of Risers:* **21**

8. In the *Modify | Create Stair* tab>Tools panel, click
   (Railing). In the Railings dialog box, select **Handrail - Residential**, as shown in Figure 10–29. Verify that the *Position* is set to **Treads** and click **OK**.

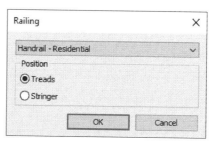

Figure 10–29

9. Pick the start point of the run just above the trim on the framed doorway opening between the foyer and the dining room, as shown in Figure 10–30. Use the DWG to find the start of the stairs.

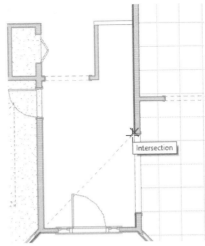

Figure 10–30

10. Pick a second point close to the midpoint of the framed opening leading from the great room to the kitchen area. Make sure all 21 risers are showing, as shown in Figure 10–31.

Figure 10–31

11. Stay in the **Stair** command and select the stairs.

12. In the *Modify | Create Stair* tab>Tools panel, click (Convert to sketch-based).

13. A Stair - Convert to Custom dialog box opens. Click **Close**. It is a reminder that converting the stair means it is no longer a component stair.

14. With the stairs still selected, in the *Modify | Create Stair* tab> Mode panel, click (Edit Sketch).

15. Click (Riser). Use the **Start-End-Radius Arc** tool to create the rounded step, as shown in Figure 10–32.

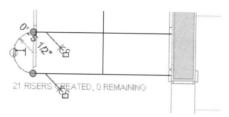

Figure 10–32

16. Pull the existing boundary line back to the center of the arc.

17. Click (Finish Edit Mode) to complete editing the stair run sketch.

18. Click (Finish Edit Mode) again to end the Stair command.

19. The railing will be off from the DWG, but you will fix that in the next practice.

20. Save the project.

Task 2 - Modify the second floor stair openings.

1. Open the **Floor Plans: Second Floor** view.

2. Select the floor by the loft area. (Hint: The easiest way is to select the floor edge near the balcony or turn on the **Select By Face** selection option and select the floor. By default, it should already be turned on.)

3. In the *Modify | Floors* tab>Mode panel, click (Edit Boundary).

4. Modify the boundary line so that it creates an opening for the stairs, as shown in Figure 10–33.

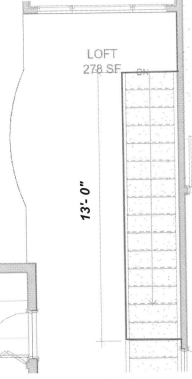

Figure 10–33

5. Use (Trim/Extend to Corner) to clean up the intersections of the boundary lines.

6. Click (Finish Edit Mode). Do not attach the walls to the floor.

7. Save the project.

Task 3 - (Optional) Add the stairs in the garage.

1. Activate the **First Floor** view, then pan and zoom in on the garage area.

2. Start the **Stair** command.

3. In the Options Bar, set the following:

   • *Location Line:* **Run: Left**
   • *Actual Run Width:* **3'-11"**

4. In Properties, set the following:

   • *Base Level:* **Grade**
   • *Top Level:* **First Floor**
   • *Desired Number of Risers:* **4**

5. In the *Modify | Create Stair* tab>Tools panel, click
   (Railing). In the Railings dialog box, select **None** from the drop-down list and click **OK**.

6. Draw the stairs in the garage, as shown in Figure 10–34.

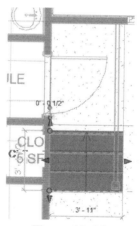

Figure 10–34

7. Stay in the **Stair** command.

8. In the *Modify | Create Stairs* tab>Components panel, select
   (Landing)> (Create Sketch)> (Rectangle).

9. Draw the rectangle landing shown in Figure 10–35.

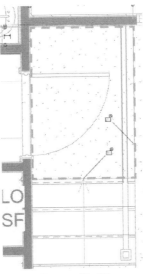

Figure 10–35

10. Click (Finish Edit Mode) twice to end the Stair command.

11. Select the stairs. In the *Modify | Stairs* tab>View panel, click

   (Selection Box) to view the stairs.

12. Save and close the project.

10.3 Working with Railings

Railings can be automatically created with stairs, but you can modify or delete them independently of the stair element. You can also add railings separate from stairs for other locations, as shown in Figure 10–36.

Hosts for sketched railings include floors, slabs, slab edges, the tops of walls, and roofs. You can also add railings to topographic surfaces.

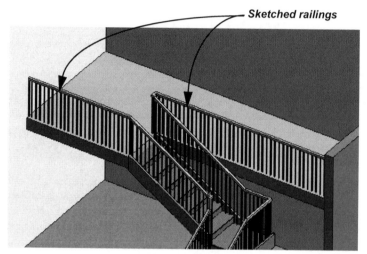

Sketched railings

Figure 10–36

- You can add railings to existing stairs and ramps if the railings were not included when they were created.

How To: Add Railings by Sketching

1. Open a plan or 3D view.
2. In the *Architecture* tab>Circulation panel, expand

   (Railing) and click (Sketch Path).
3. In the Type Selector, specify the railing type.
4. In the *Modify | Create Railing Path* tab>Tools panel, click

   (Pick New Host) and select the element that you want the railing to associate to, such as a stair, floor, or top of a wall.

   - If you are working in a 3D or section view, you can select **Preview** in the *Modify | Create Railing Path* tab>Options panel and the railing displays while you are still in Edit mode. This only works if you have selected a host.

- If the host is sloped, the railing will follow the slope, as shown in Figure 10–37. The sketch displays at the host's level.

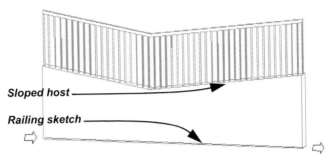

Sloped host —

Railing sketch —

Figure 10–37

5. Use the Draw tools to sketch the lines that define the railing.

6. Click (Finish Edit Mode) to create the railing.

- The railing must be a single connected sketch. If it is not, you are prompted with an error, such as that shown in Figure 10–38.

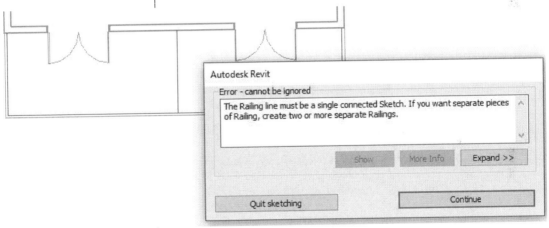

Figure 10–38

How To: Add Railings by Place on Stair/Ramp

1. In the *Architecture* tab>Circulation panel, expand (Railing) and click (Place on Stair/Ramp).

2. In the *Modify | Create Railing Place on Stair/Ramp* tab>Position panel, click (Treads) or (Stringer).

3. Select the stair or ramp where you want to add the railing.

*   (Place on Stair/Ramp) only works if there is no railing on the stairs. If you want to add an additional railing (e.g., down the middle of a wide stair), you need to sketch the railing.

Modifying Railings

Modifying railings can be as simple as changing their type, as shown in Figure 10–39. You can also edit the path of a railing.

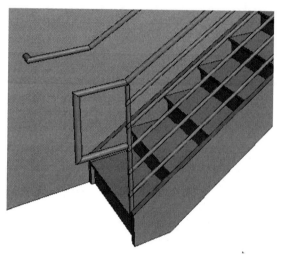

Figure 10–39

*   You can delete railings separately from stairs or ramps. However, deleting a stair or ramp automatically deletes related railings.

*   You can use the (Split Element) command on railings. Doing so results in separate railings, as shown in Figure 10–40.

Figure 10–40

Editing the Path of a Railing

To edit the path of a railing, double-click on the railing or select the railing and in the *Modify | Railings* tab>Mode panel, click

(Edit Path). This places you in Edit mode, in which you can modify the individual lines that define the railing, as shown in Figure 10–41. You can create additional lines, but they must be connected to the existing lines.

Unlike many other elements in Edit mode, railings do not have to be in a closed loop.

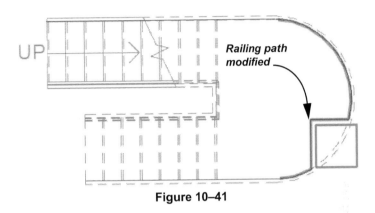

Figure 10–41

Practice 10c | Work with Railings

Practice Objectives

- Modify railings and handrails.
- Add standalone railings.

In this practice, you will modify the railings on the interior stair by changing the railings to a new type, as well as modify the porch stair railings so that the newel posts sit on the treads properly. You will also add standalone railings to the porches and upstairs balcony, as shown in Figure 10–42.

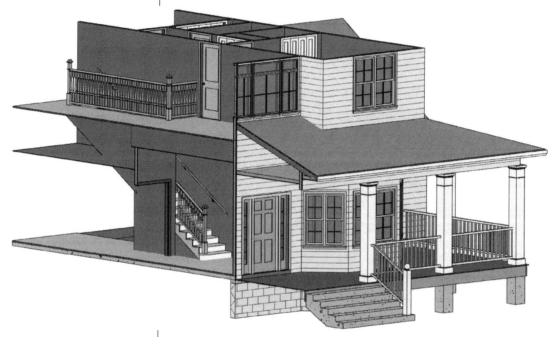

Figure 10–42

Task 1 - Modify railings on stairs.

1. Open the project **Residential-Railings.rvt** from the practice files folder.

2. Open the **Floor Plans: First Floor** view.

3. Zoom in to the bottom porch.

4. Note that the newel posts are facing the wrong direction.

5. Select one of the railing systems.

6. In the *Modify | Railings* tab>Mode panel, click  (Edit Path).

7. Select one of the arrow controls so that it faces away from the porch.

8. Verify that the path itself is centered on the column. Drag the line to the face of the column, as shown in Figure 10–43.

Figure 10–43

9. Click ✓ (Finish Edit Mode).

10. Repeat the process for the remaining railing on this stair. If needed, also repeat the process for the railings on the porch stair at the top of the view.

11. Open a 3D view to see the results.

12. Save the project.

Task 2 - Change and modify the railing for custom stairs.

---

1. In the First Floor view, zoom in to the interior stairs.

2. Select the railing on the right side of the stair, against the wall.

3. In the Type Selector, select **Handrail – Pipe – Wall**.

4. In Properties, in the *Constraints* group, ensure that the *Offset from Path* is set to **0'-2"**.

5. Click ⌖ (Modify).

6. Select the other railing on the stairs. In the *Modify | Railings* tab>Mode panel, select ▱ (Edit Path).

7. Ensure that the arrow controls point upward.

8. Select the Drag Line End control at the top of the railing and drag it down until it aligns with the corner of the wall, as shown in Figure 10–44.

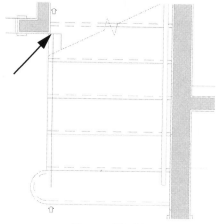

Figure 10–44

9. Ensure that the Drag Line End control at the bottom of the stair is centered on the bottom tread.

10. Click ✓ (Finish Edit Mode).

Task 3 - Add standalone railings.

1. Each segment of railing around the porch needs to be its own railing. Zoom out until the bottom porch is entirely visible.

2. In the *Architecture* tab>Circulation panel, expand ▥ (Railing) and click ▥ (Sketch Path).

3. In the Type Selector, select **Railing: Handrail – Residential Porch**.

4. Ensure that the *Base Level* is set to **First Floor**.

5. Set the *Base Offset* to (negative) **-0'-4"**.

6. Draw a sketch line that is centered on the face of the column, as shown in Figure 10–45.

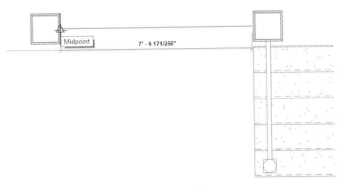

Figure 10–45

7. Click 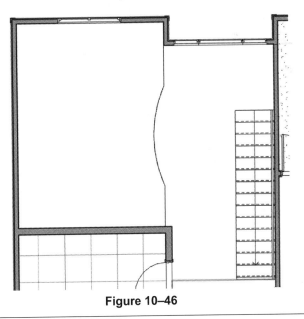 (Finish Edit Mode).

8. Continue to create railings between the other columns. Make sure that where one side ends in a wall, it extends to the exterior face of the wall.

9. Repeat this process for the railings on the porch at the top of the view.

Task 4 - Add a railing to the second floor.

---

1. Open the **Floor Plans: Second Floor** view. Pan and zoom over to the interior balcony, as shown in Figure 10–46.

Figure 10–46

2. In the *Architecture* tab>Circulation panel, expand
   (Railing) and click (Sketch Path).

3. In the Type Selector, select **Railing: Handrail -
   Residential 3**.

4. In the Options Bar, set the *Offset* to **3"**.

5. In Properties, set the *Base Offset* to **0'-0"**.

6. Use the **Pick Lines** draw tool to select the edge of the
   balcony floor over the great room, as shown in Figure 10–47.

   • Hint: You can use <Tab> to select the entire edge of the
     balcony.

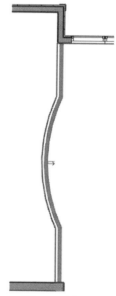

Figure 10–47

7. Click (Finish Edit Mode).

8. Open the **3D view: 3D View 1** to see the railing.

9. Save and close the project.

Chapter Review Questions

1. Which of the following is NOT a stair component?

   a. Runs

   b. Landings

   c. Treads

   d. Supports

2. How do you modify a stair so that it is wider at the bottom than at the top, as shown in Figure 10–48?

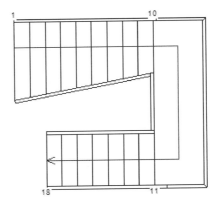

Figure 10–48

   a. Use the grips located at each corner of the stair and drag them to a new location.

   b. Convert the run to a sketch and modify the boundary and riser lines.

   c. Use <Tab> to cycle through components so that you only select the tread that you want to modify.

   d. Explode the stair into components, and then use grips to modify the stair width.

3. When do you need to use the 📝 (Railing) command? (Select all that apply.)

   a. When you want an extra railing in the middle of very wide stairs.

   b. When you create a stair or ramp.

   c. When you create railings that are not attached to stairs or ramps.

   d. When you use the **Stair by Sketch** command.

Command Summary

Button	Command	Location
Stairs		
	Convert to sketch-based	• **Ribbon:** *Modify	Create Stair* tab> Tools panel
	Connect Levels	• **Ribbon:** *Modify	Stairs* tab>Multistory Stairs panel
	Edit Sketch	• **Ribbon:** *Modify	Create Stair* tab> Tools panel
	Edit Stairs	• **Ribbon:** *Modify	Stairs* tab>Edit panel
	Flip	• **Ribbon:** *Modify	Create Stair* tab> Tools panel
	Landing (Stair)	• **Ribbon:** *Modify	Create Stair* tab> Components panel
	Run (Stair)	• **Ribbon:** *Modify	Create Stair* tab> Components panel
	Stair	• **Ribbon:** *Architecture* tab>Circulation panel
	Support (Stair)	• **Ribbon:** *Modify	Create Stair* tab> Components panel
Railings		
	Edit Path (Railings)	• **Ribbon:** *Modify	Railings* tab>Mode panel
	Railing	• **Ribbon:** *Modify	Create Stair (Create Stairs Sketch) (Create Ramp)* tab> Tools panel
	Railing>Place on Stair/Ramp	• **Ribbon:** *Architecture* tab>Circulation panel>expand Railing
	Railing>Sketch Path	• **Ribbon:** *Architecture* tab>Circulation panel>expand Railing
	Pick New Host	• **Ribbon:** *Modify	Create Railing Path (Railings)* tab>Tools panel

Chapter

11

Adding Components

As you construct a building model, you add component families such as furniture, lighting fixtures, HVAC equipment, and structural framing elements. These components can be loaded from your company's template, the Autodesk® Revit® library, or a custom library.

Learning Objectives in This Chapter

- Place components in a project to further develop the design.
- Load components from the Autodesk Revit Library.
- Change component types and locations.
- Purge unused component elements to increase the processing speed of the model.

11.1 Adding Components

Many types of elements are added to a project using component families. These can include freestanding components, such as the furniture, floor lamp, and table lamp shown in Figure 11–1. They can also include wall, ceiling, floor, roof, face, and line-hosted components. These hosted components must be placed on the referenced element.

Floor-based
light fixture

Figure 11–1

- You can load more components into a project or create your own as needed.

- Components are located in family files with the extension .RFA. For example, a component family can contain several types and sizes.

How To: Place a Component

1. In the *Architecture* tab>Build panel, click ▨ (Place a Component), or type **CM**.
2. In the Type Selector, select the component you want to add to the project.

3. Proceed as follows, based on the type of component used:

If the component is...	Then...
Not hosted	Set the *Level* and *Offset* in Properties, as shown in Figure 11–2.
Wall hosted	Set the *Elevation* in Properties, as shown in Figure 11–3.
Face hosted	Select the appropriate method in the contextual tab> Placement panel, as shown in Figure 11–4. • Vertical faces include walls and columns. • Faces include ceilings, beams, and roofs. • Work planes can be set to levels, faces, and named reference planes.

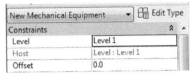

Figure 11–2

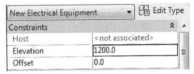

Figure 11–3

Figure 11–4

4. Place the component in the model.

• Many components can be quickly rotated by pressing <Spacebar> when placing them. This will rotate them in 90-degree increments.

• In the Options Bar, many components will have an option to **Rotate after placement**, as shown in Figure 11–5. This allows you to rotate the element by any degree immediately after placing the family.

Modify | Place Component   ☐ Rotate after placement

Figure 11–5

Create Similar works with all elements.

• A fast way to add components that match those already in your project is to select one, right-click on it, and select **Create Similar**. This starts the **Component** command with the same type selected.

Loading Components

If the components you are looking for are not available, you can look in the Autodesk Revit Library, which contains many options. You can also check which custom components your company has and find vendor-specific components.

- You can also copy a component to the clipboard in one project and past it into a different project.

- In the *Insert* tab>Load from Library panel, you can check for updated content or load Autodesk Families to get updated links for the latest Autodesk content.

How To: Load a Component Family

1. In the *Architecture* tab>Build panel, click ⬜ (Place a Component).
2. In the *Modify | Place Component* tab>Mode panel, click ⬛ (Load Family).
3. In the Load Family dialog box, locate the folder that contains the family or families you want to load and select them, as shown in Figure 11–6. To load more than one family at a time, hold <Ctrl> while selecting.

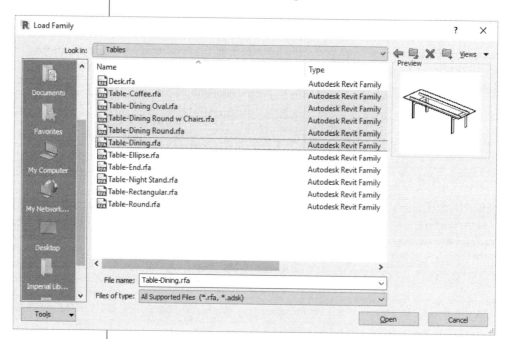

Figure 11–6

- The program remembers the last folder used.

4. Click **Open**.

5. Once the family (or families) is loaded, in the Type Selector, select the type you want to use, as shown in Figure 11–7.

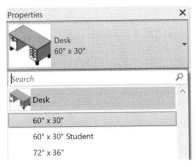

Figure 11–7

Hint: Family Library Location

If you need to load a family file that is not an out-of-box family, you can easily return to the default Revit family folder location by clicking on the **Imperial Library** folder icon in the Places panel within the Load Family dialog box, as shown in Figure 11–8.

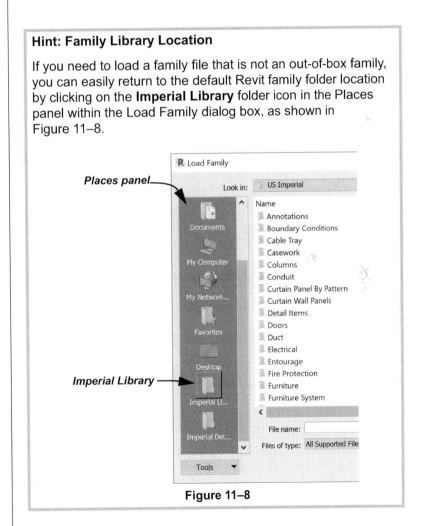

Figure 11–8

How To: Check for Updated Revit Content

1. In the *Insert* tab>Load from Library panel, click 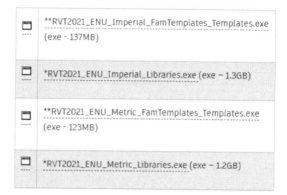 (Get Autodesk Content).
2. This takes you to the Autodesk website. If Autodesk has updated their content, you will see a link to download templates and family content (as shown in Figure 11–9).

English - United States

🖿	**RVT2021_ENU_Imperial_FamTemplates_Templates.exe (exe - 137MB)
🖿	*RVT2021_ENU_Imperial_Libraries.exe (exe – 1.3GB)
🖿	**RVT2021_ENU_Metric_FamTemplates_Templates.exe (exe - 123MB)
🖿	*RVT2021_ENU_Metric_Libraries.exe (exe – 1.2GB)

Figure 11–9

How To: Load Autodesk Content from the Website

1. In the *Insert* tab>Load from Library panel, click 🖿 (Load Autodesk Family).
2. In the Load Autodesk Family - Technology Preview dialog box, select the required family.
   - You can filter your search by typing in what kind of family you are looking for or click on a category in the *Browse* section, as shown in Figure 11–10.

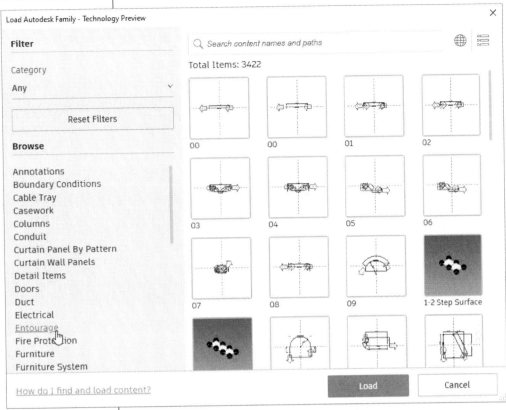

Figure 11–10

3. Click **Load** to load the family into your project.

11.2 Modifying Components

Components can be modified when they are selected by changing the type in the Type Selector. For example, you might have placed a task chair in a project (as shown in Figure 11–11), but now you need to change it to an executive chair. With some types, you can use controls to modify the component. You can also select a new host for a component and move components with nearby elements.

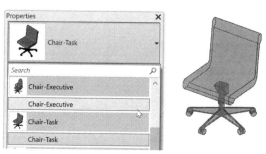

Figure 11–11

Working with Host Elements

If you need to move a component from the level on which it was inserted, you can change its host. For example, one of the desks in Figure 11–12 is floating above the floor. It was placed on Level 1 when it was inserted, but needs to be located on the floor that is below the level.

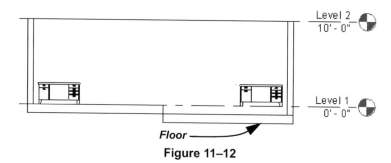

Figure 11–12

How To: Pick a New Host Element

1. Select a component.
2. In the *<component type>* contextual tab>Host panel, click

   (Pick New Host).
3. Select the new host (e.g., the floor).

- You can select a floor, surface, or level to be the new host for the components depending on the requirements of the component.

Moving with Nearby Host Elements

Components have the capacity to move with nearby host elements (such as walls) when they are moved. Select the component and in the Options Bar, select **Moves with Nearby Elements**. The component is automatically assigned to the closest host elements.

For example, a chair near the corner of two walls is linked to those two walls. If you move either wall, the chair moves as well. However, you can still move the chair independently of the walls.

- You cannot specify which elements the component should be linked to; the software determines this automatically. This option only works with host elements (such as walls), not with other components.

Purging Unused Elements

To reduce file size and remove unused elements from a project, including individual component types, you can purge the project, as shown in Figure 11–13.

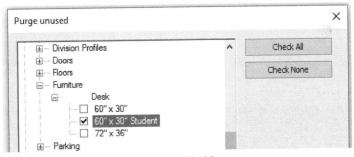

Figure 11–13

- Some elements are nested in other elements and it might require several rounds of purging the project to remove them. A good rule of thumb is to run the command three times to ensure everything is purged.

How To: Purge Unused Elements

1. In the *Manage* tab>Settings panel, click (Purge Unused).
2. In the Purge unused dialog box, click **Check None** and select the elements you want to purge.
3. Click **OK**.

- Purging unused components helps simplify the list of families loaded in a project.

Practice 11a | Add Components

Practice Objective

- Load and add components.

In this practice, you will place appliances and casework, as shown in Figure 11–14. You will load a component from a custom library and use controls to modify the placement. If you have time, add utilities in the garage and a fireplace. Finally, you will add footing components to the foundation.

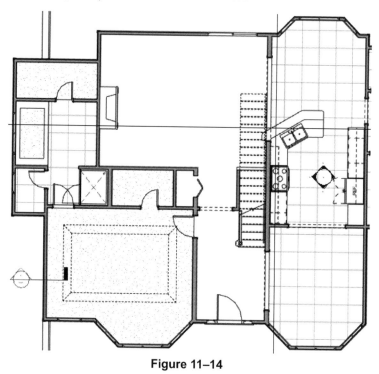

Figure 11–14

Task 1 - Add casework to the kitchen.

1. Open the project **Residential-Components.rvt** from the practice files folder.

2. Close any other projects you may have open.

3. Open the **Floor Plans: First Floor** view and close any other views that are open.

4. Verify that the DWG is set to **Foreground** so you can see the kitchen components.

5. Zoom in to the kitchen area.

6. Double-click on the **Kitchen - West** interior elevation arrow to open the view. Type **TW** to tile the first floor and elevation views.

7. Activate the **First Floor** view. For clarity, while adding components, select the floor and temporary hide the components by category.

8. In the *Architecture* tab>Build panel, expand 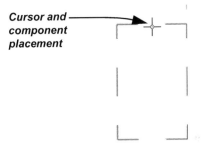 (Component) and click (Place a Component).

9. In the Type Selector, review the various **Base Cabinet** options that are available for the project. Select **Base Cabinet-Single Door & Drawer 15"**.

10. Press <Spacebar> to rotate the cabinet so your cursor or placement point is along the wall.

- Hint: Where your cursor is located is the back of the cabinet (as shown in Figure 11–15).

Cursor and component placement

Figure 11–15

11. Place the cabinet in the bottom-left corner of the kitchen area, near the stairs.

12. Press <Esc> twice to clear the selection, and adjust the cabinet as needed to match the DWG.

- You may need to use the Flip controls on the cabinet to face it in the correct direction. In the casement families used for this project, the Flip controls are located on the front side of the casement.

13. Start the **Component** command.

14. In the *Modify | Place Component* tab>Mode panel, click  (Load Family).

Make sure you have the latest Revit family library installed.

15. In the Load Family dialog box, in the Revit Library, navigate to the folders and open the families listed below. After each time you click **Open**, you will need to click on 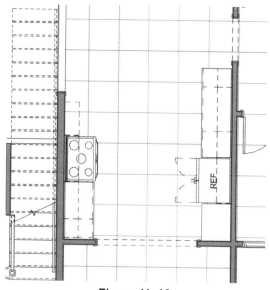 (Load Family) again.

   - In the *Casework>Base Cabinets* folder:
     Base Cabinet-Double Door & 2 Drawer.rfa

   - In the *Casework>Tall Cabinets* folder:
     Tall Cabinet-Single Door (2).rfa

   - In the *Casework>Wall Cabinets* folder:
     Upper Cabinet-Double Door-Wall.rfa
     Upper Cabinet-Single Door-Wall.rfa

   - In the *Casework>Counter Tops* folder:
     Counter Top.rfa

16. Place and arrange the components, placing the cabinets, refrigerator, and range in the kitchen area (as shown in Figure 11–16). Place the upper cabinets over the base cabinets and add the countertop. You can follow the suggested layout or create your own design.

   - Use your Interior Elevation views to see how your kitchen is being laid out and if you need to move or rotate anything.

Figure 11–16

17. Save the project.

Task 2 - Load and place custom components.

1. Start the **Component** command and, in the *Modify |*

   Place Component tab>Mode panel, click 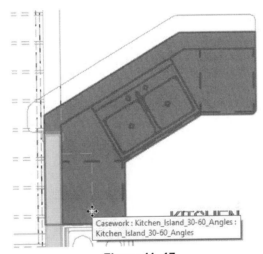 (Load Family).

2. In the Load Family dialog box, navigate to the practice files *Custom Families* folder. Load the following components:

   - **Kitchen_Island_30-60_Angles.rfa**
   - **Mantel 1.rfa**
   - **Shower Tray.rfa**
   - **72x36 Deep Bath Tub.rfa**
   - **Finish Based Fireplace 2.rfa**

3. Press <Esc> to clear the component.

4. Place the kitchen island, as shown in Figure 11–17.

Casework : Kitchen_Island_30-60_Angles : Kitchen_Island_30-60_Angles

Figure 11–17

5. Figure 11–18 shows the east and west kitchen elevations with all of the components placed. Set the *Detail Level* to **Fine** to see more details on the elements.

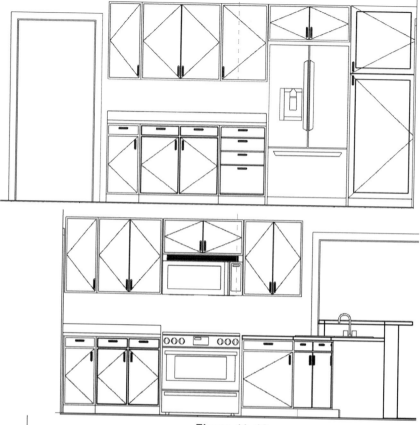

Figure 11–18

6. Pan over to the master bathroom area. Note that there is a small knee-wall and a floor opening in the bathroom, near the window.

   • If prompted that there are no tags loaded for what you are placing, click **No**.

7. In the *Architecture* tab>Build panel, expand (Component) and click (Place a Component). In the Type Selector, select **72x36 Deep Bath Tub**.

8. Ensure that the edges of the tub lay on top of the raised floor opening.

   • To get a better view of this offset, place a section through the floor object and go to that view. Adjust the crop region if needed.

9. Place the shower tray in the shower area, as shown in Figure 11–19.

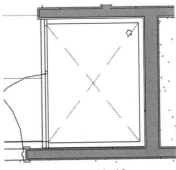

Figure 11–19

10. Click ⌖ (Modify).

11. Pan over to the great room. In the *Architecture* tab>Build panel, expand ⬚ (Component) and click ⬚ (Place a Component). In the Type Selector, select **Finish Based Fireplace 2** and place it centered on the wall opposite the stairs. It should be centered with the door leading to the garage.

12. In the Type Selector, select **Mantel 1: 61" x 52 3/4"**. Place it against the firebox and above the hearth plate that are part of the fireplace family, as shown in Figure 11–20.

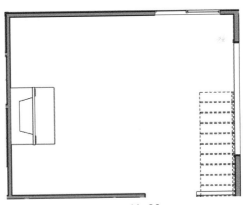

Figure 11–20

13. Create a section in the great room to see the mantel.

14. Save and close the project.

Chapter Review Questions

1. What do you use to change the family type when inserting a component?

   a. Quick Access Toolbar

   b. Type Selector

   c. Options Bar

   d. Properties

2. If the component you want to use is not available in the current project, where do you go to get the component? (Select all that apply.)

   a. In another project, copy the component to the clipboard and paste it into the current project.

   b. In the current project, use (Insert from File) and select the family from the list in the dialog box.

   c. In the current project, use (Load Family) and select the family from the list in the dialog box.

   d. Search a manufacturer's site for a component and download it.

3. When you use the **Moves with Nearby Elements** option, can you control which elements a component moves with?

   a. Yes, select the element with which you want it to move.

   b. No, it moves with the closest host element.

4. What can you do if the Load Family dialog box does not default to the Revit Library?

   a. Close the dialog box and reopen it.

   b. Click **Imperial Library** in the Places panel.

   c. Purge the model.

5. Which of the following commands would you use if you want to move a furniture component to a floor that is lower than the level where it was originally placed, as shown in Figure 11–21?

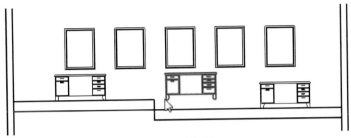

Figure 11–21

a. Use (Level) and add a level at the height of the lower floor.

b. Use (Ref Plane) and draw a plane aligned with the lower floor.

c. Use (Pick New Host) and select the lower floor.

d. Use (Edit Family) and change the work plane in the family so that it matches the height of the lower floor.

Command Summary

Button	Command	Location
	Load Family	• **Ribbon:** *Modify* | *Place Component* tab>Load panel or *Insert* tab>Load from Library panel
	Pick New Host	• **Ribbon:** *Modify* | *Multi-Select* or *component type* contextual tab>Host panel
	Place Component	• **Ribbon:** *Architecture* tab>Build panel> expand Component • **Shortcut:** CM
	Place on Face	• **Ribbon**: *Modify* | *Place Component* tab> Placement panel
	Place on Vertical Face	• **Ribbon**: *Modify* | *Place Component* tab> Placement panel
	Place on Work Plane	• **Ribbon**: *Modify* | *Place Component* tab> Placement panel
	Purge Unused	• **Ribbon:** *Manage* tab>Settings panel

Chapter
12

Design Options

Design options enable you to create different examples for part of a building, and then display each example in separate views. Once you have decided which option to use, you can make the option part of the main model.

Learning Objectives in This Chapter

- Create design options.
- Add existing and new elements to design options.
- Create views for design options.

12.1 Using Design Options

Design options provide a way to set up multiple layouts for a section of a building model. For example, you could design several roof options, window layouts, or entry areas and view each in context with the main building.

You can create a variety of design option sets that define an area that changes and then add design options under each set. For example, you can create a design option set with two options for a balcony, as shown in Figure 12–1 and Figure 12–2.

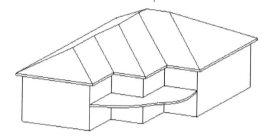

Figure 12–1

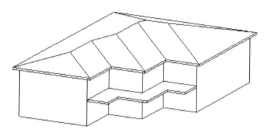

Figure 12–2

- The part of the building that is NOT modified by options is called the *main model*.

- Design options are rarely used in MEP projects, as systems such as plumbing, HVAC, and power do not work in the options.

The Design Options tools are located in the *Manage* tab>Design Options panel, as shown in Figure 12–3. Additional tools can be found in the Status Bar, as shown in Figure 12–4.

Figure 12–3

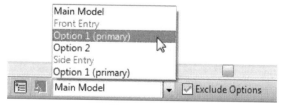

Figure 12–4

- Once you make a decision on the option to use, you can accept the primary option in a set and delete the rest of the options.

- Design options, when linked into another Revit model, will show the primary design option by default, but they can be edited and changed in the Visibility/Graphic Overrides dialog box with the other options.

How To: Set Up Design Options

1. In the *Manage* tab>Design Options panel, or in the Status Bar, click 🗒 (Design Options). The Design Options dialog box opens, as shown in Figure 12–5.

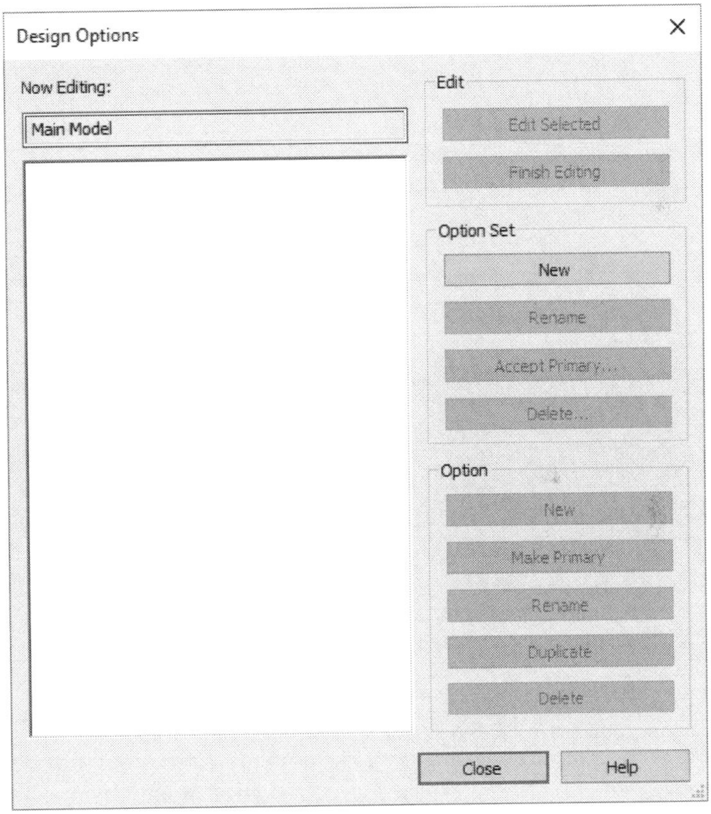

You can have as many option sets and options under a set as required. Each set always contains one primary option.

Figure 12–5

2. In the *Option Set* area, click **New**. An option set with a corresponding option is created, as shown in Figure 12–6.

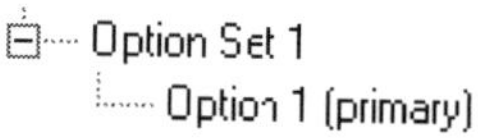

⊟···· Option Set 1
      └···· Option 1 (primary)

Figure 12–6

3. To add more options, select the Option Set title. In the *Option* area in the dialog box, click **New**.
4. Rename the option sets and options so that they convey more information. In the *Option Set* or *Option* area, click **Rename** and type a new name in the Rename dialog box.
5. Once you have defined the option sets and options, you are ready to work on the various options. Close the dialog box.

- Once you have added design options, you can set the current design option in the *Manage* tab or in the Status Bar, as shown in Figure 12–7.

Figure 12–7

How To: Add Existing Elements to Design Options

1. In the Status Bar or *Manage* tab>Design Options panel, verify that **Main Model** displays as the active design option, as shown in Figure 12–8.

Active design option

Figure 12–8

2. Select the elements that you want to include in a design option. The *Modify* tab displays.
3. Switch to the *Manage* tab. In the Design Options panel, click ⬛ (Add to Set).

4. In the Add to Design Option Set dialog box, expand the drop-down list and select the design option set, then select the option(s) to which you want to add the selected elements, as shown in Figure 12–9. You can select more than one option.

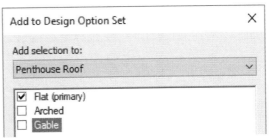

Figure 12–9

5. Click **OK** to close the dialog box. The elements are added to the option and can no longer be modified in the main model.

- Only elements in the primary design option display in standard views. They cannot be selected unless you clear the **Exclude Options** option in the Status Bar before selecting.

- **Exclude Options** is only available in the Status Bar if design options have been set up in the project.

How To: Add New Elements to a Design Option

1. Set the active design option in the drop-down list in the Status Bar or in the *Manage* tab>Design Options panel, as shown in Figure 12–10.

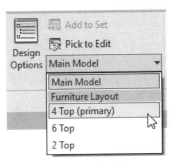

Figure 12–10

2. Only the elements that are part of the active design option display in black. Elements in the main model are grayed out, as shown in Figure 12–11.

Figure 12–11

3. Use standard commands to add or modify elements in the design option.
4. Set the active design option to **Main Model** when you are finished.

Viewing Design Options

You can set up views that specify design options. These can then be used to quickly see the various design options without having to edit them, as shown in Figure 12–12.

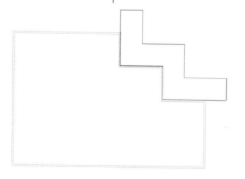

Design option 1

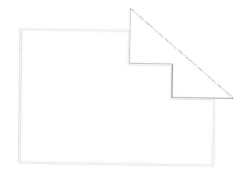

Design option 2

Figure 12–12

How To: View Design Options

1. Create a view (a 3D, plan, elevation, or section view) that displays the information that you want to present.
2. In the view, open the Visibility/Graphic Overrides dialog box (type **VV** or **VG**).

3. In the *Design Options* tab, in the drop-down list for each *Design Option Set*, select a design option, as shown in Figure 12–13. **<Automatic>** displays the primary option or the option that is currently being edited. Setting the view to a specific choice displays that option regardless of what is being edited.

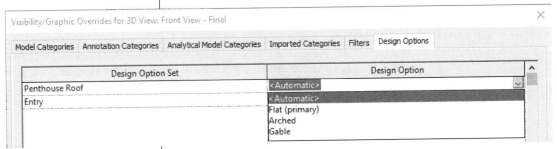

Figure 12–13

- If elements in a design option display in a view, you can click

  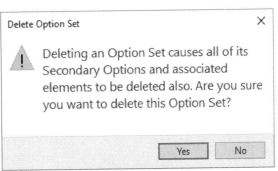 (Pick to Edit) in the Design Options panel and select one of the elements to activate that option.

How To: Delete Design Options

When you have decided on the design option you want to use, you can delete any other options in the project.

*If you did not set the active option to Main Model, you must select **Finish Editing** in the dialog box to continue the process.*

1. Set the active design option to **Main Model**.
2. Open the Design Options dialog box.
3. Select the option you want to keep and click **Make Primary**.
4. Select the option set and click **Accept Primary...**.
5. An alert box opens, as shown in Figure 12–14, warning you that all secondary options are going to be deleted. Click **Yes** if you are sure.

Figure 12–14

6. If views are associated with the options being deleted, you are prompted to delete the associated views, as shown in Figure 12–15. Select the view(s) and click **Delete**.

   • If you want to keep all of the views, you can uncheck them and click **Delete**. This will finish the command but not delete any views.

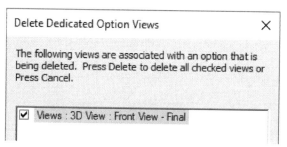

Figure 12–15

7. Close the Design Options dialog box.

Practice 12a | Use Design Options

Practice Objectives

- Set up design options.
- Draw elements in each design option.
- Create views that show variations on the design options.

In this practice, you will create two design option sets and several options for each set. You will modify the elements in each design option and create views that display the options, such as the one shown in Figure 12–16.

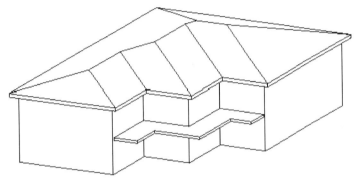

Figure 12–16

- Note: This practice uses a different house than the one that is used in previous practices.

Task 1 - Set up design options.

1. Open the project **Residential-Options.rvt** from the practice files folder.

2. In the *Manage* tab>Design Options panel or in the Status Bar, click (Design Options).

3. In the Design Options dialog box, in the *Option Set* area, click **New**. A new option set and a primary option are created, as shown in Figure 12–17.

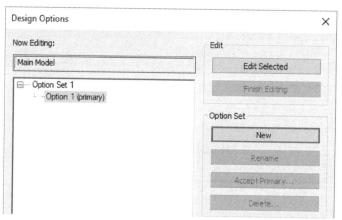

Figure 12–17

4. Select **Option Set 1** and in the *Option Set* area, click **Rename**. In the Rename dialog box, set its name as **Main Roof** and click **OK**.

5. Select **Option 1 (primary)** and in the *Option* area, click **Rename**. Set its name as **Shallow Slope**.

6. In the *Option* area, click **New** twice to add two more options. Rename them as **Medium Slope** and **Steep Slope**.

7. Create an additional option set and name it **Entry Roof**. Add three options to the set, making **Curved** the primary option, as shown in Figure 12–18.

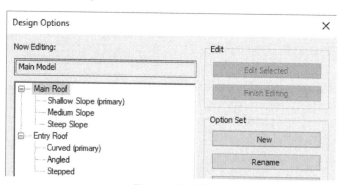

Figure 12–18

8. In the **Main Roof** option set, select **Medium Slope** and click **Make Primary**.

9. Close the Design Options dialog box.

Task 2 - Create main roof design options.

1. In the Design Options panel or in the Status Bar, use the drop-down list to set the **Main Roof>Medium Slope (primary)** option as the active design option. The main model is grayed out.

2. Open the **Floor Plans: Roof** view.

3. Draw a **Roof by Footprint** with a deep overhang, all edges sloped, and a medium slope angle, as shown in Figure 12–19.

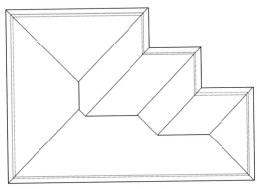

Figure 12–19

4. When prompted to attach highlighted walls to the roof, select **Don't attach**. You are prompted only for the primary option and not for other design options.

5. View the roof in a 3D view. Type **VV** and in the Visibility/Graphic Overrides dialog box, select the *Design Options* tab and set the *Main Roof* to **<Automatic>**.

6. Click **OK**.

7. Set the active design option to **Main Roof>Steep Slope**. The main model is grayed out and the medium sloped roof is toggled off.

8. Return to the **Floor Plans: Roof** view. Draw a **Roof by Footprint** using a steep slope angle.

9. Repeat the process using the **Shallow Slope** design option and a shallow roof slope.

10. Set the active design option to **Main Model**. The primary **Medium Slope** design option displays.

11. Save the project.

Task 3 - Create entry roof design options.

1. Set the active design option to **Entry Roof>Curved**. The main model and main roof are grayed out.

2. Open the **Floor Plans: Level 2** view.

3. Use **Roof by Footprint** to draw a curved flat roof over the entry area, as shown in Figure 12–20. You can use the **Spline** or **Arc** sketch options. Use a generic roof type.

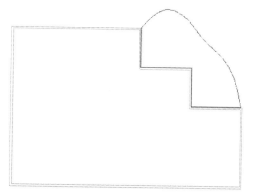

Figure 12–20

4. Create additional flat roofs similar to those shown in Figure 12–21 for the **Angled** and **Stepped** entry roof options.

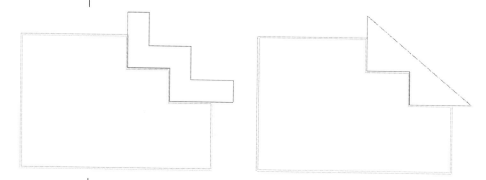

Figure 12–21

5. Set the active design option back to the **Main Model**. The curved roof displays as it is the primary design option that shows at this level.

6. Save the project.

Task 4 - Create views of design options.

1. Switch to a 3D view that displays both the main and entry roofs. The primary option currently displays for each.

2. Type **VG** to open the Visibility/Graphic Overrides dialog box.

3. In the *Design Options* tab, specify the *Design Options* for the sets as follows, then click **OK**.

   - *Main Roof:* **Medium Slope (primary)**
   - *Entry Roof:* **Curved (primary)**

4. Rename the 3D view shown in Figure 12–22 as **Medium Slope and Curved**.

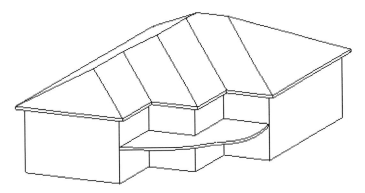

Figure 12–22

5. Duplicate the 3D view. Rename the view as **Shallow Slope and Stepped**.

6. Open the Visibility/Graphic Overrides dialog box and in the *Design Options* tab, specify the *Design Options* for the sets as follows, then click **OK**. The new layout displays, as shown in Figure 12–23.

- *Main Roof:* **Shallow Slope**
- *Entry Roof:* **Stepped**

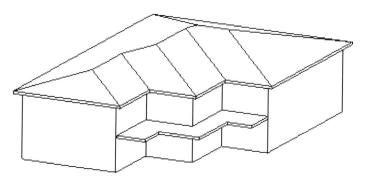

Figure 12–23

7. Repeat this with other combinations of the options if you have time.

8. Switch between the various views to see the differences.

9. Save the project.

Chapter Review Questions

1. What is the difference between *Option Set* and *Option*, as shown in Figure 12–24?

Figure 12–24

a. You can have multiple options but only one option set.

b. You can have multiple options without any option sets.

c. You can have multiple option sets without any options.

d. You can have multiple option sets with multiple options in each set.

2. What method do you use to set up a view to display specific design options?

a. Set the active design option.

b. Select the primary design option in the Design Options dialog box.

c. Open the Visibility/Graphic Overrides dialog box and select the options.

d. Right-click in the view and select **Override Graphics in View>By Element**.

3. Design options enable you to create different examples for part of a building, and then display each example in a separate view.

a. True

b. False

4. The part of the building that is NOT modified by options is called what?

   a. Primary

   b. Option set

   c. Main model

   d. Level 1

Command Summary

Button	Command	Location
Main Model ▾	**Active Design Option**	• **Ribbon:** *Manage* tab>Design Options panel • **Status Bar**
	Add to Set	• **Ribbon:** *Manage* tab>Design Options panel • **Status Bar**
	Design Options	• **Ribbon:** *Manage* tab>Design Options panel • **Status Bar**
	Pick to Edit	• **Ribbon:** *Manage* tab>Design Options panel

Creating Construction Documents

The accurate creation of construction documents in the Autodesk® Revit® software ensures that the design is correctly communicated to downstream users. Construction documents are created primarily in special views called sheets. Knowing how to select title blocks, assign title block information, place views, and print the sheets is essential for the construction documentation process.

Learning Objectives in This Chapter

- Add sheets with title blocks and views of a project.
- Enter the title block information for individual sheets and for an entire project.
- Place and organize views on sheets.
- Print sheets using the default Print dialog box.

13.1 Setting Up Sheets

While you are modeling a project, the foundations of the working drawings are already in progress. Any view (such as a floor plan, section, callout, or schedule) can be placed on a sheet, as shown in Figure 13–1.

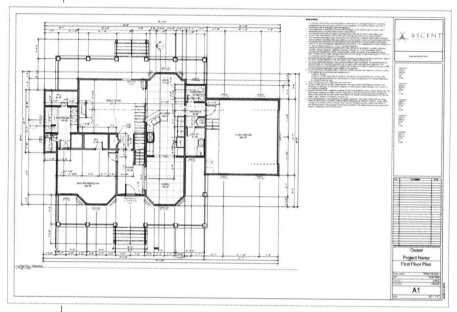

Figure 13–1

- Company templates can be created with standard sheets using the company (or project) title block and related views already placed on the sheet.

- The sheet size is based on the selected title block family.

- Sheets are listed in the *Sheets* area in the Project Browser.

- Most information on sheets is included in the views. You can add general notes and other non-model elements directly to the sheet, though it is better to add them using drafting views or better yet legends, as these can be placed on multiple sheets.

How To: Set Up Sheets

1. In the Project Browser, right-click on the *Sheets* area header and select **New Sheet...**, or in the *View* tab>Sheet Composition panel, click ⬚ (Sheet).

2. In the New Sheet dialog box, select a title block from the list, as shown in Figure 13–2. Alternatively, if there is a list of placeholder sheets, select one or more from the list.

*Click **Load...** to load a sheet from the Revit Library.*

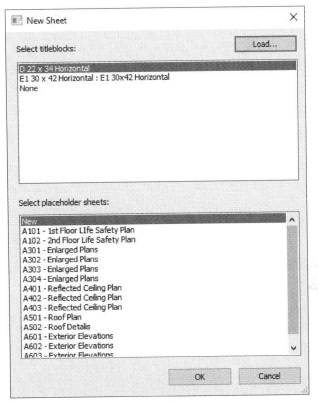

Hold <Ctrl> to select multiple placeholder sheets.

Figure 13–2

3. Click **OK**. A new sheet is created using the selected title block.
4. Fill out the information in the title block, as needed.
5. Add views to the sheet.

- When you create sheets, the next sheet is incremented numerically.

- Slowly click twice on the sheet name to change the name and number in the Sheet Title dialog box.

- When you change the *Sheet Name* and/or *Number* in the title block, it automatically changes the name and number of the sheet in the Project Browser.

- The plot stamp on the side of the sheet automatically updates according to the current date and time. The format of the display uses the regional settings of your computer.

- The *Scale* is automatically entered when a view is inserted onto a sheet. If a sheet has multiple views with different scales, the scale displays **As Indicated.**

Sheet (Title Block) Properties

Each new sheet includes a title block. You can change the title block information in Properties, as shown in Figure 13–3, or by selecting any blue label you want to edit (*Sheet Name, Sheet Number, Drawn by*, etc.), as shown in Figure 13–4.

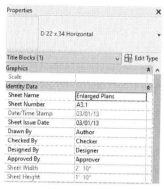

Figure 13–3

Figure 13–4

Properties that apply to all sheets can be entered in the Project Information dialog box (as shown in Figure 13–5). In the *Manage* tab>Settings panel, click (Project Information).

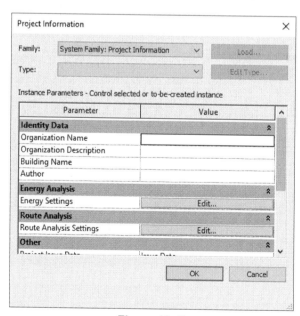

Figure 13–5

13.2 Placing and Modifying Views on Sheets

The process of adding views to a sheet is simple. Drag and drop a view from the Project Browser onto the sheet. The new view on the sheet is displayed at the scale specified in the original view. The view title displays the name, number, and scale of the view, as shown in Figure 13–6.

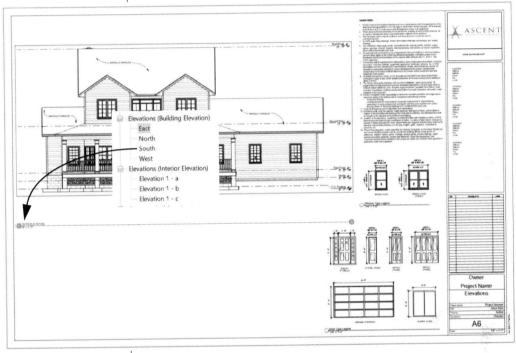

Figure 13–6

How To: Place Views on Sheets

Alignment lines from existing views display to help you place additional views.

1. Set up the view as you want it to display on the sheet, including the scale and visibility of elements.
2. Create or open the sheet where you want to place the view.
3. Select the view in the Project Browser, and drag and drop it onto the sheet.
4. The center of the view is attached to the cursor. Click to place it on the sheet.

Placing Views on Sheets

- Views can only be placed on a sheet once. However, you can duplicate the view and place that copy on a sheet.

- Views on a sheet are associative. They automatically update to reflect changes to the project.

- Each view on a sheet is listed under the sheet name in the Project Browser, as shown in Figure 13–7.

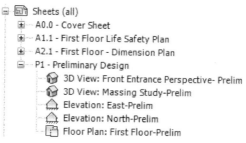

Figure 13–7

- You can also use two other methods to place views on sheets:

    - In the Project Browser, right-click on the sheet name and select **Add View...**.

    - In the *View* tab>Sheet Composition panel, click

      (Place View).

    Then, in the Views dialog box (shown in Figure 13–8), select the view you want to use and click **Add View to Sheet.**

This method lists only those views which have not yet been placed on a sheet.

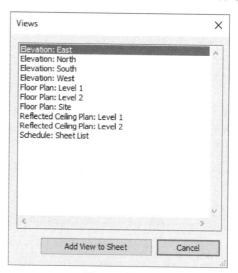

Figure 13–8

- To remove a view from a sheet, select it and press <Delete>. Alternatively, in the Project Browser, expand the individual sheet information to show the views, right-click on the view name, and select **Remove From Sheet**.

Hint: Setting Up the Project Browser

To view and change the Project Browser's types, select the top level node of the Project Browser (which is set to *Views (all)* by default) and select the type you want to use from the Type Selector. For example, you can set the Project Browser to only display views that are **not on sheets**, as shown in Figure 13–9.

Figure 13–9

Moving Views and View Titles

You can also use the **Move** *command or the arrow keys to move a view.*

- To move a view on a sheet, select the edge of the view and drag it to a new location. The view title moves with the view.

- To move only the view title, make sure to not have the view selected, then select the title and drag it to the new location.

- To modify the length of the line under the title name, select the edge of the view and drag the controls, as shown in Figure 13–10.

North-South Entry
1
1/8" = 1'-0"

Figure 13–10

- To change the title of a view on a sheet without changing its name in the Project Browser, in Properties, in the *Identity Data* area, type a new title for the *Title on Sheet* parameter, as shown in Figure 13–11.

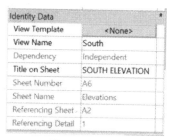

Figure 13–11

Rotating Views

- When creating a vertical sheet, you can rotate the view on the sheet by 90 degrees. Select the view and set the direction of rotation in the Rotation on Sheet drop-down list in the Options Bar, as shown in Figure 13–12.

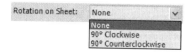

Figure 13–12

- To rotate a view to an angle other than 90 degrees, open the view, toggle on and select the crop region, and use the **Rotate** command to change the angle.

Working Inside Views

To make small changes to a view while working on a sheet:

- Double-click *inside* the view to activate it.
- Double-click *outside* the view to deactivate it.

Only use this method for small changes. Significant changes should be made directly in the view.

Only elements in the viewport are available for modification. The rest of the sheet is grayed out, as shown in Figure 13–13.

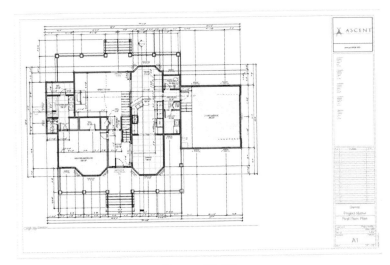

Figure 13–13

- You can activate and deactivate views by right-clicking on the edge of the view or by using the tools found in the *Modify | Viewports* and *Views* tab>Sheet Composition panel.

- Changes you make to elements when a view is activated also display in the original view.

- If you are unsure which sheet a view is on, right-click on the view in the Project Browser and select **Open Sheet**. This item is grayed out if the view has not been placed on a sheet and is not available for schedules and legends, which can be placed on more than one sheet.

Resizing Views on Sheets

Each view displays the extents of the model or the elements contained in the crop region. If the view does not fit on a sheet (as shown in Figure 13–14), you might need to crop the view or move the elevation markers closer to the building.

If the extents of the view change dramatically based on a scale change or a crop region, it is easier to delete the view on the sheet and drag it over again.

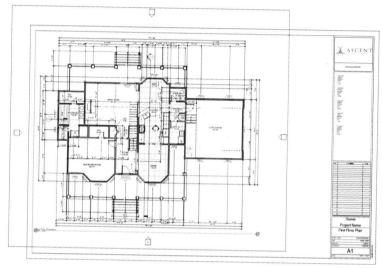

Figure 13–14

- For information about laying out views on sheets using guide grids, see *A.4 Working with Guide Grids on Sheets.*

- For information about working with revisions in views and on sheets, see *A.5 Importing and Exporting Schedules.*

Hint: Add an Image to a Sheet

Company logos and renderings saved to image files (such as .JPG and .PNG) can be added directly on a sheet or in a view.

1. In the *Insert* tab>Import panel, click  (Image).
2. In the Import Image dialog box, select and open the image file. The extents of the image display, as shown in Figure 13–15.

Figure 13–15

3. Place the image where you want it.
4. The image is displayed. Pick one of the grips and extend it to modify the size of the image.

- In Properties, you can adjust the height and width and also set the *Draw Layer* to either **Background** or **Foreground**, as shown in Figure 13–16.

Dimensions	⌃
Width	1' 5 185/256"
Height	1' 1 41/64"
Horizontal Scale	1.000000
Vertical Scale	1.000000
Lock Proportions	☑
Other	⌃
Draw Layer	Background

Figure 13–16

- You can select more than one image at a time and move them as a group to the background or foreground.

- In the *Modify | Raster Images* tab (as shown in Figure 13–17), you can access the *Arrange* options and the **Manage Images** tool.

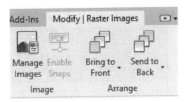

Figure 13–17

Practice 13a | Create Construction Documents

Practice Objectives

- Set up project properties.
- Create sheets individually.
- Modify views to prepare them to be placed on sheets.
- Place views on sheets.

In this practice, you will complete the project information, add new sheets, and use existing sheets. You will fill in title block information and then add views to sheets, as shown in Figure 13–18. Complete as many sheets as you have time for.

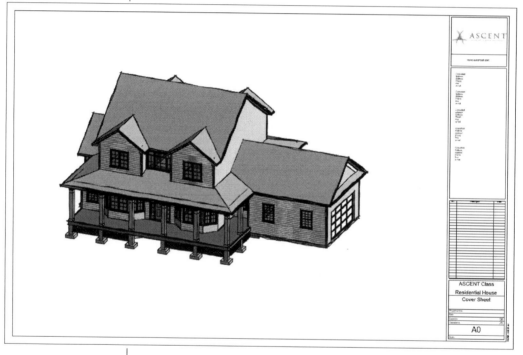

Figure 13–18

Task 1 - Complete the project information.

1. Open the project **Residential-Sheets.rvt** from the practice files folder.

2. In the *Manage* tab>Settings panel, click (Project Information).

3. In the Project Information dialog box, in the *Other* area, set the following parameters:

- *Project Issue Date:* **Issue Date**
- *Project Status:* **Design Development**
- *Client Name:* **ASCENT Class**
- *Project Address:* Click ▦ (Browse) and enter your address
- *Project Name:* **Residential House**
- *Project Number:* **1234-5678**

These properties are used across the entire sheet set and do not need to be entered on each sheet.

4. Click **OK**.

5. Save the project.

Task 2 - Create a cover sheet and floor plan sheets.

1. In the *View* tab>Sheet Composition panel, click ▨ (Sheet).

2. In the New Sheet dialog box, select the **ASCENT_D 22 x 34 Horizontal** title block. In the *Select placeholder sheets* area, select **New**.

3. Click **OK**.

4. Zoom in on the lower-right corner of the title block. The project properties filled out earlier are automatically added to the sheet.

5. Continue filling out the title block, as shown in Figure 13–19.

Figure 13–19

6. Zoom back out to display the whole sheet.

7. In the *View* tab>Sheet Composition panel, select 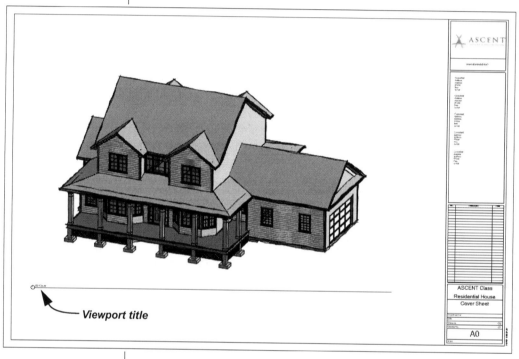 (View).

8. In the Views dialog box, select **3DView: 3D Cover** and click **Add View to Sheet**.

9. Move your cursor around and note that the view is attached to your cursor and ready to be placed where you want it. Click in the center of the sheet to place the 3D cover view, as shown in Figure 13–20.

— *Viewport title*

Figure 13–20

10. The viewport title is not required on the cover sheet. To remove the viewport title, select the edge of the viewport and in the Type Selector, select **Viewport: No Title**.

11. In the Project Browser, right-click on the **Sheets (all)** node and select **New Sheet**.

12. Using the ASCENT D-sized title block, create the following new sheets:

Sheet Number and Name	View Name
A1: First Floor Plan	First Floor-Dimension Plan
A2: Second Floor Plan	Second Floor-Dimension Plan
A5: Roof Plan	Roof Plan
S1.0 Foundation Plan	Foundation Plan

13. Save the project.

Task 3 - Add views to existing sheets.

1. Open sheet **S1.0**, then from the Project Browser, expand the **Structural Plans** node.

2. Drag and drop the **Foundation Plan** view onto the sheet.

3. Select the view. In Properties, in the *Graphics* area, change the *View Scale* to **1/4"=1'-0"**.

4. Click ⌕ (Modify).

5. Select the viewport and adjust the view title at the bottom of the viewport.

6. Click in an empty area in the view to clear the selection.

7. Move the view to the lower-right corner. This will leave room for any notes or schedules that need to be added later.

8. Save and close the project.

13.3 Printing Sheets

With the **Print** command, you can print individual sheets or a list of selected sheets. You can also print an individual view or a portion of a view for check prints or presentations. To open the Print dialog box (shown in Figure 13–21), in the *File* tab, click

🖨 (Print), or press **<Ctrl>+<P>**.

Figure 13–21

Printing Options

The Print dialog box is divided into the following areas: *Printer, File, Print Range, Options*, and *Settings*. Modify them as needed to produce the plot you want.

- **Printing Tips** opens Autodesk WikiHelp online, in which you can find help with troubleshooting printing issues.

- **Preview** opens a preview of the print output so that you can see what is going to be printed.

Printer

Select from the list of available printers, as shown in
Figure 13–22. Click **Properties...** to adjust the properties of the
selected printer. The options vary according to the printer. Select
the **Print to file** option to print to a file rather than directly to a
printer. You can create .PLT or .PRN files.

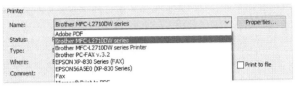

Figure 13–22

- You must have a PDF print driver installed on your system to
  print to PDF.

File

The *File* area is only available if the **Print to file** option has been
selected in the *Printer* area or if you are printing to an
electronic-only type of printer. You can create one file or multiple
files depending on the type of printer you are using, as shown in
Figure 13–23. Click **Browse...** to select the file location and
name.

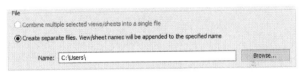

Figure 13–23

Print Range

The *Print Range* area enables you to print individual views/sheets or sets of views/sheets, as shown in Figure 13–24.

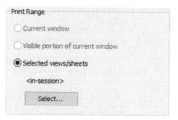

Figure 13–24

- **Current window** prints the entire current sheet or view you have open.

- **Visible portion of current window** prints only what is displayed in the current sheet or view.

- **Selected views/sheets** prints multiple views or sheets. Click **Select...** to open the View/Sheet Set dialog box to choose what to include in the print set. You can save these sets by name so that you can more easily print the same group again.

Options

If your printer supports multiple copies, you can specify the number in the *Options* area, as shown in Figure 13–25. You can also reverse the print order or collate your prints. These options are also available in the printer properties.

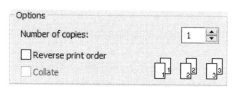

Figure 13–25

Settings

Click **Setup...** to open the Print Setup dialog box, as shown in Figure 13–26. Here you can specify the *Orientation* and *Zoom* settings, among others. You can also save these settings by name.

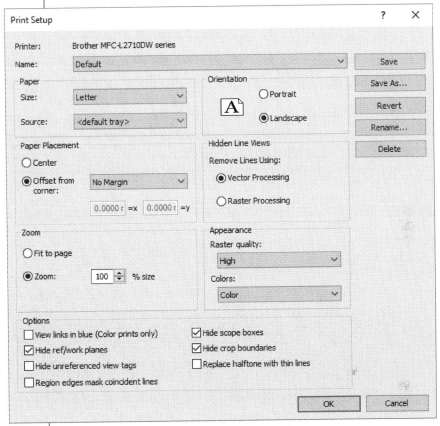

Figure 13–26

- In the *Options* area, specify the types of elements you want to print or not print. Unless specified, all of the elements in a view or sheet print.

- Sheets should always be printed using **Zoom** set to **100%** size unless you are creating a quick markup set that does not need to be exact.

Chapter Review Questions

1. How do you specify the size of a sheet?

    a. In the Sheet Properties, specify the **Sheet Size**.

    b. In the Options Bar, specify the **Sheet Size**.

    c. In the New Sheet dialog box, select a title block to control the sheet size.

    d. In the Sheet view, right-click and select **Sheet Size**.

2. How is the title block information filled in, as shown in Figure 13–27? (Select all that apply.)

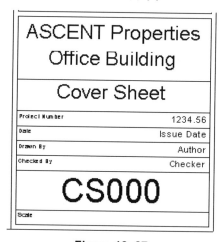

Figure 13–27

    a. Select the title block and select the label that you want to change.

    b. Select the title block and modify it in Properties.

    c. Right-click on the sheet in the Project Browser and select **Information**.

    d. Some of the information is filled in automatically.

3. On how many sheets can a floor plan view be placed?

    a. 1

    b. 2-5

    c. 6+

    d. As many as you want

4. Which of the following is the best method to use if the size of a view is too large for a sheet, as shown in Figure 13–28?

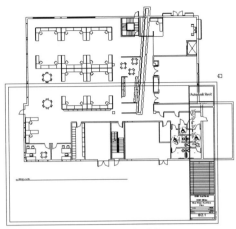

Figure 13–28

a. Delete the view, change the scale, and place the view back on the sheet.

b. Change the scale of the sheet.

5. How do you set up a view on a sheet that only displays part of a floor plan, as shown in Figure 13–29?

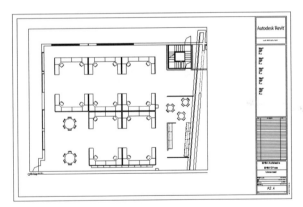

Figure 13–29

a. Drag and drop the view to the sheet and use the crop region to modify it.

b. Activate the view and rescale it.

c. Create a callout view displaying the part that you want to use and place the callout view on the sheet.

d. Open the view in the Project Browser and change the view scale.

Command Summary

Button	Command	Location
	Activate View	• **Ribbon:** (*select the view*) *Modify | Viewports* tab>Viewport panel • **Double-click:** (*in viewport*) • **Right-click:** (*on view*) Activate View
	Deactivate View	• **Ribbon:** *View* tab>Sheet Composition panel>expand Viewports • **Double-click:** (*on sheet*) • **Right-click:** (*on view*) Deactivate View
	Place View	• **Ribbon:** *View* tab>Sheet Composition panel
	Print	• **File tab**
	Sheet	• **Ribbon:** *View* tab>Sheet Composition panel

Annotating Construction Documents

When you create construction documents, annotations are required to show the design intent. Annotations such as dimensions and text can be added to views at any time during the creation of a project. Legends can be created to provide a place to document any symbols that are used in a project.

Learning Objectives in This Chapter

- Add dimensions to the model as a part of the working drawings.
- Add text to a view and use leaders to create notes pointing to a specific part of the model.
- Create text types using different fonts and sizes to suit your company standards.
- Create legend views and populate them with symbols of elements in the project.

14.1 Working with Dimensions

You can create permanent dimensions using aligned, linear, angular, radial, diameter, and arc length dimensions. These can be individual or a string of dimensions, as shown in Figure 14–1. With aligned dimensions, you can also dimension entire walls with openings, grid lines, and/or intersecting walls.

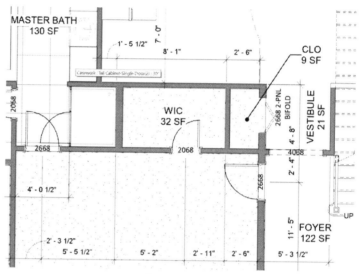

Figure 14–1

- Dimensions referencing model elements must be added to the model in a view. You can dimension on sheets, but only to items added directly on the sheets.

- Dimensions are available in the *Annotate* tab>Dimension panel (shown in Figure 14–2) and in the *Modify* tab>Measure panel.

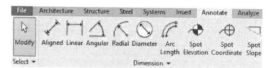

Figure 14–2

How To: Add Aligned Dimensions with Options

1. Start the ✎ (Aligned) command or type **DI**.
2. In the Type Selector, select a dimension style.

✎ *(Aligned) is also located in the Quick Access Toolbar.*

3. In the Options Bar, select the location line of the wall to dimension from, as shown in Figure 14–3.

   • This option can be changed as you add dimensions.

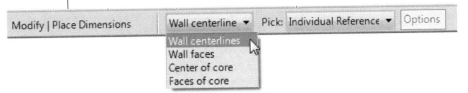

Figure 14–3

4. In the Options Bar, select your preference from the Pick drop-down list:

   • **Individual References:** Select the elements in order (as shown in Figure 14–4) and then click in an empty space in the view to position the dimension string.

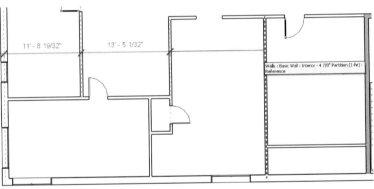

Figure 14–4

   • **Entire Walls:** Select the wall you want to dimension and then click the cursor to position the dimension string, as shown in Figure 14–5.

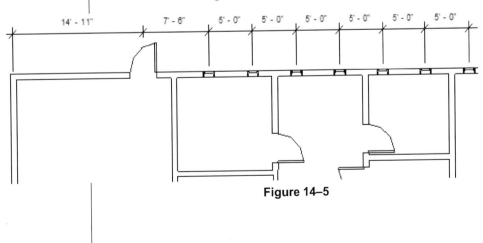

Figure 14–5

- When dimensioning entire walls, you can specify how you want *Openings*, *Intersecting Walls*, and *Intersecting Grids* to be treated by the dimension string. In the Options Bar, click **Options**. In the Auto Dimension Options dialog box, shown in Figure 14–6, select the references you want to have automatically dimensioned.

*If the **Entire Walls** option is selected without specifying additional options, an overall wall dimension will be placed.*

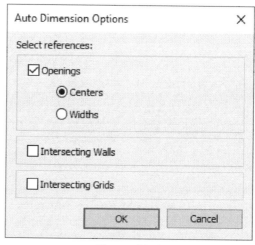

Figure 14–6

How To: Add Other Types of Dimensions

*When the **Dimension** command is active, the dimension methods are also accessible in the Modify | Place Dimensions tab.*

1. In the *Annotate* tab>Dimension panel, select a dimension method.

	Aligned	Most commonly used dimension type. Select individual elements or entire walls to dimension.
	Linear	Used when you need to specify certain points on elements.
	Angular	Used to dimension the angle between two elements.
	Radial	Used to dimension the radius of circular elements.
	Diameter	Used to dimension the diameter of circular elements.
	Arc Length	Used to dimension the length of the arc of circular elements.

2. In the Type Selector, select the dimension type.
3. Follow the prompts for the selected method.

Modifying Dimensions

When you move elements that are dimensioned, the dimensions automatically update. You can also modify dimensions by selecting a dimension or dimension string and making changes, as shown in Figure 14–7.

Toggle dimension equality

Click to edit dimension text

Move (dimension line)

Drag text

Lock/Unlock

Move witness line

Set gap between witness line and reference

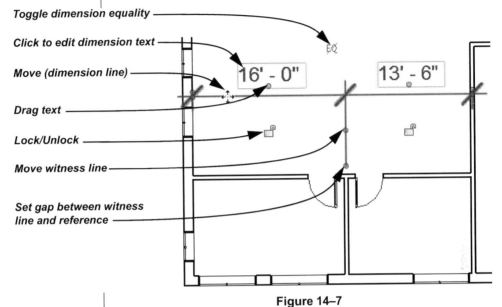

Figure 14–7

- To move the dimension text, select the **Drag text** control under the text and drag it to a new location. It automatically creates a leader from the dimension line if you drag it away. The style of the leader (arc or line) depends on the dimension style.

- To move the dimension line (the line parallel to the element being dimensioned), simply drag the line to a new location or select the dimension and drag the ⁺ (Drag to new position) control.

- To change the gap between the witness line and the element being dimensioned, drag the control at the end of the witness line.

- To move the witness line (the line perpendicular to the element being dimensioned) to a different element or face of a wall, use the **Move Witness Line** control in the middle of the witness line. While moving the witness line, you can hover your cursor over an element or component and press <Tab> repeatedly to cycle through the various options. You can also drag this control to move the witness line to a different element, or right-click on the control and select **Move Witness Line**.

Adding and Deleting Dimensions in a String

- To add a witness line to a string of dimensions, select the dimension and, in the *Modify | Dimensions* tab>Witness Lines panel, click ⊢⊣ (Edit Witness Lines). Select the element(s) you want to add to the dimension. Click in an empty space in the view to finish.

- To delete a witness line, drag the **Move Witness Line** control to a nearby witness line's element. Alternatively, you can hover the cursor over the control, right-click, and select **Delete Witness Line**.

- To delete one dimension in a string and break the string into two separate dimensions, select the string, hover your cursor over the dimension that you want to delete, and press <Tab>. When it highlights (as shown on the top in Figure 14–8), pick it and press <Delete>. The selected dimension is deleted and the dimension string is separated into two elements, as shown on the bottom in Figure 14–8.

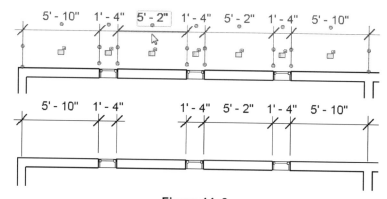

Figure 14–8

Modifying the Dimension Text

Because the Autodesk® Revit® software is parametric, changing the dimension text without changing the elements dimensioned would cause problems throughout the project. These issues could cause problems beyond the model if you use the project model to estimate materials or work with other disciplines.

You can append the text with prefixes and suffixes (as shown in Figure 14–9), which can help you in renovation projects.

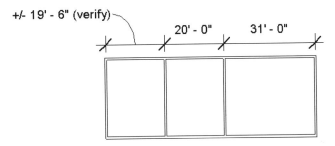

Figure 14–9

Slowly click twice on the dimension text to open the Dimension Text dialog box, as shown in Figure 14–10, and make modifications as needed.

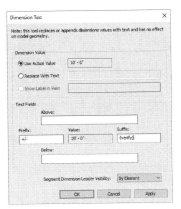

Figure 14–10

Setting Constraints

The three types of constraints that work with dimensions are locks and equal settings, as shown in Figure 14–11, as well as labels.

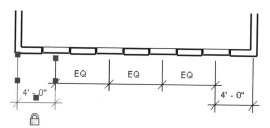

Figure 14–11

Locking Dimensions

When you lock a dimension, the value is set and you cannot make a change between it and the referenced elements. If it is unlocked, you can move it and change its value.

Note that when you use this and move an element, any elements that are locked to the dimension also move.

Setting Dimensions Equal

For a string of dimensions, select the **EQ** symbol to constrain the elements to be at an equal distance apart. This actually moves the elements that are dimensioned.

- The equality text display can be changed in Properties, as shown in Figure 14–12. The style for each of the display types is set in the dimension type.

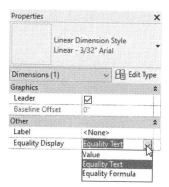

Figure 14–12

Labeling Dimensions

If you have a distance that needs to be repeated multiple times (such as the *Wall to Window* label shown in Figure 14–13) or one where you want to use a formula based on another dimension, you can create and apply a global parameter, also called a label, to the dimension.

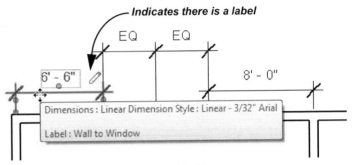

Figure 14–13

- To apply an existing label to a dimension, select the dimension and in the *Modify | Dimension* tab>Label Dimension panel, select the label in the drop-down list, as shown in Figure 14–14.

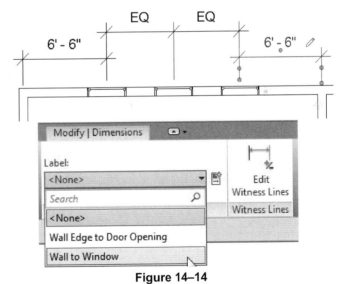

Figure 14–14

How To: Create a Label

1. Select a dimension.
2. In the *Modify | Dimension* tab>Label Dimension panel, click
   (Create Parameter)
3. In the Global Parameter Properties dialog box, type in a *Name*, as shown in Figure 14–15, and click **OK**.

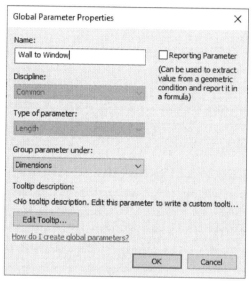

Figure 14–15

4. The label is applied to the dimension.

How To: Edit the Label Information

1. Select a labeled dimension.

2. Click (Global Parameters), as shown in Figure 14–16.

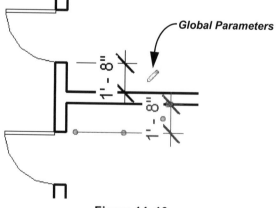

Figure 14–16

3. In the Global Parameters dialog box, in the *Value* column, type the new distance, as shown in Figure 14–17.

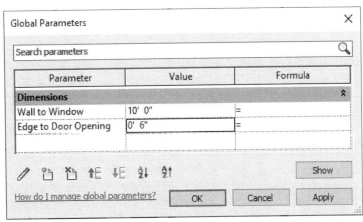

Figure 14–17

4. Click **OK**. The selected dimension and any other dimensions using the same label are updated.

- You can also edit, create, and delete global parameters in this dialog box.

Working with Constraints

To find out which elements have constraints applied to them, in the View Control Bar, click ⊟ (Reveal Constraints). Constraints display, as shown in Figure 14–18.

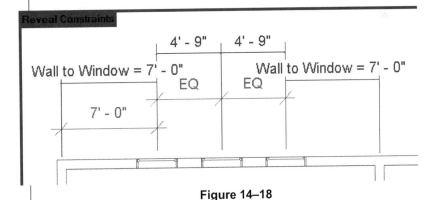

Figure 14–18

- If you try to move the element beyond the appropriate constraints, a warning dialog box displays, as shown in Figure 14–19.

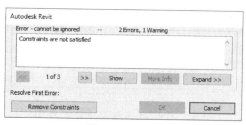

Figure 14–19

- If you delete dimensions that are constrained, a warning dialog box displays, as shown in Figure 14–20. Click **OK** to retain the constraint or click **Unconstrain** to remove the constraint.

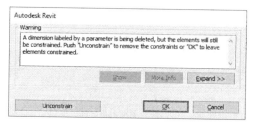

Figure 14–20

Practice 14a | Add Dimensions

Practice Objectives

- Add a string of dimensions.
- Dimension using the **Entire Walls** option.
- Edit the witness lines of dimensions.

In this practice, you will add dimensions using several different methods to a floor plan view, as shown on the sheet in Figure 14–21. You will also modify the dimensions so that they show what you are expecting.

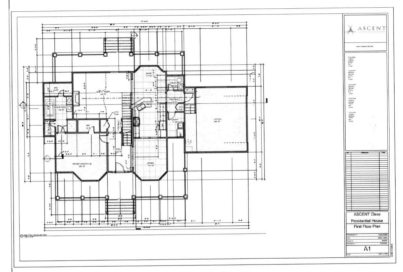

Figure 14–21

Task 1 - Add dimensions to the floor plan.

1. Open the project **Residential-Dimensions.rvt** from the practice files folder.

2. In the Project Browser, open the **Floor Plans: First Floor-Dimension Plan** view.

3. Zoom in to the west exterior walls by the master bathroom.

4. In the Quick Access Toolbar, click ✏ (Aligned).

5. In the Options Bar, select **Faces of Core** and set *Pick* to **Entire Walls**.

6. Click **Options** and verify the *Openings* is set to **Centers**, as shown in Figure 14–22. Click **OK**.

Figure 14–22

7. Select the west walls and place dimensions beside them. Be sure to select other walls that may appear along that string as well, as shown in Figure 14–23 (for clarity, section marks have been hidden in the image).

8. Adjust the section markers as needed.

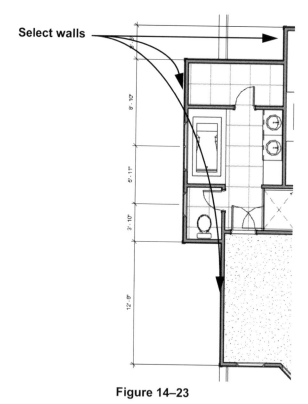

Figure 14–23

9. Click ⌖ (Modify).

10. Pan to the south of the model and repeat the process to dimension the entire wall.

11. Click ⌖ (Modify) and select the dimension string.

12. In the *Modify | Dimensions* tab>Witness Lines panel, click 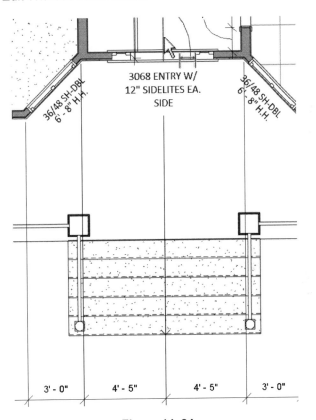 (Edit Witness Lines). Select the center of the front door, as shown in Figure 14–24. Note that it removes that dimension from the overall dimension string, and you are still in Edit Witness Lines mode.

3068 ENTRY W/
12" SIDELITES EA.
SIDE

36/48 SH-DBL
6' - 8" H.H.

36/48 SH-DBL
6' - 8" H.H.

3' - 0"   4' - 5"   4' - 5"   3' - 0"

Figure 14–24

13. Click the center of the door to add that dimension back, then press <Esc> twice to end the command.

14. Pan along the overall dimension string and note that there are dimensions of **3 1/2"** showing the thickness of the core of the wall (in this case, the framing stud). You need to remove these dimensions.

15. Select the dimension string, right-click on the Move Witness Line grip, and select **Delete Witness Line** (as shown in Figure 14–25).

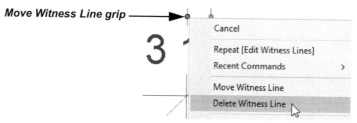

Figure 14–25

16. Continue removing the stud thickness dimensions, as needed.

17. Pan along the overall dimension string and drag out any dimensions that are overlapping another dimension. This is done by selecting the dimension string and clicking on the Drag text grip to drag the dimension outside of the string, as shown in Figure 14–26.

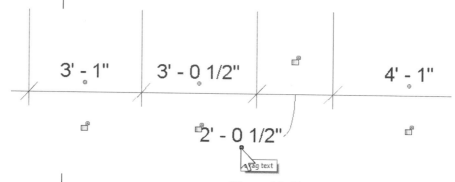

Figure 14–26

18. Continue adding dimensions to the exterior walls. Move elevation and section markers, as well as dimension text and lines, to keep the dimensions clear.

19. Use the various dimensioning commands and methods to dimension the interior spaces, as shown in Figure 14–27. (Hint: Do not forget to change from **Pick: Entire Walls** to **Pick: Individual References**.) The dimensions might not be exactly as shown.

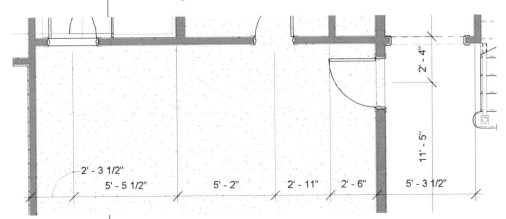

Figure 14–27

20. Save the project.

21. If time permits, dimension the **Floor Plans: Second Floor-Dimension Plan** view. Make adjustments as needed to the locations of the walls and doors.

22. Save the project.

Task 2 - Add a view to a sheet.

1. In the Project Browser, expand *Sheets (all)* and open **A1 - First Floor Plan**.

2. Drag and drop the **First Floor-Dimension Plan** view from the Project Browser onto the sheet.

3. Adjust it on the sheet as needed.

4. Save and close the project.

14.2 Working with Text

The **Text** command enables you to add notes to views or sheets, such as the plan shown in Figure 14–28. The same command is used to create text with or without leaders.

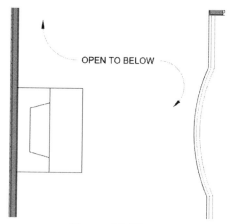

OPEN TO BELOW

Figure 14–28

The text height is automatically set by the text type in conjunction with the scale of the view (as shown in Figure 14–29, using the same size text type at two different scales). Text types display at the specified height, both in the views and on the sheet.

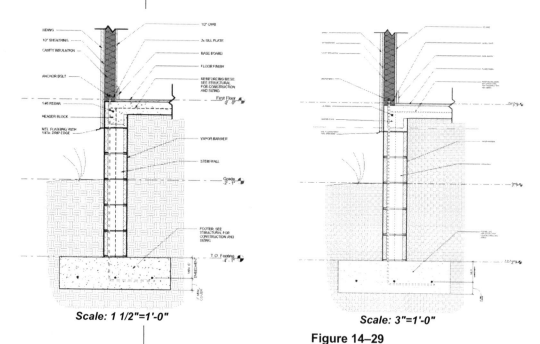

Scale: 1 1/2"=1'-0"   *Scale: 3"=1'-0"*

Figure 14–29

How To: Add Text

The text type sets the font and height of the text.

1. In the Quick Access Toolbar or *Annotate* tab>Text panel, click **A** (Text).
2. In the Type Selector, set the text type.
3. In the *Modify | Place Text* tab>Leader panel, select the method you want to use: **A** (No Leader), **←A** (One Segment), **↙A** (Two Segments), or **⌒A** (Curved).
4. In the Alignment panel, set the overall justification for the text and leader, as shown in Figure 14–30.

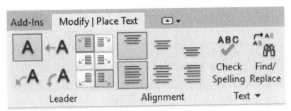

Figure 14–30

Use alignment lines to help you align the text with other text elements.

5. Select the location for the leader and text.
   - If **No leader** is selected, select the start point for the text and begin typing.
   - If using a leader, the first point places the arrow and you then select points for the leader. The text starts at the last leader point.
   - To set a word wrapping distance, click and drag the circle grip controls to set the start and end points of the text.
6. Type the needed text. In the *Edit Text* tab, specify additional options for the font and paragraph, as shown in Figure 14–31.

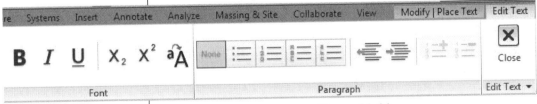

Figure 14–31

7. In the *Edit Text* tab>Edit Text panel, click **X** (Close) or click outside the text box to complete the text element.
   - Pressing <Enter> after a line of text starts a new line of text in the same text window.

How To: Add Text Symbols

1. Start the **Text** command and click to place the text.
2. As you are typing text and need to insert a symbol, right-click and select **Symbols** from the shortcut menu. Select from the list of commonly used symbols, as shown in Figure 14–32.

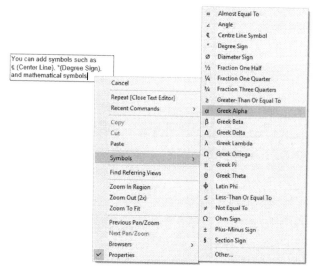

Figure 14–32

3. If the symbol you need is not listed, click **Other**.
4. In the Character Map dialog box, click on a symbol and click **Select**, as shown in Figure 14–33.

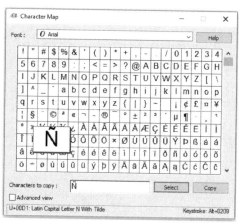

Figure 14–33

5. Click **Copy** to copy the character to the clipboard and paste it into the text box.

- The *Font* in the Character Map dialog box should match the font used by the text type. You do not want to use a different font for symbols.

Editing Text

Editing text notes takes place at two levels:

- Modifying the text note, which includes the **Leader** and **Paragraph** styles.

- Editing the text, which includes changes to individual letters, words, and paragraphs in the text note.

Modifying the Text Note

Click once on the text note to modify the text box and leaders using controls, as shown in Figure 14–34, or using the tools in the *Modify | Text Notes* tab.

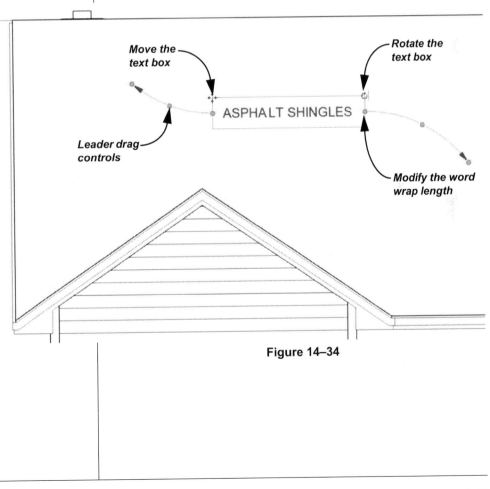

Move the text box

Rotate the text box

ASPHALT SHINGLES

Leader drag controls

Modify the word wrap length

Figure 14–34

How To: Add a Leader to Text Notes

1. Select the text note.
2. In the *Modify | Text Notes* tab>Leader panel, select the direction and justification for the new leader, as shown in Figure 14–35.
3. The leader is applied, as shown in Figure 14–36. Use the drag controls to place the arrow as needed.

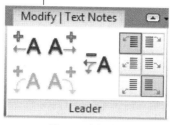

Figure 14–35

Figure 14–36

- You can remove leaders by clicking ⤴A (Remove Last Leader).

Editing the Text

The *Edit Text* tab enables you to make various customizations. These include modifying the font of selected words, as well as creating bulleted and numbered lists, as shown in Figure 14–37.

<u>General Notes</u>
1. Notify designer of intention to start construction at least 10 days prior to start of site work.
2. Installer shall provide the following:
    - 24-hour notice of start of construction
    - Inspection of bottom of bed or covering required by state inspector
    - All environmental management inspection sheets must be emailed to designer's office within 24 hours of inspection.

Figure 14–37

- You can **Cut**, **Copy**, and **Paste** text using the clipboard. For example, you can copy text from a document and then paste it into the text editor in Revit.

- To help you see the text better as you are modifying it, in the *Edit Text* tab, expand the Edit Text panel and select one or both of the options, as shown in Figure 14–38.

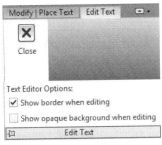

Figure 14–38

How To: Modify the Font

1. Select individual letters or words.
2. Click on the font modification you want to include:

B (Bold)	X$_2$ (Subscript)
I (Italic)	X^2 (Superscript)
U̲ (Underline)	ᵃA (All Caps)

- When pasting text from a document outside of Autodesk Revit, font modifications (e.g., bold, italics, etc.) are retained.

How To: Create Lists

1. In Edit Text mode, place the cursor in the line where you want to add a list.
2. In the *Edit Text* tab>Paragraph panel, click the type of list you want to create:

(Bullets)	(Uppercase Letters)
(Numbers)	(Lowercase Letters)

3. As you type, press <Enter> and the next line in the list is incremented.

The indent distance is set up by the text type Tab Size.

4. To include sub-lists, at the beginning of the next line, click

   ☰ (Increase Indent) or press <Tab>. This indents the line and applies the next level of lists, as shown in Figure 14–39.

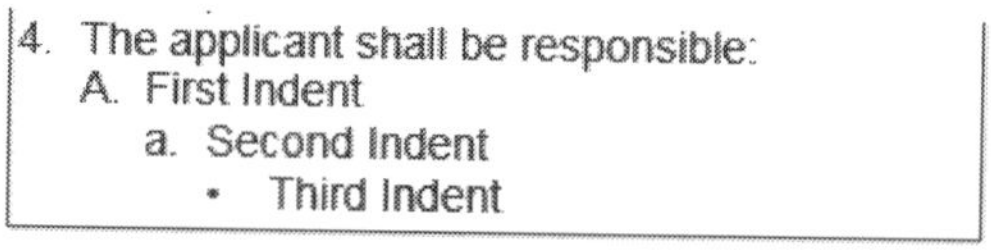

   > 4. The applicant shall be responsible:
   >   A. First Indent
   >   a. Second Indent
   >   • Third Indent

   Figure 14–39

   • You can change the type of list after you have applied the first increment. For example, you might want to use bullets for the sub-list instead of letters, as shown in Figure 14–40.

5. Click ☰ (Decrease Indent) or press <Shift>+<Tab> to return to the previous list style.

   • Press <Shift>+<Enter> to create a blank line in a numbered list.

   • To create columns or other separate text boxes that build on a numbering system (as shown in Figure 14–40), create the second text box and list. Then, place the cursor on one of the lines and in the Paragraph panel, click ☰ (Increment List Value) until the list matches the next number in the sequence.

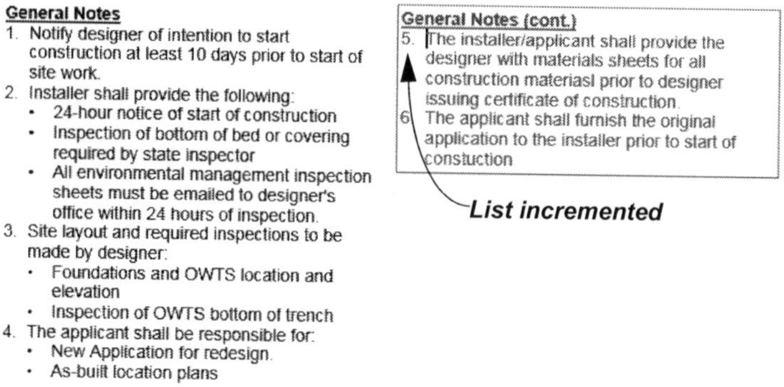

   General Notes
   1. Notify designer of intention to start construction at least 10 days prior to start of site work.
   2. Installer shall provide the following:
      • 24-hour notice of start of construction
      • Inspection of bottom of bed or covering required by state inspector
      • All environmental management inspection sheets must be emailed to designer's office within 24 hours of inspection.
   3. Site layout and required inspections to be made by designer:
      • Foundations and OWTS location and elevation
      • Inspection of OWTS bottom of trench
   4. The applicant shall be responsible for:
      • New Application for redesign.
      • As-built location plans

   General Notes (cont.)
   5. The installer/applicant shall provide the designer with materials sheets for all construction materiasl prior to designer issuing certificate of construction.
   6. The applicant shall furnish the original application to the installer prior to start of constuction

   List incremented

   Figure 14–40

6. Click ☰ (Decrement List Value) to move back a number.

Hint: Model Text

Model text is different from annotation text. It is designed to create full-size text on the model itself. For example, you would use model text to create a sign on a door, as shown in Figure 14–41. One model text type is included with the default template. You can create other types as needed.

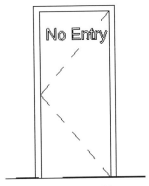

Figure 14–41

- Model text can be viewed in all views.
- Model text is added from the *Architecture* tab>Model panel

  by clicking 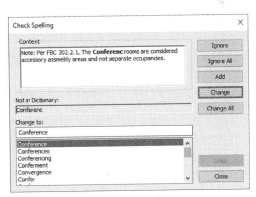 (Model Text).

Spell Checking

The Check Spelling dialog box displays any misspelled words in context and provides several options for changing them, as shown in Figure 14–42.

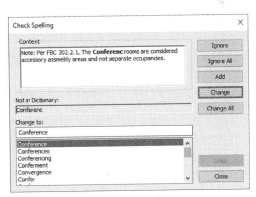

Figure 14–42

- Revit does not have active spell checking. It will only spell check when the command is activated.

- To spell check all text in a view, in the *Annotate* tab>Text panel, click ABC (Spelling) or press <F7>. As with other spell checkers, you can **Ignore**, **Add**, or **Change** the word.

- You can also check the spelling in selected text. With text selected, in the *Modify | Text Notes* tab>Tools panel, click ABC (Check Spelling).

Creating Text Types

If you need text types with a different text size or font (such as for a title or hand-lettering), you can create new ones, as shown in Figure 14–43. It is recommended that you create these in a project template so they are available in future projects.

General Notes

1. This project consists of
furnishing and installing...

Figure 14–43

- You can copy and paste text types from one project to another or use **Transfer Project Standards**.

How To: Create Text Types

1. In the *Annotate* tab>Text panel, click (Text Types).
2. In the Type Properties dialog box, click **Duplicate**.
3. In the Name dialog box, type a new name and click **OK**.
4. Modify the text parameters, as needed. The parameters are shown in Figure 14–44.

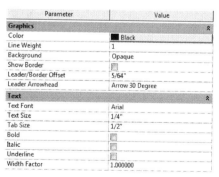

Parameter	Value
Graphics	
Color	Black
Line Weight	1
Background	Opaque
Show Border	
Leader/Border Offset	5/64"
Leader Arrowhead	Arrow 30 Degree
Text	
Text Font	Arial
Text Size	1/4"
Tab Size	1/2"
Bold	
Italic	
Underline	
Width Factor	1.000000

Figure 14–44

- The *Background* parameter can be set to **Opaque** or **Transparent**. An opaque background includes a masking region that hides lines or elements behind the text.

- In the *Text* area, the *Width Factor* parameter controls the width of the lettering, but does not affect the height. A width factor greater than **1** spreads the text out and a width factor less than **1** compresses it.
- The *Show Border* parameter, when selected, includes a rectangle around the text.

5. Click **OK** to close the Type Properties dialog box.

Practice 14b | Work with Text

Practice Objectives

- Create text types.
- Add text with and without leaders to a view.
- Add a numbered and bulleted list to a sheet.

In this practice, you will add text with and without leaders to a view. You will also add a text note with a numbered and bulleted list on an elevation plan sheet, as shown in Figure 14–45.

Figure 14–45

Task 1 - Create text types.

1. Open the project **Residential-Text.rvt** from the practice files folder.

2. In the *Annotate* tab>Text panel, click **A** (Text).

3. In Properties, click ⊞ (Edit Type).

4. In the Type Properties dialog box, duplicate the **3/32" Arial** text type and create the following text types as outlined below.

	1/8" Arial	**1/8" Arial Narrow**	**1/8" Arial Narrow Italic**
Text Font	Arial	Arial Narrow	Arial Narrow
Text Size	1/8"	1/8"	1/8"
Tab Size	1/4"	1/4"	1/4"
Width Factor	1.0	0.9	0.9
Italic	No	No	Yes

5. Click **OK**.

Task 2 - Add text to a view.

1. Open the **Elevations (Building Elevations): South** view.

2. In the *Annotate* tab>Text panel, click **A** (Text).

3. In the Type Selector, select **Text: 3/32"**.

4. Add text to all the roofs stating ASPHALT SHINGLES, as shown in Figure 14–46.

Figure 14–46

*   To add the leaders to the text, select the text and in the *Modify | Text Notes* tab>Leader panel, click ⁺A (Add Left Side Straight Leader), A⁺ (Add Right Side Straight Leader), ⁺A (Add Left Side Arc Leader), and A⁺ (Right Side Arc Leader), as required. Modify the Drag controls, as needed.

Task 3 - Create text with a list.

Note: In this task, you are placing the text directly on the sheet. Check your office standards, as using a legend view or schedule for general notes might be preferred.

1. Open sheet **A6 - Elevations**.

2. Add the **Elevations (Building Elevations): South** view to the sheet, as shown in Figure 14–47.

Figure 14–47

3. In a text editor (such as Word or Notepad), navigate to the practice files folder and open either **General Notes.docx** or **General Notes.txt**.

4. Copy the entire contents of the file to the clipboard.

5. In Revit, start the **Text** command.

6. Verify that no leader is selected, set the text type to **1/8" Arial Narrow**, and draw a text box similar to the one shown in Figure 14–48.

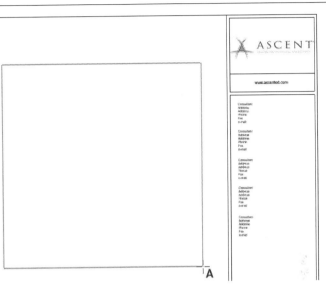

Figure 14–48

7. In the Edit Text dialog box>Clipboard panel, click 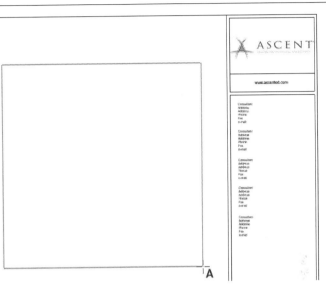 (Paste).

8. Remain in Edit Text mode and zoom in on the text box. Note that the formatting is not quite correct.

You do not need to do this with the .DOCX file as the numbered list will be retained.

- If you have copied the text from the General Notes.txt file, select all of the text and, in the *Edit Text* tab>Paragraph

  panel, click (List: Numbers).

- The paragraphs are recognized and numbered but some of the existing numbers are still there. You will need to delete the existing numbering and possibly fix the indents.

9. Zoom in and remove any additional numbering. After number 11, indent and use a bullet for the "Contractors shall be responsible" paragraph. Make the General Notes title bold and underlined, as shown in Figure 14–49.

General Notes:

1. It is the intent of the Architect that this work be in conformance with all requirements of the authorities having jurisdiction over this type of construction and occupancy. All contractors shall do their work in conformance with all applicable codes and regulations.
2. These documents as instruments of service are the property of the Architect and may not be used or reproduced without expressed written consent of the Architect.
3. The Contractor shall verify all conditions and dimensions at the job site prior to commencing work.
4. Do NOT scale these drawings. Written dimensions shall take precedence over scaled drawings.
5. The Contractor shall supply, locate, and build into the work all inserts, anchors, angles, plates, openings, sleeves, hangers, slab depressions, and pitches as may be required to attach and accommodate their work.
6. All materials and construction to be incorporated in the work shall be in strict accordance with the latest edition of the ASTM specifications applicable and shall conform to the Standards and Recommendations of the various trade institutes (A.C.I., A.I.S.C., etc) where applicable.
7. Contractors and all subcontractors shall install or apply, and protect all products, materials, processes, methods, coatings, equipment, appliances, hardware, software, etc. in strict accordance with the manufacturer's specifications, details, and instructions, typical. All manuals or instructions provided by these manufacturers for proper operation and maintenance of the above shall be delivered to the Owner at the completion and final inspection of the project.
8. All details and sections shown on the drawings are intended to be typical and shall be construed to apply to any similar situation elsewhere in the work except where a different detail is shown.
9. The Owner will provide contractor with a soil's investigation report and analysis. All requirements for site preparation and soil compaction specified in the soil report shall be followed unless additional, more stringent requirements are specified. Immediately notify Architect if foundation conditions encountered differ from soil exploration information made available to the contractor.
10. It is the Contractor's sole responsibility to determine erection procedure and sequence to insure the safety of the building and its component parts during erection.
11. Temporary bracing:
    - Contractors shall be responsible for temporary bracing that is required during construction to keep structure safe and plumb until the entire structure is in place. Bracing shown on structural drawings is for completed structure only.
12. Verify all dimensions prior to fabrication and construction.
13. Contractor shall verify the quantity, rough openings, and types of doors and windows in relation to the schedules and framing in the field prior to ordering. Any discrepancies shall be brought to the attention of the Architect immediately.
14. Location of Access Doors, supplied by mechanical trades and installed by others, shall be determined in the field through coordination of trades. Location of light fixtures shall govern position of ducts and pipes for which access doors are required. Access Doors shall not be placed in inaccessible positions or in the way of lights, grills, registers, concealed by casework, etc.
15. Prior to final inspection, a letter signed by the General Contractor or the Owner/ Builder (for any Owner/ Builder) projects must be provided to building official certifying that all adhesives, sealants, caulks, paints, coatings, aerosol paints, aerosol coatings, carpet systems (including carpeting, cushion and adhesive), other flooring systems, and composite wood products installed on this project are within the emission limits specified in applicable codes and regulations.

Figure 14–49

10. Click outside the text box and use the controls if needed to relocate or resize the text note.

11. Zoom out to see the full sheet.

12. Save and close the project.

14.3 Creating Legends

A legend is a separate view that can be placed on multiple sheets. Legends can be used to hold installation notes that need to be placed on a sheet with each floor plan, key plans, or any 2D items that need to be repeated. You can also create and list the annotations, line styles, and symbols that are used in your project, and provide explanatory notes next to the symbol, as shown in Figure 14–50. Additionally, legends can provide a list of materials or elevations of window types used in the project.

The elements in this figure are inserted using the ***Symbol*** *command rather that the* ***Legend Component*** *or* ***Detail Component*** *commands.*

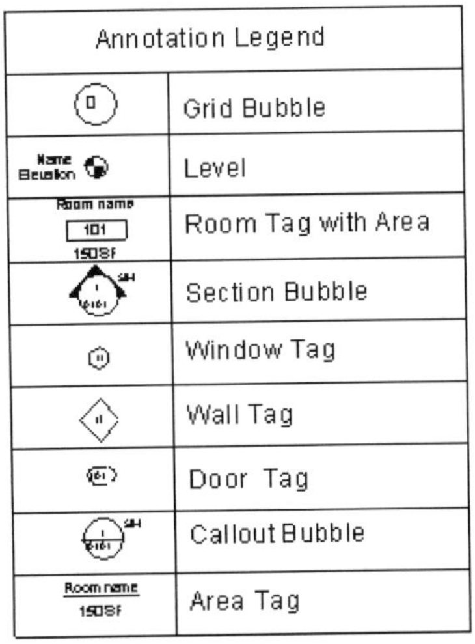
Annotation Legend
Grid Bubble
Level
Room Tag with Area
Section Bubble
Window Tag
Wall Tag
Door Tag
Callout Bubble
Area Tag

Figure 14–50

- You use (Detail Line) and (Text) to create the table and explanatory notes. Once you have a legend view, you can use commands, such as (Legend Component), (Detail Component), and (Symbol), to place elements in the view.
- Unlike other views, legend views can be attached to more than one sheet.
- You can set a legend's scale in the View Control Bar.
- Elements in legends can be dimensioned.

How To: Create a Legend

1. In the *View* tab>Create panel, expand 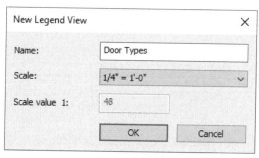 (Legends) and click (Legend), or in the Project Browser, right-click on the *Legends* area title and select **Legend**.
2. In the New Legend View dialog box, enter a name and select a scale for the legend, as shown in Figure 14–51, and click **OK**.

New Legend View		×
Name:	Door Types	
Scale:	1/4" = 1'-0" ∨	
Scale value 1:	48	
	OK	Cancel

Figure 14–51

3. Place the components in the view first, and then sketch the outline of the table when you know the sizes. Use **Ref Planes** to line up the components.

How To: Use Legend Components

1. In the *Annotate* tab>Detail panel, expand (Component) and click (Legend Component).
2. In the Options Bar, select the *Family* type that you want to use, as shown in Figure 14–52.

   • This list contains all of the elements in the project that can be used in a legend. For example, you might want to display the elevation of all door types used in the project.

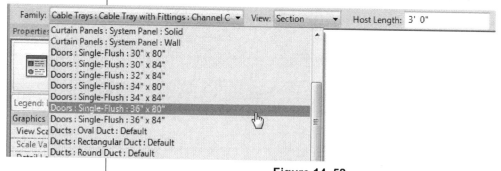

Figure 14–52

3. Select the *View* of the element that you want to use. For example, you might want to display the section of the floors or roofs, and the front elevation of the doors (as shown in Figure 14–53) and windows.

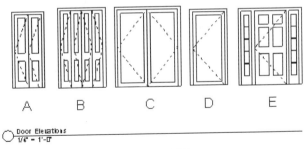

Figure 14–53

4. For section elements (such as walls, floors, and roofs), type a distance for the *Host Length*.

•   Elements that are full size, such as planting components or doors, come in at their full size.

•   Legends are views that can be placed on multiple sheets. You can use **Copy to the Clipboard** and **Paste** to copy legends from sheet to sheet.

Practice 14c | Create Legends

Practice Objective

- Create legends using legend components and text.

In this practice, you will create door and window legends (as shown in Figure 14–54) by creating legend views, adding legend components, and labeling the door and window types with text.

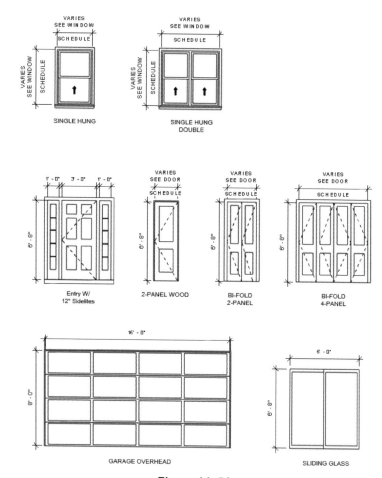

Figure 14–54

1. Open the project **Residential-Legends.rvt** from the practice files folder.

2. In the *View* tab>Create panel, expand (Legends) and click (Legend) to create a new legend view.

3. Name it **Window Type Legend** and set the *Scale* to **1/4"=1'-0"**.

4. In the *Annotate* tab>Detail panel, expand (Component) and click (Legend Component).

5. In the Options Bar, set *Family* to **Windows: Window - Single-Hung: 36" x 56"** and *View* to **Elevation: Front**. Place the component in the view. The window displays.

6. In the *Annotate* tab>Text panel, click **A** (Text).

7. In the Type Selector, select **Text: 3/32"**. Add text under the window, as shown in Figure 14–55.

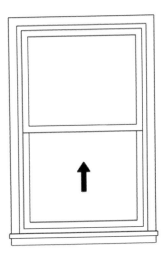

SINGLE HUNG

Figure 14–55

8. Start the **Dimension** command and dimension the top of the window. Double-click on the dimension to open the Dimension Text dialog box. Set the *Dimension Value* to **Replace With Text** and add the text **SEE WINDOW**, as shown in Figure 14–56.

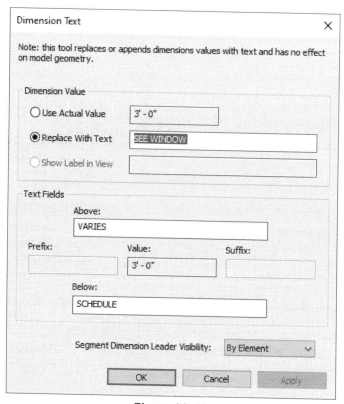

Figure 14–56

9. Continue to add text and edited dimensions to the other windows, as required.

10. Create another legend view. Name it **Door Type Legend** and set the *Scale* to **1/4"=1'-0"**.

11. In the legend view, click ⊟ (Legend Component) and add the elevations of the doors used in the project. Refer to Figure 14–57 below for door family types.

12. Label the doors as shown in Figure 14–57.

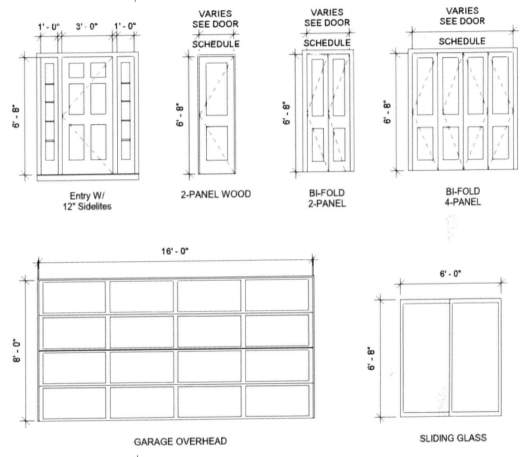

Figure 14–57

13. Save and close the project.

Chapter Review Questions

1. When a wall is moved (as shown in Figure 14–58), how do you update the dimension?

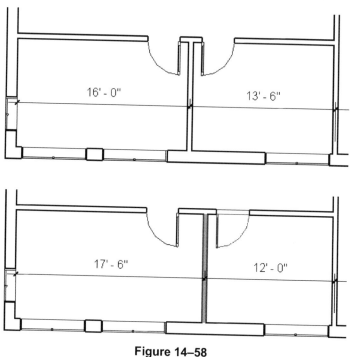

16' - 0"   13' - 6"

17' - 6"   12' - 0"

Figure 14–58

   a. Edit the dimension and move it over.
   b. Select the dimension and then click **Update** in the Options Bar.
   c. The dimension automatically updates.
   d. Delete the existing dimension and add a new one.

2. How do you create new text styles?
   a. Using the **Text Styles** command.
   b. Duplicate an existing type.
   c. They must be included in a template.
   d. Using the **Format Styles** command.

3. When you edit text, how many leaders can be added using the leader tools shown in Figure 14–59?

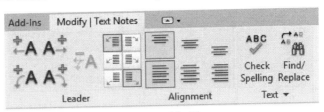

Figure 14–59

a. One

b. One on each end of the text

c. As many as you want at each end of the text

4. When creating a legend, which of the following elements cannot be added?

a. Legend components

b. Tags

c. Rooms

d. Symbols

Command Summary

Button	Command	Location
Dimensions and Text		
	Aligned (Dimension)	• **Ribbon:** *Annotate* tab>Dimension panel or *Modify* tab>Measure panel, expanded drop-down list • **Quick Access Toolbar** • **Shortcut:** DI
	Angular (Dimension)	• **Ribbon:** *Annotate* tab>Dimension panel or *Modify* tab>Measure panel, expanded drop-down list
	Arc Length (Dimension)	• **Ribbon:** *Annotate* tab>Dimension panel or *Modify* tab>Measure panel, expanded drop-down list
	Diameter (Dimension)	• **Ribbon:** *Annotate* tab>Dimension panel or *Modify* tab>Measure panel, expanded drop-down list
	Linear (Dimension)	• **Ribbon:** *Annotate* tab>Dimension panel or *Modify* tab>Measure panel, expanded drop-down list
	Radial (Dimension)	• **Ribbon:** *Annotate* tab>Dimension panel or *Modify* tab>Measure panel, expanded drop-down list
	Text	• **Ribbon:** *Annotate* tab>Text panel • **Shortcut:** TX
Legends		
	Legend (View)	• **Ribbon:** *View* tab>Create panel>expand Legends
	Legend Component	• **Ribbon:** *Annotate* tab>Detail panel>expand Component

Chapter 15

Adding Tags and Schedules

Adding tags to your views helps you to identify elements such as doors, windows, or walls in the model. Tags are 2D annotation families with labels that extract information about the elements being tagged from their properties. Tags are typically added when you insert an element, but can also be added at any point of the design process. The information captured in the elements in a project is used to populate schedules, which can be added to sheets to complete the construction documents.

Learning Objectives in This Chapter

- Add tags to elements in 2D and 3D views to prepare the views to be placed on sheets.
- Load tags that are required for projects.
- Modify schedule content including the instance and type properties of related elements.
- Add schedules to sheets as part of the construction documents.

15.1 Adding Tags

Tags identify elements that are listed in schedules. Door and window tags are inserted automatically if you use the **Tag on Placement** option when inserting the door or window or other elements. You can also add tags later to specific views, as needed. Many other types of tags are available in the Autodesk® Revit® software, such as wall tags and furniture tags, as shown in Figure 15–1.

Additional tags are stored in the Revit Library in the Annotations folder.

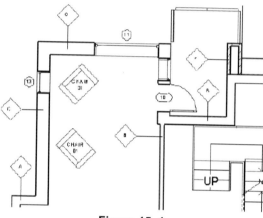

Figure 15–1

- The **Tag by Category** command works for most elements, except for a few that have separate commands.

- Tags can be letters, numbers, or a combination of the two.

You can place three types of tags, as follows:

- (Tag by Category): Tags according to the category of the element. It places door tags on doors and wall tags on walls.

- (Multi-Category Tag): Tags elements belonging to multiple categories. The tags display information from parameters that they have in common.

- (Material Tag): Tags that display the type of material. They are typically used in detailing.

How To: Add Tags

1. In the *Annotate* tab>Tag panel, click (Tag by Category), (Multi-Category Tag), or (Material Tag) depending on the type of tag you want to place.

2. In the Options Bar, set the options as needed, as shown in Figure 15–2.

Figure 15–2

In the Load Family dialog box, if you are not routed to the Revit families folder location, click on Imperial Library in the Places panel.

3. Select the element you want to tag. If a tag for the selected element is not loaded, you are prompted to load it from the library.

Tag Options

- You can set tag options for leaders and tag rotation, as shown in Figure 15–3. You can also press <Spacebar> to toggle the orientation while placing or modifying the tag.

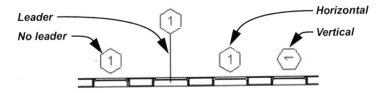

Figure 15–3

- Leaders can have an **Attached End** or a **Free End**, as shown in Figure 15–4. The attached end must be connected to the element being tagged. A free end has an additional drag control where the leader touches the element.

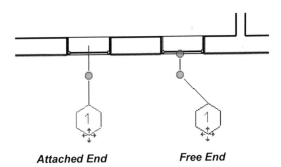

Figure 15–4

- If you change between **Attached End** and **Free End**, the tag does not move and the leader does not change location.

- The **Length** option specifies the length of the leader in plotting units. It is grayed out if **Leader** is not selected or if a **Free End** leader is defined.

- If a tag is not loaded, a warning box opens, as shown in Figure 15–5. Click **Yes** to open the Load Family dialog box in which you can select the appropriate tag.

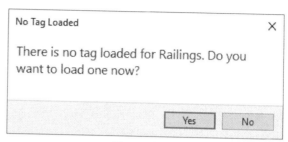

Figure 15–5

- Tags can be pinned to stay in place if you move the element that is tagged. This is primarily used when tags have leaders, as shown in Figure 15–6.

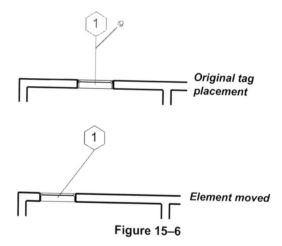

Original tag placement

Element moved

Figure 15–6

Room Tags

If tags were not added to rooms when they were created or you wish to add room tags to another view, you must use a specific command. In the *Architecture* tab>Room & Area panel, click

 (Tag Room), or in the *Annotate* tab>Tag panel, click

(Room Tag). You can also type **RT**.

How To: Add Multiple Tags

1. In the *Annotate* tab>Tag panel, click 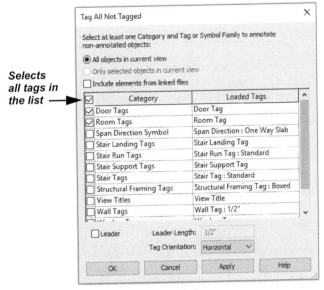 (Tag All).
2. In the Tag All Not Tagged dialog box, shown in Figure 15–7, select the checkbox beside one or more categories to tag. Selecting the checkbox beside the *Category* title selects all of the tags.

*To tag only some elements, select them before starting this command. In the Tag All Not Tagged dialog box, select **Only selected objects in current view**.*

Selects all tags in the list →

Figure 15–7

3. Set the *Leader* and *Tag Orientation*, as needed.
4. Click **Apply** to apply the tags and stay in the dialog box. Click **OK** to apply the tags and close the dialog box.

• When you select a tag, the properties of that tag display. To display the properties of the tagged element, in the

   Modify | <contextual> tab>Host panel, click 🔳 (Select Host).

• Rooms can be tagged using **Tag All Not Tagged**.

How To: Load Tags

1. In the *Annotate* tab, expand the Tag panel and click

   🔳 (Loaded Tags And Symbols) or, when a **Tag** command is active, in the Options Bar, click **Tags...**.

2. In the Loaded Tags And Symbols dialog box (shown in Figure 15–8), click **Load Family...**.

Figure 15–8

3. In the Load Family dialog box, navigate to the appropriate *Annotations* folder in the Revit Library, select the tag(s) needed, and click **Open**.
4. The tag is added to the category in the dialog box. Click **OK**.

Instance vs.Type Based Tags

Default doors are tagged in a numbered sequence, with each instance of the door having a separate tag number. Other elements (such as windows and walls) are, by default, tagged by type, as shown in Figure 15–9. Changing the information in one tag changes all instances of that element.

*An additional window tag (**Window Tag-Number.rfa**) is stored in the Annotations> Architectural folder in the Revit Library. It tags windows using sequential numbers.*

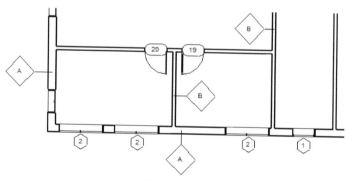

Figure 15–9

• To modify the number of an instance tag (such as a door or room), slowly click twice directly on the number in the tag and modify it, or you can modify the *Mark* property, as shown in Figure 15–10. Only that one door instance updates.

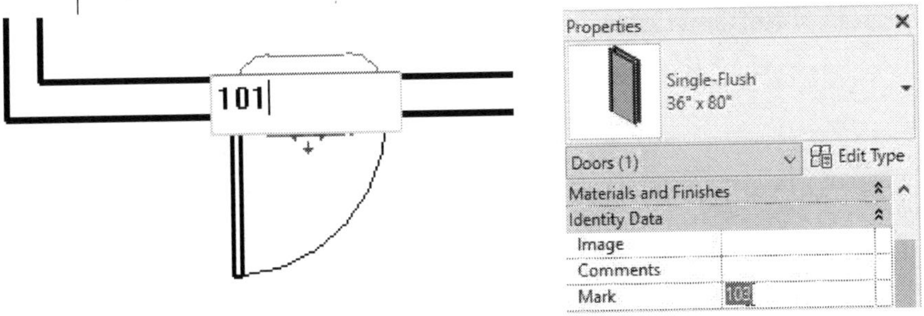

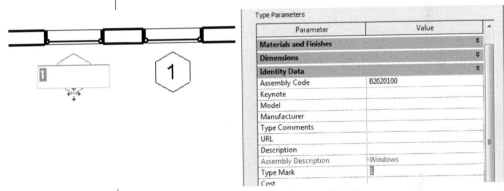

Figure 15–10

- To modify the number of a type tag, you can slowly click twice directly on the number in the tag and modify it. Alternatively, you can select the element and in the *Modify | <contextual>* tab>Host panel, click ⬛ (Select Host), then in Properties, click 🔲 (Edit Type). In the Type Properties dialog box, in the *Identity Data* area, modify the *Type Mark*, as shown in Figure 15–11. All instances of this element then update.

Figure 15–11

- When you change a type tag, an alert box opens to warn you that changing a type parameter affects other elements, as shown in Figure 15–12. If you want this tag to modify all other elements of this type, click **Yes**.

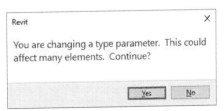

Figure 15–12

- If a tag displays with a question mark, it means that no information has been assigned to that parameter yet.

Tagging in 3D Views

You can add tags to isometric 3D views, as shown in Figure 15–13, as long as the views are locked first.

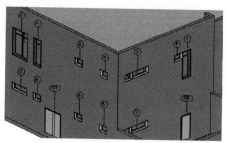

Figure 15–13

- Dimensions can be added to isometric 3D views whether they are locked or not. Proceed with caution when selecting the items to dimension to. Ensure that the witness lines and text orient is snapping to and extending in the correct direction as intended.

- Locked views can be used with perspective views. This enables you to create the view as you want it and then save it from being modified.

How To: Lock a 3D View

1. Open a 3D view and set it up as you want it to display.

2. In the View Control Bar, click 🏠 (Unlocked 3D View), then click 🏠 (Save Orientation and Lock View).

- If you are using the default 3D view and it has not been saved, you are prompted to name and save the view first.

- You can modify the orientation of the view by clicking 🏠 (Locked 3D View), then clicking 🏠 (Unlock View). This also removes any tags you have applied.

- To return to the previous locked view, click 🏠 (Unlocked 3D View), then click 🏠 (Restore Orientation and Lock View).

Hint: Stair and Railing Tags

Tag by Category can be used to tag the overall stairs, stair runs, landings, and railings, as shown in Figure 15–14. An additional type of tag, **Stair Tread/Riser Number**, creates a sequence of numbers for each tread or riser.

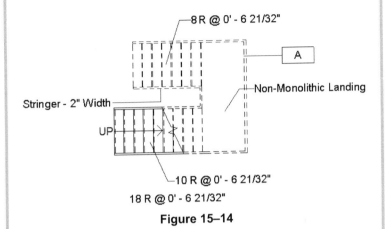

Figure 15–14

How To: Add Tread/Riser Number Tags to Stairs

1. Open a plan, elevation, or section view.

2. In the *Annotate* tab>Tag panel, click ✏ (Stair Tread/Riser Number).

3. In Properties, set up the *Tag Type*, *Display Rule*, and other parameters. These remain active for the project.

4. Select a reference line of a stair to place the numbers, as shown in Figure 15–15.

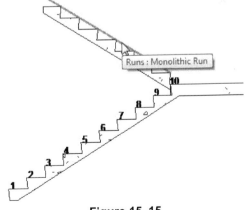

Figure 15–15

5. Continue selecting runs as needed.

Practice 15a | Add Tags

Practice Objectives

- Add door and window tags to a model using the Tag All Not Tagged dialog box.
- Set the *Type Comments* parameter for tags.
- Add room tags.

In this practice, you will add door and window tags in a floor plan, as shown in Figure 15–16. You will also modify the *Type Comments* numbers for the windows. Finally, you will tag the room elements. Note: Dimensions have been hidden in the view for clarity.

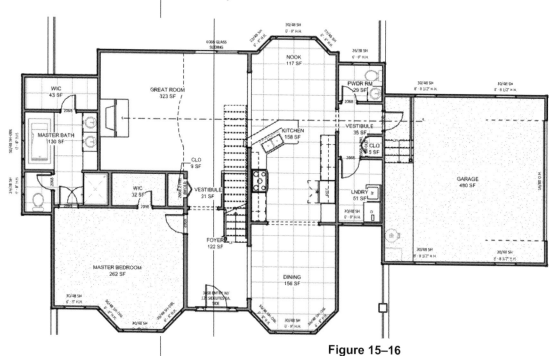

Figure 15–16

Task 1 - Add tags to a floor plan.

1. Open the project **Residential-Tags.rvt** from the practice files folder.

2. Verify you are in the **Floor Plan: First Floor-Dimension Plan** view and zoom in to the garage area.

3. In the *Annotate* tab>Tag panel, click 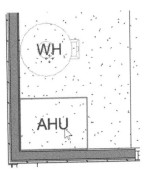 (Tag by Category). In the Options Bar, select **Horizontal** and verify that **Leader** is deselected.

4. Select the water heater and then the furnace, as shown in Figure 15–17.

Figure 15–17

5. Click ⌖ (Modify).

6. Zoom out so you can see the entire house.

7. Save the project.

Task 2 - Tag all the doors and windows, then modify tag locations.

1. In the *Annotate* tab>Tag panel, click (Tag All).

2. In the Tag All Not Tagged dialog box, do the following:

- Choose **All objects in current view**.
- Check the boxes next to the **Door Tags** and **Window Tags** categories.
- Verify the box next to **Leader** in the bottom-left corner is unchecked and leave the *Tag Orientation* set to **Horizontal**, as shown in Figure 15–18.

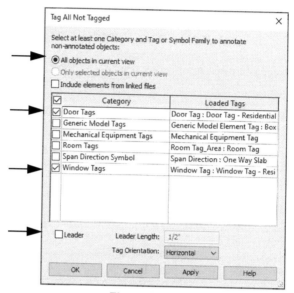

Figure 15–18

3. Click **OK** to add door and window tags to all the doors and windows.

- Window and door tags typically follow the direction of the components.

4. Save the project.

Task 3 - Modify windows to update the window tags.

Note that some of the windows are showing question marks. This means that those windows do not have the information that is being pulled by the tag. In this task, you will update the windows so the proper information displays.

1. Pan and zoom over to the master bedroom and select the large window in the bay window area.

2. In Properties, click ⊞ (Edit Type).

3. In the Type Properties dialog box, in the *Identity Data* area, set the *Type Comments* to **50/48 SH-DBL**, as shown in Figure 15–19. Click **OK**.

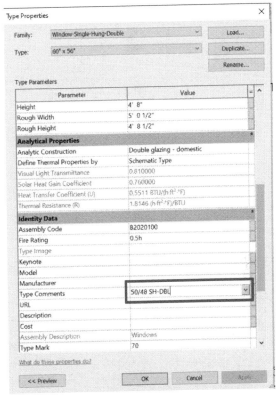

Figure 15–19

- Note that similar windows in the model update as well.

4. If time permits, modify any window tags that still have question marks following the table below.

Window Type	Type Comments
Window-Single-Hung_Double: 60" x 56"	50/48 SH-DBL
Window-Single-Hung_Double: 42" x 56"	36/48 SH-DBL
Window-Single-Hung: 36" x 56"	30/48 SH
Window-Single-Hung: 30" x 44"	26/38 SH
Window-Single-Hung: 26" x 56"	22/48 SH
Window-Single-Hung-Double: 60" x 44"	26/38 SH-DBL

5. Zoom out to display the entire floor plan.

6. To make the dimension plan more readable, move the window tags above the windows. Select a window tag that is overlapping the window and use the move grip to move the tag above the window, as shown in Figure 15–20.

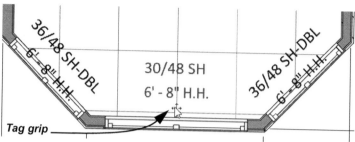

Figure 15–20

7. Save the project.

Task 4 - Add room tags.

1. Still in the First Floor-Dimension Plan view, verify that **Select Elements By Face** is turned off in the Status Bar.

   • This will allow you to select the room elements more easily.

2. Hover the cursor over the open area inside the front door until you see the room element, as shown in Figure 15–21. The room elements do not display in this view but are available.

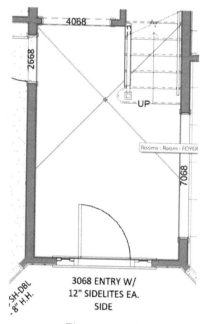

Figure 15–21

3. In the *Annotate* tab>Tag panel, click 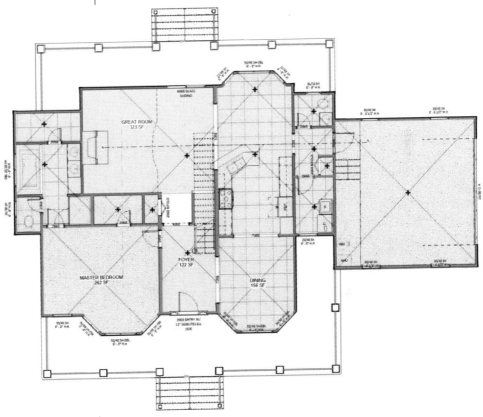 (Tag by Category). Note that rooms cannot be tagged this way.

4. Select ⮁ (Modify) to end the command.

5. In the *Annotate* tab>Tag panel, click (Tag Room). The room elements display. Place tags in one or two rooms, as shown in Figure 15–22 (dimensions have been turned off in the image for clarity).

Figure 15–22

6. Click ⮁ (Modify).

7. In the *Annotate* tab>Tag panel, click (Tag All).

8. In the Tag All Not Tagged dialog box, select **Room Tags: Room Tag** and click **OK**. Room tags are added to all of the rooms in the view.

9. Zoom in on the closet next to the stairs and move the tag outside the room. It is no longer connected to the room element, as shown in Figure 15–23.

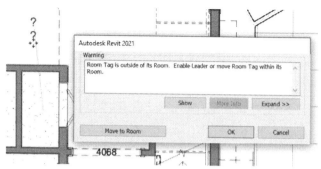

Figure 15–23

10. Read the warning information and click **OK** to close the dialog box.

11. The tag is still selected. In the Options Bar, select **Leader**. The room tag is now connected to the room element and displays the information, as shown in Figure 15–24.

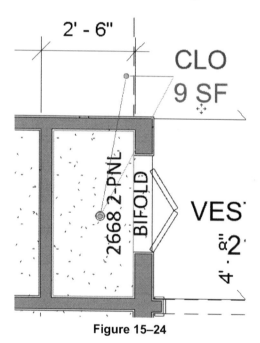

Figure 15–24

12. Save and close the project.

15.2 Working with Schedules

Schedules extract information from a project and display it in table form. Each schedule is stored as a separate view and can be placed on sheets, as shown in Figure 15–25. Any changes you make to the project elements that affect the schedules are automatically updated in both views and sheets.

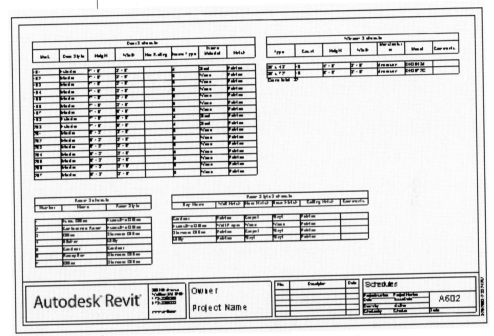

Figure 15–25

- The architectural template (**Default.rte**) does not include any schedules. The **Construction-Default.rte**, **Residential-Default.rte**, and **Commercial-Default.rte** template files do include useful schedules.

How To: Work with Schedules

1. In the Project Browser, expand the *Schedules/Quantities* area, as shown in Figure 15–26, and double-click on the schedule you want to open.

Figure 15–26

---

2. Schedules are automatically filled out with the information stored in the instance and type parameters of related elements that are added to the model.
3. Fill out additional information either in the schedule or in Properties.
4. In the *Modify Schedule/Quantities* tab>Appearance panel, you can select ▦ (Freeze Header) to keep the header row visible while you scroll through the schedule.
5. When selecting on a schedule's row, it will highlight in blue.
6. Drag and drop the schedule onto a sheet.

- You can zoom in to read small text in schedule views. Hold down <Ctrl> and scroll using the mouse wheel, or press <Ctrl>+<+> to zoom in or <Ctrl>+<-> to zoom out.

Modifying Schedules

Information in schedules is bi-directional:

- Make changes to elements and the schedule automatically updates.

- Make changes to information in the schedule cells and the elements automatically update.

How To: Modify Schedule Cells

1. Open the schedule view.
2. Select the cell you want to change. Some cells have drop-down lists, as shown in Figure 15–27. Others have edit fields.

If you change a type property in the schedule, it applies to all elements of that type. If you change an instance property, it only applies to that one element.

<Door Schedule>			
A	**B**	**C**	**D**
Mark	Type	Width	Height
101	36" x 84"	3' - 0"	7' - 0"
103	24" x 82"	3' - 0"	6' - 8"
104	30" x 80"	3' - 0"	6' - 8"
105	30" x 8"	3' - 0"	6' - 8"
106	32" x 84"	3' - 0"	6' - 8"
107	36" x 80"	3' - 0"	6' - 8"
108	36" x 84"	3' - 0"	7' - 0"

Figure 15–27

3. Add the new information. The change is reflected in the schedule, on the sheet, and in the elements of the project.

- If you change a type property, an alert box opens, as shown in Figure 15–28.

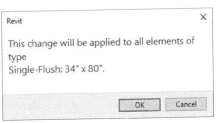

Figure 15–28

- When you select an element in a schedule, in the *Modify Schedule/Quantities* tab>Element panel, you can click

  (Highlight in Model). This opens a close-up view of the element with the Show Element(s) In View dialog box, as shown in Figure 15–29. Click **Show** to display more views of the element. Click **Close** to finish the command.

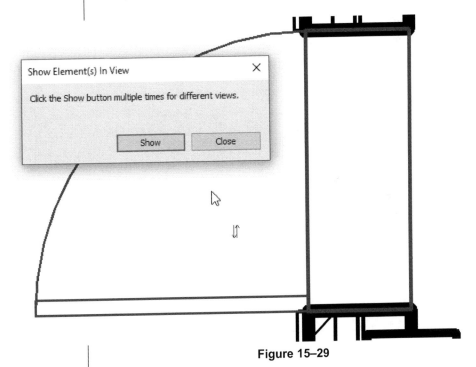

Figure 15–29

Hint: Customizing Schedules

Schedules are typically included in project templates, which are set up by the BIM manager or other advanced users. They can be complex to create as there are many options.

- For information about creating basic schedules, see *A.6 Creating Building Component Schedules*.

- For information on using schedule data outside of Autodesk Revit, see *A.5 Importing and Exporting Schedules*.

- For more information about creating schedules, refer to the ASCENT guide *Autodesk Revit: BIM Management: Template and Family Creation*.

Modifying a Schedule on a Sheet

Once you have placed a schedule on a sheet, you can manipulate it to fit the information into the available space. Select the schedule to display the controls that enable you to modify it, as shown in Figure 15–30.

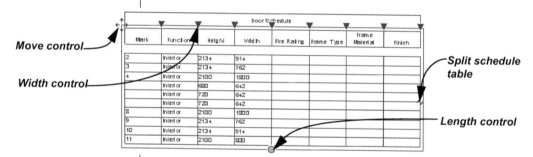

Figure 15–30

- The blue triangles modify the width of each column.

- The break mark splits the schedule into two parts.

- In a split schedule, you can use the arrows in the upper-left corner to move that portion of the schedule table. The control at the bottom of the first table changes the length of the table and impacts any connected splits, as shown in Figure 15–31.

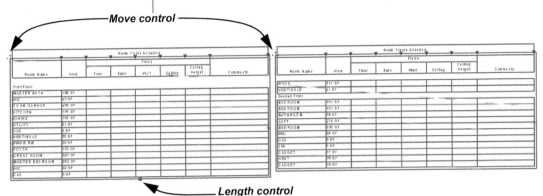

Figure 15–31

- To unsplit a schedule, drag the Move control from the side of the schedule that you want to unsplit back to the original column.

Practice 15b | Work with Schedules

Practice Objectives

- Update schedule information.
- Add a schedule to a sheet.

In this practice, you will add information to a door schedule and to elements that are connected to the schedule. You will then place the schedule on a sheet, as shown in Figure 15–32.

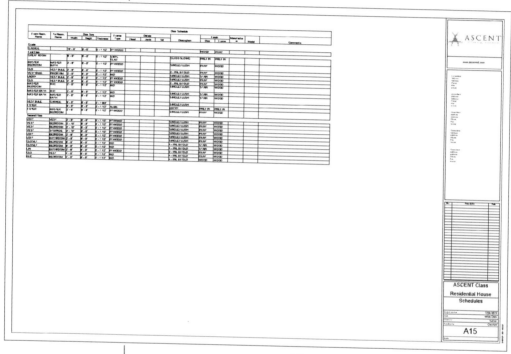

Figure 15–32

Task 1 - Fill in schedules.

1. Open the project **Residential-Schedules.rvt** from the practice files folder.

2. Verify you are in the default **3D** view.

3. In the Project Browser, expand *Schedules/Quantities*. Two schedules have been added to this project.

4. Double-click on **Door Schedule** to open it. The existing doors in the project are already populated with some of the basic information included with the door, as shown in Figure 15–33.

<Door Schedule>

A	B	C	D	E	F	G	H	I	J
			Door Size				Details		
From Room Name	To Room Name	Width	Height	Thickness	Frame Type	Head	Jamb	Sill	Descriptio
Grade									
GARAGE		16' - 0"	8' - 0"	0' - 1 1/2"					
First Floor									
GREAT ROOM		6' - 0"	6' - 8"	0' - 1 1/2"					
MASTER BEDROOM	MASTER BATH	2' - 6"	6' - 8"	0' - 1 1/2"					
CLO	VESTIBULE	2' - 6"	6' - 8"	0' - 1 1/2"					
VESTIBULE	PWDR RM	2' - 0"	6' - 8"	0' - 1 1/2"					
UTILITY	VESTIBULE	2' - 6"	6' - 8"	0' - 1 1/2"					
CLO	VESTIBULE	2' - 6"	6' - 8"	0' - 1 1/2"					
MASTER BEDROOM	WIC	2' - 0"	6' - 8"	0' - 1 1/2"					
MASTER BATH	WIC	2' - 0"	6' - 8"	0' - 1 1/2"					
MASTER BATH	MASTER BATH	2' - 0"	6' - 8"	0' - 1 1/2"					
VESTIBULE	GARAGE	3' - 0"	6' - 8"	0' - 1 3/8"					
FOYER		3' - 0"	6' - 8"	0' - 1 1/2"					
FOYER	MASTER BEDROOM	2' - 6"	6' - 8"	0' - 1 1/2"					
Second Floor									
LOFT	VEST	2' - 6"	6' - 8"	0' - 1 1/2"					
VEST	BEDROOM	2' - 10"	6' - 8"	0' - 1 1/2"					
VEST	BEDROOM	2' - 10"	6' - 8"	0' - 1 1/2"					
VEST		2' - 10"	6' - 8"	0' - 1 1/2"					
LOFT	BEDROOM	2' - 6"	6' - 8"	0' - 1 1/2"					
LOFT	BATHROOM	2' - 6"	6' - 8"	0' - 1 1/2"					
CLOSET	BEDROOM	6' - 0"	6' - 8"	0' - 1 1/2"					
CLOSET	BEDROOM	6' - 0"	6' - 8"	0' - 1 1/2"					
LIN	BATHROOM	2' - 6"	6' - 8"	0' - 1 1/2"					
CLO	VEST	4' - 0"	6' - 8"	0' - 1 1/2"					
WIC	BEDROOM	4' - 0"	6' - 8"	0' - 1 1/2"					

Figure 15–33

5. Close the 3D view and any other projects that are opened.

6. Select **GARAGE**.

7. In the *Modify Schedules/Quantities* tab>Element panel, click 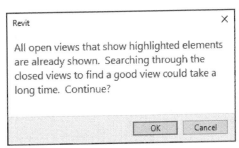 (Highlight in Model).

8. In the dialog box that pops up (as shown in Figure 15–34), click **OK**. It will search for a view that shows the selected door.

Revit ✕

All open views that show highlighted elements are already shown. Searching through the closed views to find a good view could take a long time. Continue?

[OK] [Cancel]

Figure 15–34

9. In the Show Element(s) In View dialog box, click **Show** until you see a plan view of the door, as shown in Figure 15–35. Then, click **Close**.

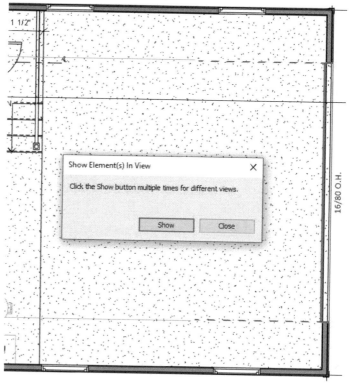

Figure 15–35

10. The door is still selected and you are in a plan view. In Properties, set the following:

    *   *Frame Type:* **PT-WOOD**
    *   *Frame Material:* **WOOD**
    *   *Finish:* **PAINT**

11. Click (Edit Type).

12. In the Type Properties dialog box, in the *Identity Data* area, set the *Description* to **OVERHEAD**.

13. Click **OK** to finish.

14. Click on the *Door Schedule* tab to open the view.

15. Close any views except the Door Schedule view. Open the **First Floor** view and type **WT** to tile the views.

16. Activate the **Door Schedule** view.

17. In the schedule, select **FOYER** (that goes into the master bedroom). The door highlights in the model, as shown in Figure 15–36.

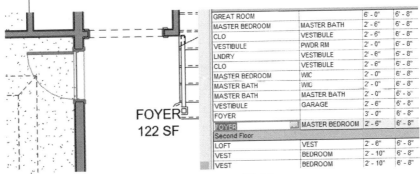

GREAT ROOM		6' - 0"	6' - 8"
MASTER BEDROOM	MASTER BATH	2' - 6"	6' - 8"
CLO	VESTIBULE	2' - 6"	6' - 8"
VESTIBULE	PWDR RM	2' - 0"	6' - 8"
LNDRY	VESTIBULE	2' - 6"	6' - 8"
CLO	VESTIBULE	2' - 6"	6' - 8"
MASTER BEDROOM	WIC	2' - 0"	6' - 8"
MASTER BATH	WIC	2' - 0"	6' - 8"
MASTER BATH	MASTER BATH	2' - 0"	6' - 8"
VESTIBULE	GARAGE	2' - 6"	6' - 8"
FOYER		3' - 0"	6' - 8"
FOYER	MASTER BEDROOM	2' - 6"	6' - 8"
Second Floor			
LOFT	VEST	2' - 6"	6' - 8"
VEST	BEDROOM	2' - 10"	6' - 8"
VEST	BEDROOM	2' - 10"	6' - 8"

FOYER 122 SF

Figure 15–36

18. With the door selected, in Properties, set the following:

- *Frame Type:* **WD**
- *Frame Material:* **WOOD**
- *Finish:* **STAIN**

19. Click ▦ (Edit Type).

20. In the Type Properties dialog box, in the *Identity Data* area, set the *Description* to **SINGLE-2-PANEL**.

21. Click **OK**.

22. Click ▷ (Modify).

23. Click on the *Door Schedule* tab to activate the view and note that all of the descriptions for the same door type updated. You may need to expand the *Description* column so you can see the entire name.

Note: The *Frame Type* and *Frame Material* did not populate on similar door types because the information you changed was in the element property; however, some properties, such as *Description*, are type properties and will update on all elements of the same family and type in the schedule.

24. In the schedule, select **VESTIBULE** (that leads to the powder room). The door highlights in the First Floor view.

25. Activate the **First Floor** view. If the door deselects, select it again.

26. Right-click on the door and select **Select All Instances>In Entire Project**. This selects all doors of the same type.

27. In Properties, set the following:

    • *Frame Type:* **WD**
    • *Frame Material:* **WOOD**
    • *Finish:* **PRE FIN**

28. Click ⌖ (Modify).

29. Click on the *Door Schedule* tab to activate the view.

30. Note how all of the door type's finishes updated.

31. Close the First Floor view.

32. In the **Schedule** view, fill in the frame type, material, and finish for the rest of the door types by going to each row and entering the values (it does not matter which values you choose). If a value already exists, you can select it from the drop-down list, as shown in Figure 15–37.

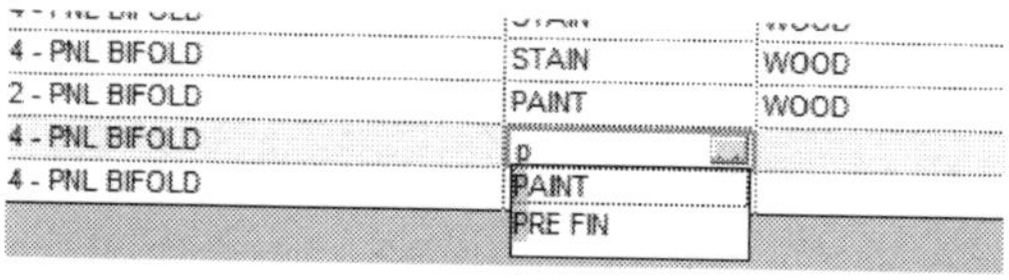

Figure 15–37

33. Save the project.

Task 2 - Add schedules to a sheet.

1. In the Project Browser, open the sheet **A15 - Schedules**.

2. Drag and drop the **Door Schedule** view onto the sheet, as shown in Figure 15–38.

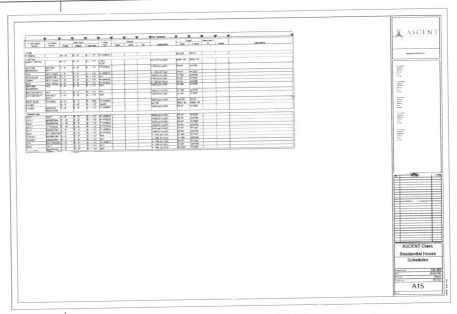

Figure 15–38

- Note that your schedule might look different than the one shown in Figure 15–38.

3. Zoom in and use the arrows at the top to modify the width of the columns so that the titles display correctly.

4. Click in an empty space on the sheet to finish placing the schedule.

5. Switch back to the **Floor Plans: First Floor-Dimension Plan** view and select the single panel door leading to the garage.

6. In the Type Selector, change the size to **36" x 80"**. In Properties, set the *Frame Type* to **ALUM**.

7. Return to the sheet **A15 - Schedules**. The information is automatically populated for the door that is going from the vestibule to the garage.

8. Save and close the project.

Chapter Review Questions

1. You can tag in a 3D view, but you first have to do what to the view?

   a. You cannot tag in a 3D view.

   b. Rename the view.

   c. Lock the view.

   d. Unlock the view.

2. Which of the following elements cannot be tagged using **Tag by Category**?

   a. Rooms

   b. Floors

   c. Walls

   d. Doors

3. What happens when you delete a door in an Autodesk Revit model?

   a. You must delete the door on the sheet.

   b. You must delete the door from the schedule.

   c. The door is removed from the model, but not from the schedule.

   d. The door is removed from the model and the schedule.

4. In a schedule, if you change type information (such as a *Type Mark*), all instances of that type update with the new information.

   a. True

   b. False

Command Summary

Button	Command	Location
	Material Tag	• **Ribbon:** *Annotate* tab>Tag panel
	Multi-Category	• **Ribbon:** *Annotate* tab>Tag panel
	Stair Tread/ Riser Number	• **Ribbon:** *Annotate* tab>Tag panel
	Tag All Not Tagged	• **Ribbon:** *Annotate* tab>Tag panel
	Tag by Category	• **Ribbon:** *Annotate* tab>Tag panel • **Shortcut:** TG
	Tag Room (Room Tag)	• **Ribbon:** *Architecture* tab>Room & Area panel • Ribbon: *Annotate* tab>Tag panel • **Shortcut:** RT

Creating Details

Creating details is a critical part of the design process, as it is the step where you specify the exact information that is required to build a construction project. The elements that you can add to a model include detail components, detail lines, text, tags, symbols, and filled regions. Details can be created from views in the model, but you can also add 2D details in separate views.

Learning Objectives in This Chapter

- Create drafting views where you can add 2D details.
- Add detail components that show the typical elements in a detail.
- Annotate details using detail lines, text, tags, symbols, and patterns that define materials.

16.1 Setting Up Detail Views

Most of the work you do in the Autodesk® Revit® software is exclusively with *smart* elements that interconnect and work together in the model. However, the software does not automatically display how elements should be built to fit together. For this, you need to create detail drawings, as shown in Figure 16–1.

Details are created either in 2D drafting views, or in callouts from plan, elevation, or section views.

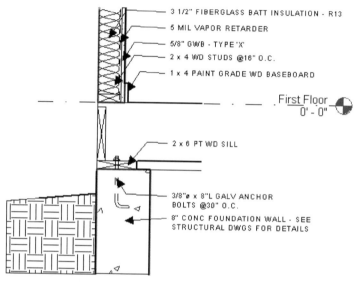

Figure 16–1

How To: Create a Drafting View

1. In the *View* tab>Create panel, click 🖨 (Drafting View).
2. In the New Drafting View dialog box, enter a *Name* and set a *Scale*, as shown in Figure 16–2.

Drafting views are listed in their own section in the Project Browser.

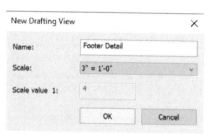

Figure 16–2

3. Click **OK**. A blank view is created with space in which you can sketch the detail.

How To: Create a Detail View from Model Elements

1. Start the **Section** or **Callout** command.
2. In the Type Selector, select the **Detail View: Detail** type.
   - The marker indicates that it is a detail, as shown for a section in Figure 16–3.

Callouts also have a Detail View type that can be used in the same way.

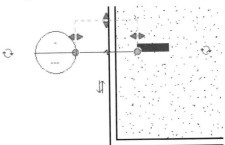

Figure 16–3

3. Place the section or a callout of the area you want to use for the detail.
4. Open the new detail.

- Change the *Detail Level* to see more or less of the element materials.

- Use the **Detail Line** tool to sketch on top of or add to the building elements.

- Because you are working with smart elements, a detail of the model is a true representation. When the building elements change, the detail changes as well, as shown in Figure 16–4.

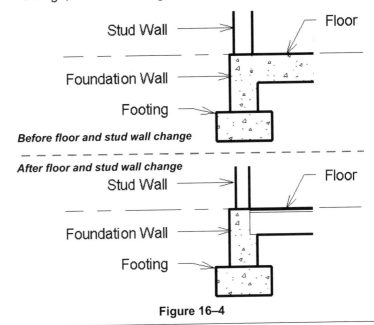

Figure 16–4

- You can create detail elements on top of the model and then toggle the model off so that it does not show in the detail view. In Properties, in the *Graphics* area, change *Display Model* to **Do not display**. You can also set the model to **Halftone**, as shown in Figure 16–5.

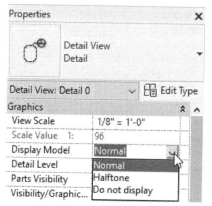

Figure 16–5

Referencing a Drafting View

Once you have created a drafting view, you can reference it in another view (such as a callout, elevation, or section view), as shown in Figure 16–6. For example, in a section view, you might want to reference an existing roof detail. You can reference drafting views, sections, elevations, and callouts.

Figure 16–6

- You can use the search feature to limit the information displayed.

How To: Reference a Drafting View

1. Open the view in which you want to place the reference.
2. Start the **Section**, **Callout**, or **Elevation** command.
3. In the *Modify | <contextual>* tab>Reference panel, select **Reference Other View**.
4. In the drop-down list, select **<New Drafting View>** or an existing drafting view.
5. Place the view marker.
6. When you place the associated drafting view on a sheet, the marker in this view updates with the appropriate information.

- If you select **<New Drafting View>** from the drop-down list, a new view is created in the *Drafting Views (Detail)* area in the Project Browser. You can rename it as needed. The new view does not include any model elements.

- When you create a detail based on a section, elevation, or callout, you do not need to link it to a drafting view.

- You can change a referenced view to a different view. Select the view marker and in the ribbon, select the new view from the list.

Saving Drafting Views

To create a library of standard details, save the non-model specific drafting views to your server. They can then be imported into a project and modified to suit. They are saved as .RVT files.

Drafting views can be saved in two ways:

- Save an individual drafting view to a new file.
- Save all of the drafting views as a group in one new file.

How To: Save One Drafting View to a File

1. In the Project Browser, right-click on the drafting view you want to save and select **Save to New File...**, as shown in Figure 16–7.

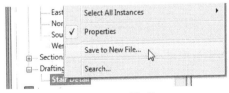

Figure 16–7

2. In the Save As dialog box, specify a name and location for the file and click **Save**.

You can save sheets, drafting views, model views (floor plans), schedules, and reports.

How To: Save a Group of Drafting Views to a File

1. In the *File* tab, expand ⬛ (Save As), expand ⬛ (Library), and click ⬛ (View).
2. In the Save Views dialog box, in the *Views:* pane, select **Show drafting views only** from the drop-down list.
3. Select the drafting views that you want to save, as shown in Figure 16–8.

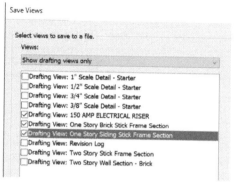

Figure 16–8

4. Click **OK**.
5. In the Save As dialog box, specify a name and location for the file and click **Save**.

How To: Use a Saved Drafting View in Another Project

1. Open the project to which you want to add the drafting view.

2. In the *Insert* tab>Load from Library panel, expand ⬛ (Insert from File) and click ⬛ (Insert Views from File).
3. In the Open dialog box, select the project in which you saved the detail and click **Open**.
4. In the Insert Views dialog box, limit the types of views to **Show drafting views only**, as shown in Figure 16–9.

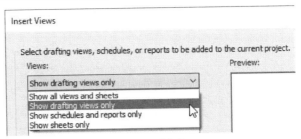

Figure 16–9

5. Select the view(s) that you want to insert and click **OK**.

Hint: Importing Details from Other CAD Software

You might already have a set of standard details created in a different CAD program, such as the AutoCAD® software. You can reuse the details in the Autodesk Revit software by importing them into a temporary project. Once you have imported the detail, it helps to clean it up and save it as a view before bringing it into your active project.

1. In a new project, create a drafting view and make it active.

2. In the *Insert* tab>Import panel, click 🔲 (Import CAD).
3. In the Import CAD dialog box, select the file to import. Most of the default values are what you need. You might want to change the *Layer/Level colors* to **Black and White**.
4. Click **Open**.

•   If you want to modify the detail, select the imported data. In the *Modify | [filename]* tab>Import Instance panel, expand

    🔲 (Explode) and click 🔲 (Partial Explode) or 🔲 (Full

    Explode). Click 🔲 (Delete Layers) before you explode the detail. A full explode greatly increases the file size.

•   Modify the detail using tools in the Modify panel. Change all the text and line styles to Autodesk Revit specific elements.

16.2 Adding Detail Components

Autodesk Revit elements, such as the casework section shown in Figure 16–10, typically require additional information to ensure that they are constructed correctly. To create details such as the one shown in Figure 16–11, you add detail components, detail lines, and various annotation elements.

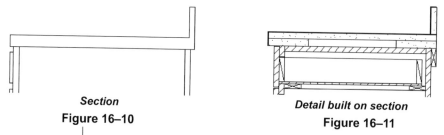

Section
Figure 16–10

Detail built on section
Figure 16–11

- Detail elements are not directly connected to the model, even if model elements display in the view.

- If you want to draw detail lines in 3D, use the **Model Line** tool. The **Detail Line** tool is grayed out when you are in a 3D view or perspective view.

Detail Components

Detail components are families made of 2D and annotation elements. Over 500 detail components organized by CSI format are found in the *Detail Items* folder of the Revit Library, as shown in Figure 16–12.

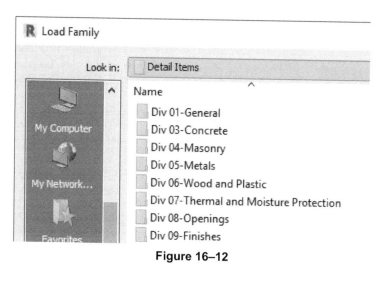

Figure 16–12

How To: Add a Detail Component

1. In the *Annotate* tab>Detail panel, expand 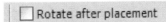 (Component) and click (Detail Component).
2. In the Type Selector, select the detail component type. You can load additional types from the Revit Library.
3. Many detail components can be rotated as you insert them by pressing <Spacebar>. Alternatively, select **Rotate after placement** in the Options Bar, as shown in Figure 16–13.

☐ Rotate after placement

Figure 16–13

4. Place the component in the view.

Adding Break Lines

The break line is a detail component found in the *Detail Items> Div 01-General* folder. It consists of a rectangular area (shown highlighted in Figure 16–14) that is used to block out elements behind it. You can modify the size of the area that is covered and change the size of the cut line using the controls.

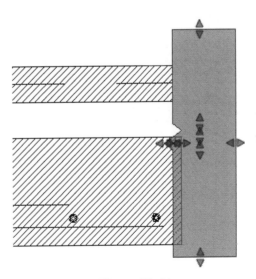

Figure 16–14

Hint: Working with the Draw Order of Details

When you select detail elements in a view, you can change the draw order of the elements in the *Modify | Detail Items* tab> Arrange panel. You can bring elements in front of other elements or place them behind elements, as shown in Figure 16–15.

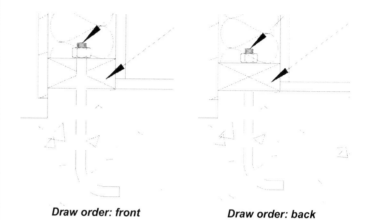

Draw order: front   Draw order: back

Figure 16–15

- ⬜ **(Bring to Front):** Places element in front of all other elements.

- ⬜ **(Send to Back):** Places element behind all other elements.

- ⬜ **(Bring Forward):** Moves element one step to the front.

- ⬜ **(Send Backward):** Moves element one step to the back.

- You can select multiple detail elements and change the draw order of all of them in one step. They keep the relative order of the original selection.

Repeating Details

Instead of having to insert a component multiple times (such as brick or concrete block), you can use ⬛ (Repeating Detail Component) and create a string of components, as shown in Figure 16–16.

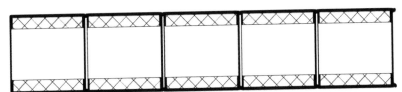

Figure 16–16

How To: Insert a Repeating Detail Component

1. In the *Annotate* tab>Detail panel, expand ▢ (Component) and click ▤ (Repeating Detail Component).
2. In the Type Selector, select the detail you want to use.
3. In the Draw panel, click ✏ (Line) or ⬊ (Pick Lines).
4. In the Options Bar, type a value for the *Offset*, if needed.
5. The components repeat to fit the length of the sketched or selected line, as shown in Figure 16–17. You can lock the components to the line.

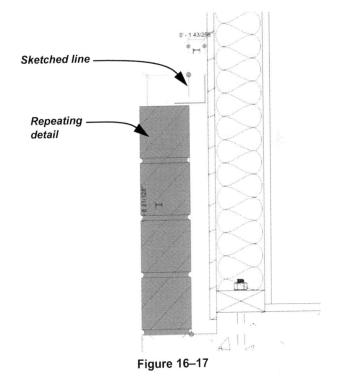

Figure 16–17

- For information on customizing repeating details, see
  A.7 Creating a Repeating Detail.

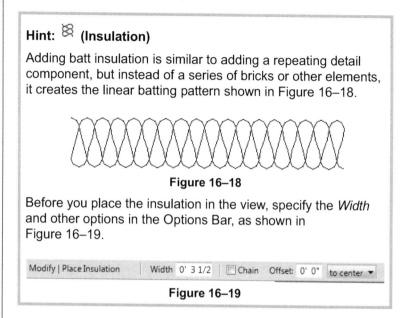

Hint: ⊠ **(Insulation)**

Adding batt insulation is similar to adding a repeating detail component, but instead of a series of bricks or other elements, it creates the linear batting pattern shown in Figure 16–18.

Figure 16–18

Before you place the insulation in the view, specify the *Width* and other options in the Options Bar, as shown in Figure 16–19.

| Modify | Place Insulation | Width | 0' 3 1/2 | ☐ Chain | Offset: 0' 0" | to center ▾ |

Figure 16–19

16.3 Adding Detail Lines and Symbols

While annotating views for construction documents, you might need to add detail lines and symbols to clarify the design intent or show information, such as the life safety plan exit information shown in Figure 16–20.

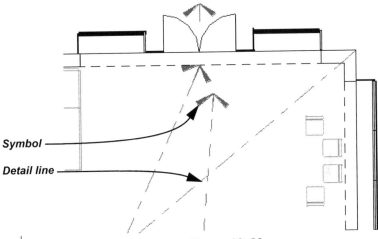

Symbol

Detail line

Figure 16–20

- Detail lines and symbols are view-specific, which means they only display in the view in which they were created.

How To: Draw a Detail Line

1. In the *Annotation* tab>Detail panel, click ⌐⌐ (Detail Line).
2. In the *Modify | Place Detail Lines* tab>Line Style panel, select the type of line you want to use, as shown in Figure 16–21.

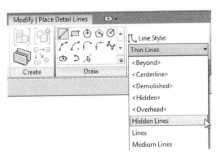

Figure 16–21

3. Use the tools in the Draw panel to create the detail line.

Using Symbols

Symbols are 2D elements that only display in one view, while components can be in 3D and display in many views.

Many of the annotations used in working drawings are frequently repeated. Several of them have been saved as symbols in the Autodesk Revit software, such as the North Arrow, Center Line, and Graphic Scale annotations shown in Figure 16–22.

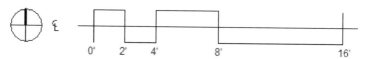

Figure 16–22

- You can also create or load custom annotation symbols.

How To: Place a Symbol

1. In the *Annotate* tab>Symbol panel, click ⊞ (Symbol).
2. In the Type Selector, select the symbol you want to use.
3. In the *Modify | Place Symbol* tab>Mode panel, click 📥 (Load Family) if you want to load other symbols.
4. In the Options Bar, as shown in Figure 16–23, set the *Number of Leaders* and select **Rotate after placement** if you want to rotate the symbol as you insert it.

Figure 16–23

5. Place the symbol in the view. Rotate it if you selected the **Rotate after placement** option. If you specified leaders, use the controls to move them into place.

- In the *Annotate* tab>Symbol panel, click ▦ (Stair Path) to label the slope direction and walk line of a stair, as shown in Figure 16–24.

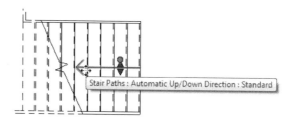

Figure 16–24

- For information about adding tags to dependent views, see *A.5 Importing and Exporting Schedules.*

16.4 Annotating Details

After you have added components and sketched detail lines, you need to add annotations to the detail view. You can place text notes and dimensions, as shown in Figure 16–25, as well as symbols and tags. Filled regions are used to add hatching.

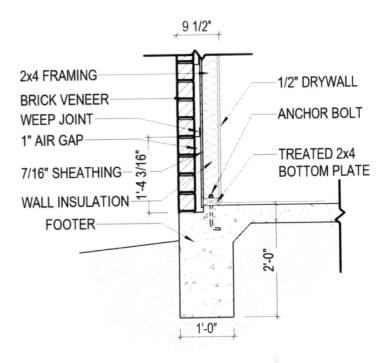

Figure 16–25

Creating Filled Regions

Many elements include material information that displays in plan and section views, while other elements need more details to be added. For example, the concrete wall shown in Figure 16–26 includes material information, while the earth to the left of the wall needs to be added using the **Filled Region** command.

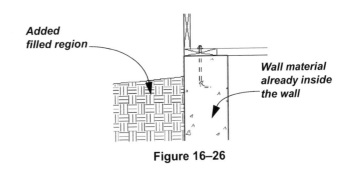

Figure 16–26

The patterns used in details are *drafting patterns*. They are scaled to the view scale and update if you modify it. You can also add full-size *model patterns*, such as a Flemish Bond brick pattern, to the surface of some elements.

How To: Add a Filled Region

1. In the *Annotate* tab>Detail panel, expand 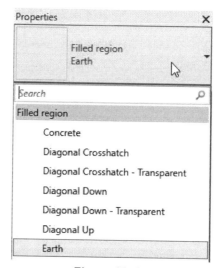 (Region) and click (Filled Region).
2. Create a closed boundary using the Draw tools.
3. In the Line Style panel, select the line style for the outside edge of the boundary. If you do not want the boundary to display, select the **<Invisible lines>** style.
4. In the Type Selector, select the fill type, as shown in Figure 16–27.

Figure 16–27

5. Click (Finish Edit Mode).

- You can modify a region by changing the fill type in the Type Selector or by editing the sketch.

- Double-click on the edge of the filled region to edit the sketch.

  If you have the Selection option set to (Select elements by face), you can select the pattern.

Hint: Creating a Filled Region Pattern Type

You can create a custom pattern by duplicating and editing an existing pattern type.

1. Select an existing region or create a boundary.

2. In Properties, click 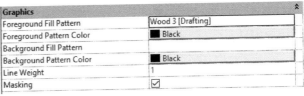 (Edit Type).

3. In the Type Properties dialog box, click **Duplicate** and name the new pattern.

4. Select the *Foreground* and *Background Fill Pattern* and *Color* and specify the *Line Weight* and *Masking*, as shown in Figure 16–28.

Graphics	
Foreground Fill Pattern	Wood 3 [Drafting]
Foreground Pattern Color	■ Black
Background Fill Pattern	
Background Pattern Color	■ Black
Line Weight	1
Masking	☑

Figure 16–28

5. Click **OK**.

• You can select from two types of fill patterns: **Drafting**, as shown in Figure 16–29, and **Model**. Drafting fill patterns scale to the view scale factor. Model fill patterns display full scale on the model.

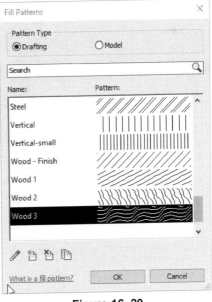

Figure 16–29

Adding Detail Tags

*The **Detail Item Tag.rfa** tag is located in the Annotations folder in the Revit Library.*

Besides adding text to a detail, you can tag detail components using 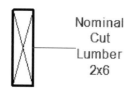 (Tag By Category). The tag name is set in the Type Parameters for that component, as shown in Figure 16–30. This means that if you have more than one copy of the component in your project, you do not have to rename it each time you place its tag.

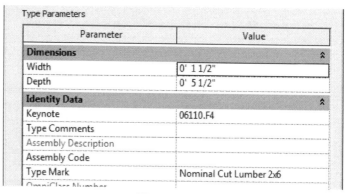

Figure 16–30

- For more information on annotating using keynotes, see *A.9 Keynoting and Keynote Legends*.

Hint: Multiple Dimension Options

If you are creating details that show one element with multiple dimension values, as shown in Figure 16–31, you can easily modify the dimension text.

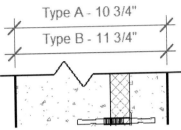

Figure 16–31

Select the dimension and then the dimension text. The Dimension Text dialog box opens. You can replace the text, as shown in Figure 16–32, or add text fields above or below, as well as a prefix or suffix.

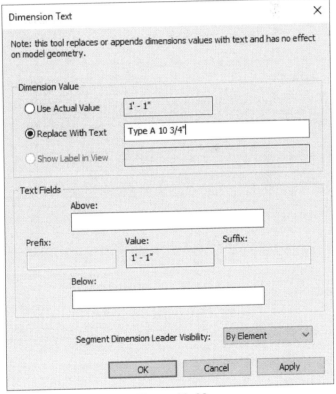

Figure 16–32

- This also works with equality text labels.

Practice 16a

Create a Detail Based on a Section Callout

Practice Objectives

- Create a detail based on a section.
- Add filled regions, detail components, and annotations.

In this practice, you will create a detail based on a callout of a wall section. You will add repeating detail components, break lines, and detail lines, and add annotations to complete the detail, as shown in Figure 16–33.

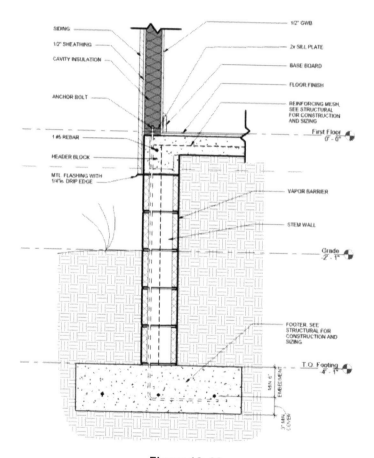

Figure 16–33

Task 1 - Create a callout of a wall section.

1. Open the project **Residential-Detailing.rvt** from the practice files folder.

2. Open the **Floor Plans: First Floor** view.

3. Double-click on the wall section head shown in the master bedroom. This guarantees that you open the right section.

4. Zoom in to the bottom of the wall showing the floor and footer.

5. In the *View* tab>Create panel, click ⟳ (Callout).

6. In the Type Selector, select **Detail View: Detail**.

7. Create a callout, as shown in Figure 16–34.

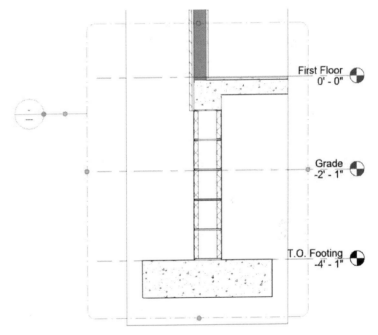

Figure 16–34

8. Double-click on the callout bubble to open the callout view.

9. In the View Control Bar, set the following parameters:

   • *Scale*: **1 1/2"=1'-0"**

   • *Detail Level*: ▨ (Fine)

10. Type **VV** to open the Visibility/Graphic Overrides dialog box. In the *Model* tab, turn off the **Furniture** category.

11. Click **OK**.

12. Adjust the crop region so the bottom is a little below the footing and the top gives you enough room to label the wall components. Then, toggle off **Crop Region Visible**.

13. In the Project Browser, in the *Detail Views (Detail)* node, rename the view to **Typ. Footer At Stemwall**.

14. Save the project.

Task 2 - Add repeating detail components and break lines.

1. In the *Annotate* tab>Detail panel, expand ◰ (Component) and click ▤ (Repeating Detail Component).

2. In the Type Selector, set the type to **Repeating Detail: 8" CMU**.

3. Draw the CMU line from the bottom of the stem wall up, as shown in Figure 16–35. Drawing from the bottom up insures that "mortar" is between the footer and the block. This is how the detail elements were created.

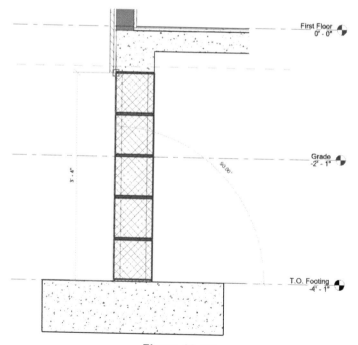

Figure 16–35

4. Click .

5. In the *Annotate* tab>Detail panel, expand ![icon] (Repeating Detail Component) and click ![icon] (Detail Component).

6. In the *Modify | Place Detail Component* tab>Mode panel, click ![icon] (Load Family).

7. In the Load Family dialog box, navigate to the Revit Library's *Detail Items>Div 01-General* folder, select **Break Line.rfa**, and click **Open**.

8. Add break lines to the top and right side of the detail. Press <Spacebar> to rotate the break line, as needed, and use the controls to modify the size and depth, as shown in Figure 16–36.

   • If you added the break line going in the wrong direction, select the break line in the view and press <Spacebar> until it is rotated correctly.

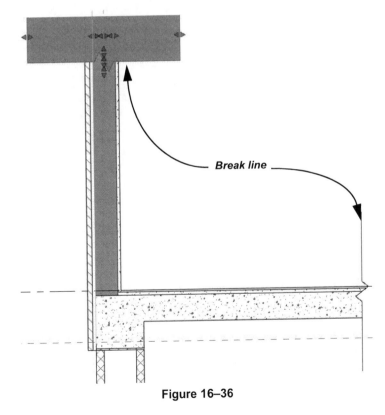

Break line

Figure 16–36

9. Click (Modify).

10. Start the **Detail Component** command.

11. In the Type Selector, select **Dimension Lumber-Section: 2x4**. Press <Spacebar> to rotate it and place it on top of the foundation, as shown in Figure 16–37.

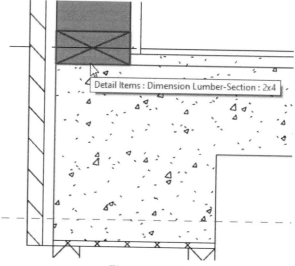

Figure 16–37

12. Still in the **Detail Component** command, from the Type Selector, add the **Anchor Bolt Hook-Side: 3/8"**, **Base Molding-Section: 3/4" x 4"**, and **Reinf BarSection: #_5** details to the view, as shown in Figure 16–38.

- Use the anchor bolt controls or Properties to adjust *Length* and *Hook Length*.

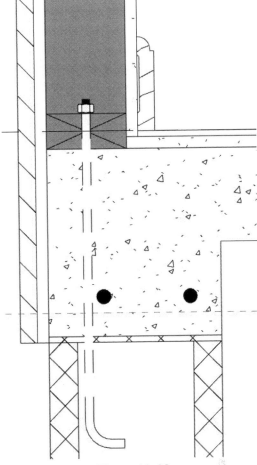

Figure 16–38

13. In the *Annotate* tab>Detail panel, click ⊗ (Insulation).

14. Verify in the Options Bar that the *Width* is **3 1/2"** and the *Offset* is set **to center**, as shown in Figure 16–39.

   • Similar to the CMU, begin the insulation from the top of the sill plate up the wall.

Figure 16–39

15. Select the break line symbol at the top of the detail.

16. Select **Bring to Front** on the contextual tab.

   • Break line symbols contain masks that will hide content under them.

17. Save the project.

Task 3 - Draw flashing and rebar using detail lines.

1. If needed, type **TL** to show the view's line thickness. Toggle it on and off to see which is best for you.

2. In the *Annotate* tab>Detail panel, click ⌐ (Detail Line).

3. In the *Modify | Place Detail Lines* tab>Line Style panel, verify that **<Wide Lines>** is selected and, from the Options Bar, that **Chain** is selected.

4. Draw flashing similar to that shown in Figure 16–40.

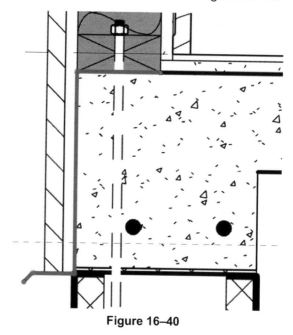

Figure 16–40

5. Click ⌖ (Modify).

6. Start the **Detail Line** command and change the *Line Style* to **Rebar**, as shown in Figure 16–41.

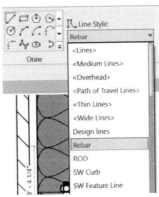

Figure 16–41

7. Draw the remaining rebar, as shown in Figure 16–42. (Elements in the image have been set to halftone for clarity.)

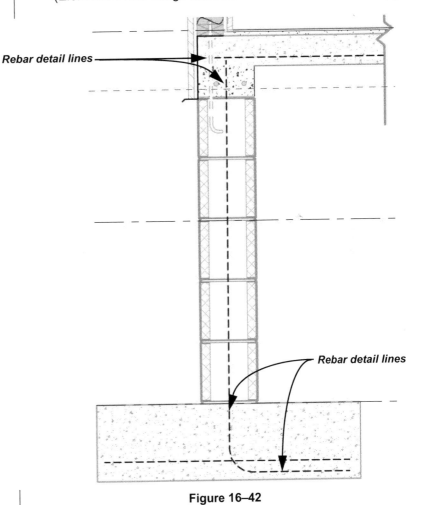

Figure 16–42

8. Use **Thin Lines** detail lines to further define the header block, as shown in Figure 16–43.

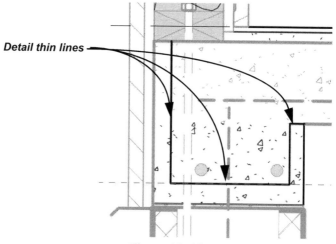

Detail thin lines

Figure 16–43

9. Click ⌖ (Modify).

10. Save the project.

Task 4 - Annotate the detail.

1. In the Quick Access Toolbar or in the *Annotate* tab>Text panel, click **A** (Text).

2. In the *Modify | Place Text* tab>Format panel, select ⟋**A** (Two-Segments).

3. Add the text and leaders shown in Figure 16–44. Use alignments to place the leader points and text.

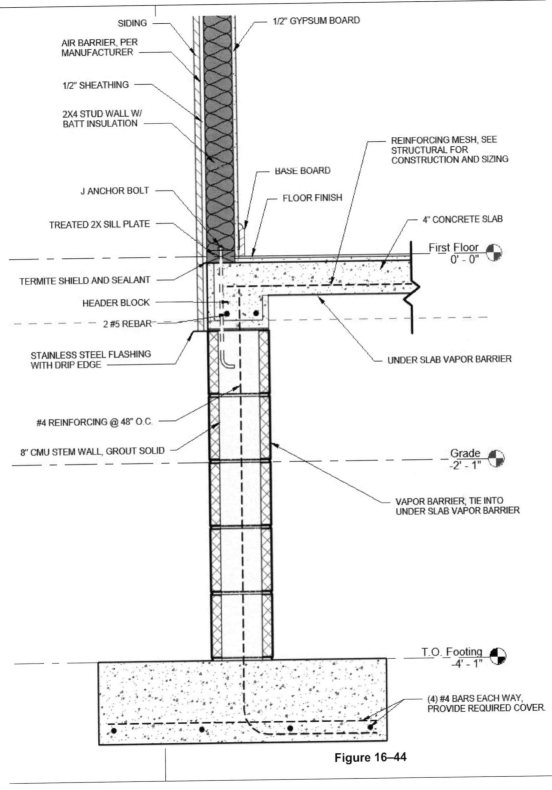

SIDING

1/2" GYPSUM BOARD

AIR BARRIER, PER MANUFACTURER

1/2" SHEATHING

2X4 STUD WALL W/ BATT INSULATION

REINFORCING MESH, SEE STRUCTURAL FOR CONSTRUCTION AND SIZING

BASE BOARD

J ANCHOR BOLT

FLOOR FINISH

TREATED 2X SILL PLATE

4" CONCRETE SLAB

First Floor
0' - 0"

TERMITE SHIELD AND SEALANT

HEADER BLOCK

2 #5 REBAR

UNDER SLAB VAPOR BARRIER

STAINLESS STEEL FLASHING WITH DRIP EDGE

#4 REINFORCING @ 48" O.C.

8" CMU STEM WALL, GROUT SOLID

Grade
-2' - 1"

VAPOR BARRIER, TIE INTO UNDER SLAB VAPOR BARRIER

T.O. Footing
-4' - 1"

(4) #4 BARS EACH WAY, PROVIDE REQUIRED COVER.

Figure 16–44

4. Save the project.

Task 5 - Add filled regions.

1. In the *Annotate* tab>Detail panel, expand 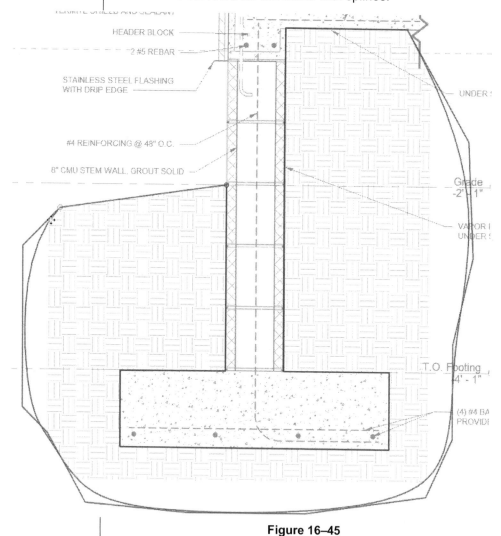 (Region) and
   click (Filled Region).

2. In the *Modify | Create Filled Region Boundary* tab>Line Style panel, set the *Line Style* to **Invisible Lines**.

3. Using the Draw tools, sketch a boundary around the footer, as shown in Figure 16–45.

   • The curved lines are made with splines.

TERMITE DRILLED AND SEALANT

HEADER BLOCK

2 #5 REBAR

STAINLESS STEEL FLASHING
WITH DRIP EDGE

#4 REINFORCING @ 48" O.C.

8" CMU STEM WALL, GROUT SOLID

UNDER

Grade
-2' - 1"

VAPOR I
UNDER

T.O. Footing
-4' - 1"

(4) #4 BA
PROVIDI

Figure 16–45

4. In the Type Selector, select **Filled region: Earth**.

5. Click 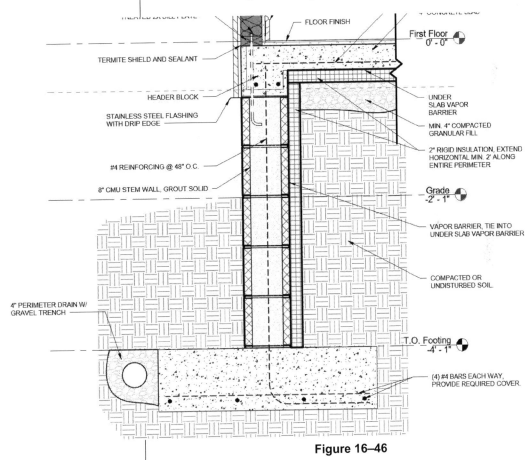 (Finish).

6. The patterns might cover over some elements. Select the filled region and in the *Modify | Detail Items* tab>Arrange panel, click (Send to Back).

7. Make any necessary adjustments to the annotation locations.

8. At this point, you have a hybrid between detail items and model items. You can continue to add detail items, such as rigid insulation, or more filled regions, such as compacted granular fill or a gravel trench with drain, if you have time (as shown in Figure 16–46).

Figure 16–46

9. Save and keep the project open.

Practice 16b | Create a Detail in a Detail View

Practice Objective

- Create and annotate details.

In this practice, you will create a footing detail in a drafting view, as shown in Figure 16–47. You will add detail components, lines, and annotations, as well as filled regions. You will place the view on a sheet and place a callout in another view that references this view.

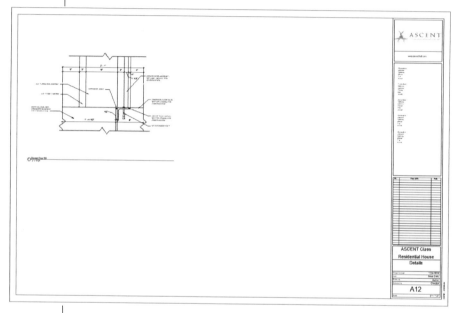

Figure 16–47

- This practice is designed with minimal direction so you can apply what you have learned.

Task 1 - Create a detail.

1. Continue working in **Residential-Detailing.rvt**.

2. In the *View* tab>Create panel, click 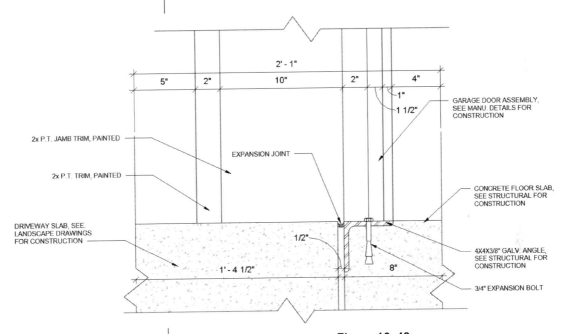 (Drafting View).

3. Create a drafting view named **Garage Door Sill** at a scale of **3"=1'-0"**.

4. Use detail lines and detail components to add the finishes, framing, and insulation, as shown in Figure 16–48.

   - Use line styles to show the different weight and patterns (such as **Medium Line** and **Thin Line**).

5. Add dimensions and text notes, as shown in Figure 16–48.

Figure 16–48

6. Click (Modify).

7. Save the project.

Task 2 - Add filled regions.

1. In the *Annotate* tab>Detail panel, expand 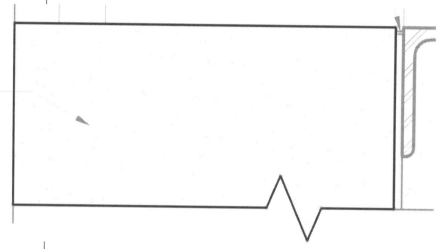 (Region) and click (Filled Region).

2. In the *Modify | Create Filled Region Boundary* tab>Line Style panel, set the *Line Style* to **Thin Lines**.

3. Using the Draw tools, sketch a boundary around the floor slabs, as shown in Figure 16–49.

Figure 16–49

4. In the Type Selector, select **Filled region: Concrete**.

5. Click (Finish).

6. The patterns might cover over some elements. Select the filled region and in the *Modify | Detail Items* tab>Arrange panel, click (Send to Back).

7. Make any necessary adjustments to the annotation locations.

8. Save the project.

Task 3 - Add the detail to a sheet and connect it to a detail callout.

1. Open sheet **A12 - Details** and drag and drop the garage detail to this sheet.

2. Open the **Sections (Wall Section): Garage Wall Section** view.

3. Start the **Callout** command and select the **Detail View: Detail** type.

4. In the *Modify | Callout* tab>Reference panel, select **Reference Other View** and in the drop-down list, select **Drafting View: Garage Door Sill**, as shown in Figure 16–50.

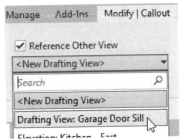

Figure 16–50

5. Place the callout around the garage door and foundation, as shown in Figure 16–51.

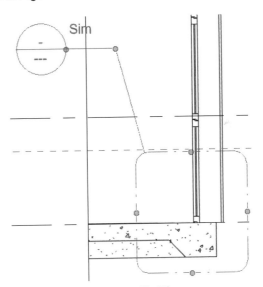

Figure 16–51

6. Place the view on sheet A-12. Note how the callout has now been labeled, as shown in Figure 16–52.

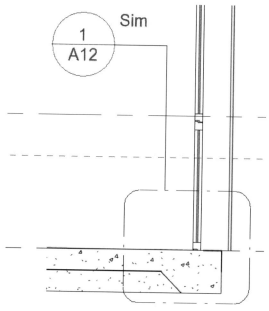

Figure 16–52

7. Save and close the project.

Chapter Review Questions

1. Which of the following are ways in which you can create a detail? (Select all that apply.)

    a. Make a callout of a section and sketch over it.

    b. Draw all of the elements from scratch.

    c. Import a CAD detail and modify or sketch over it.

    d. Insert an existing drafting view from another file.

2. In which type of view (access shown in Figure 16–53) can you NOT add detail lines?

    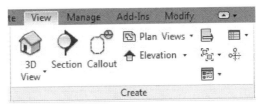

    Figure 16–53

    a. Plan

    b. Elevation

    c. 3D

    d. Legend

3. How are detail components different from building components?

    a. There is no difference.

    b. Detail components are made of 2D lines and annotations only.

    c. Detail components are made of building elements, but only display in detail views.

    d. Detail components are made of 2D and 3D elements.

4. What is a true statement about detail lines?

    a. Always the same width.

    b. Vary in width according to the view.

    c. Display in all views associated with the detail.

    d. Display only in the view in which they were created.

5. Which command do you use to add a pattern (such as concrete or earth, as shown in Figure 16–54) to part of a detail?

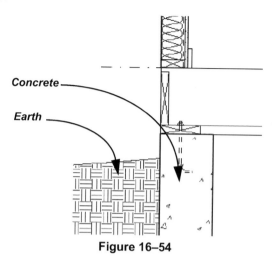

Figure 16–54

a. Region

b. Filled Region

c. Masking Region

d. Pattern Region

Command Summary

Button	Command	Location
Detail Tools		
	Detail Component	• **Ribbon:** *Annotate* tab>Detail panel> expand Component
	Detail Line	• **Ribbon:** *Annotate* tab>Detail panel
	Insulation	• **Ribbon:** *Annotate* tab>Detail panel
	Filled Region	• **Ribbon:** *Annotate* tab>Detail panel
	Repeating Detail Component	• **Ribbon:** *Annotate* tab>Detail panel> expand Component
View Tools		
	Bring Forward	• **Ribbon:** *Modify	Detail Items* tab> Arrange panel
	Bring to Front	• **Ribbon:** *Modify	Detail Items* tab> Arrange panel
	Drafting View	• **Ribbon:** *View* tab>Create panel
	Insert from File: Insert Views from File	• **Ribbon:** *Insert* tab>Load from Library panel>expand Insert from File
	Send Backward	• **Ribbon:** *Modify	Detail Items* tab> Arrange panel
	Send to Back	• **Ribbon:** *Modify	Detail Items* tab> Arrange panel

Appendix A

Additional Tools

There are many other tools available in the Autodesk® Revit® software that you can use when creating and using models. This appendix provides details about several tools and commands that are related to those covered in this guide.

Learning Objectives in This Appendix

- Save and use selection sets of multiple building elements.
- Enhance views by adjusting linework and editing plan and section profiles.
- Create structural grids and modify grid lines.
- Use guide grids to help place views on sheets.
- Import and export schedules.
- Create basic building component schedules.
- Create repeating detail types.
- Add revision clouds.
- Place keynotes in a detail and add keynote legends that describe the full content of the keynotes.

A.1 Reusing Selection Sets

When multiple elements types are selected you can save the selection set so that it can be reused. For example, a structural column and an architectural column need to move together. Instead of picking each element, create a selection set that you can quickly access as shown in Figure A–1. You can also edit selection sets to add or remove elements from the set.

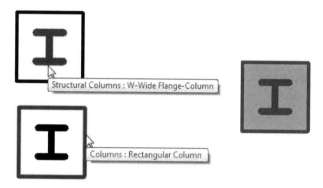

Figure A–1

- Selection sets are a filter of specific elements rather than types of elements.

How To: Save Selection Sets

1. Select the elements that you want to include in the selection set.
2. In the *Modify | Multi-Select* tab>Selection panel, click
   (Save).
3. In the Save Selection dialog box, type a name for the set as shown in Figure A–2, and click **OK**.

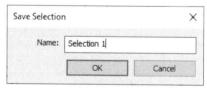

Figure A–2

How To: Retrieve Selection Sets

1. Select any other elements you might want to use. In the
   Modify | Multi-Select tab>Selection panel, click 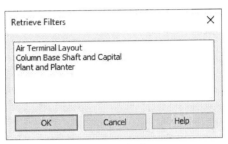 (Load).
   Alternatively, without any other selection, in the *Manage* tab>
   Selection panel, click (Load).

2. In the Retrieve Filters dialog box (shown in Figure A–3),
   select the set that you want to use and click **OK**.

Figure A–3

3. The elements are selected and you can continue to select
   other elements or use the selection.

How To: Edit Selection Sets

1. If elements are selected, in the *Modify | Multi-Select* tab>
   Selection panel, click (Edit). Alternatively, without any
   selection, in the *Manage* tab>Selection panel, click
   (Edit).

2. In the Edit Filters dialog box (shown in Figure A–4), in the **Selection Filters** node, select the set that you want to edit and click **Edit...**.

Rule-based Filters are not selection sets but apply to categories of elements, such as the Interior filter shown in Figure A–4.

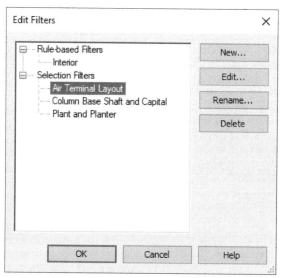

Figure A–4

- If you want to modify the name of the Filter, click **Rename...**.

3. The selection set elements remain black while the rest of the elements are grayed out. The *Edit Selection Set* contextual tab displays as well, as shown in Figure A–5.

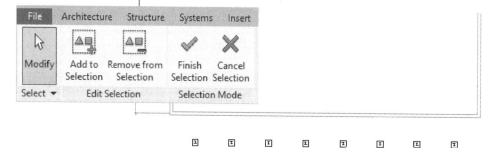

Figure A–5

4. Use ⬛ (Add to Selection) to select additional elements for the set and ⬛ (Remove from Selection) to delete elements from the set.

5. When you have finished editing, click ✔ (Finish Selection).

- In the Filters dialog box, click **OK** to finish.

A.2 Enhancing Views

Linework enables you to change the lineweight or line style of lines in a view to emphasize various components. In plan views and sections, you can use **Cut Profile** to enhance the views.

Adjusting Linework

To emphasize a particular line or change the look of a line in elevations and other views, modify the lines with the **Linework** command. Changes made to lines with the **Linework** command are view-specific, applying only to the view in which you make them, as shown in Figure A–6.

- The **Linework** command can be used on project edges of model elements, cut edges of model elements, edges in imported CAD files, and edges in linked Autodesk Revit models.

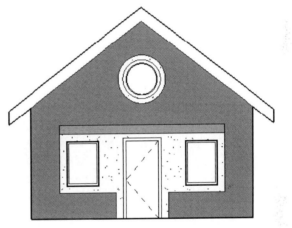

Figure A–6

How To: Adjust Linework

1. In the *Modify* tab>View panel, click ⬇ (Linework) or type the shortcut **LW**.
2. In the *Modify | Linework* tab>Line Style panel, select the line style you want to use from the list.
3. Move the cursor and highlight the line you want to change. You can use <Tab> to toggle through the lines as needed.
4. Click on the line to change it to the new line style.
5. Click on other lines as needed or return to the **Modify** command to finish.

- If the line is too long or short, you can modify the length using the controls at the end of the line.

Editing Plan and Section Profiles

*If you are working on a compound face (such as a wall with several layers of information), change the Detail Level to **Medium** or **Fine** to display the fill patterns.*

In plan and section details, you might need to modify portions of the cut to show the specific intersection of two faces, as shown in Figure A–7. This can be done using **Cut Profile**. The cut profile changes the shape of the elements at their cut plane, but does not modify their 3D information. The cut is only displayed in the view in which it is sketched.

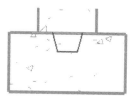 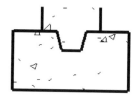

Figure A–7

• You can modify the cut of walls, floors, and roofs.

How To: Use Cut Profile

1. In the *View* tab>Graphics panel, click ⬚ (Cut Profile).
2. In the Options Bar, select to edit the **Face** or the **Boundary between faces**, as shown in Figure A–8.

Figure A–8

3. Select the face or boundary that you want to edit.
4. In the *Modify | Create Cut Profile Sketch* tab>Draw panel, use the sketch tools to sketch a new profile, as shown in Figure A–9.

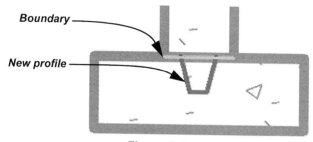

Figure A–9

5. Click ✔ (Finish Edit Mode).

• If a warning box opens, verify that the lines start and end on the same boundary line and that they do not make a closed loop or cross over each other.

A.3 Creating Structural Grids

The structural grid indicates how to space the bays of a building and where to place columns, as shown in Figure A–10. Any changes to the grid influences the elements that are referenced to them.

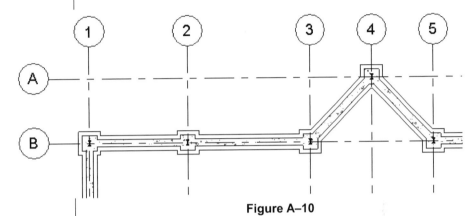

Figure A–10

Each line or arc in a grid is a separate entity and can be placed, moved, and modified individually.

How To: Create a Structural Grid

1. In the *Architecture* tab>Datum panel, click ⊞ (Grid) or type **GR**.
2. In the Properties Type Selector, select the grid type which will control the size of the bubble and the linestyle.
3. In the *Modify | Place Grid* tab>Draw panel, shown in Figure A–11, select the draw method you want to use.

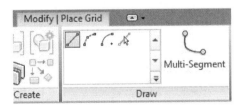

Figure A–11

4. In the Options Bar, set the *Offset* if needed.
5. Start drawing grid lines.

- Grids can be sketched at any angle, but you should ensure that all parallel grids are sketched in the same direction (i.e., from left to right, or from bottom to top).

- When using the Multi-Segment tool, shown in Figure A–12, sketch the line and click ✓ (Finish Edit Mode) to complete the command.

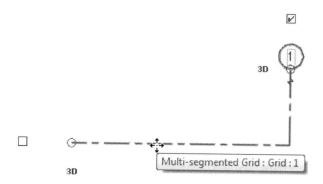

Figure A–12

Modifying Grid Lines

Grid lines are very similar to Level lines. You can modify grid lines using controls, alignments, and temporary dimensions (as shown in Figure A–13), as well as in the Properties palette and Type Selector.

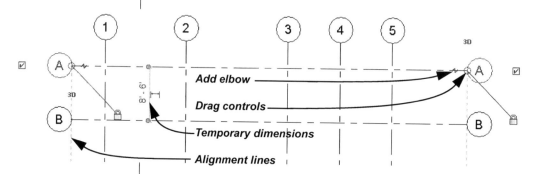

Figure A–13

- To modify a grid number, double-click on the number in the bubble and type the new number. Grid numbers can be numbers, letters, or a combination of the two.

- Grid numbers increment automatically.

A.4 Working with Guide Grids on Sheets

You can use a guide grid to help you place views on a sheet, as shown in Figure A–14. Guide grids can be set up per sheet. You can also create different types with various grid spacings.

When moving a view to a guide grid, only orthogonal datum elements (levels and grids) and reference planes snap to the guide grid.

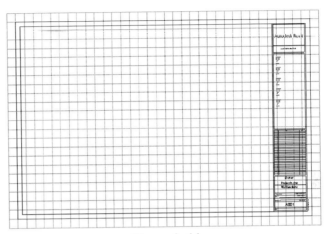

Figure A–14

• You can move guide grids and resize them using controls.

How To: Add a Guide Grid

1. When a sheet is open, in the *View* tab>Sheet Composition panel, click ⠿ (Guide Grid).

2. In the Assign Guide Grid dialog box, select from existing guide grids (as shown in Figure A–15), or create a new one and give it a name.

Figure A–15

3. The guide grid displays using the specified sizing.

How To: Modify Guide Grid Sizing

1. If you create a new guide grid you need to update it to the correct size in Properties. Select the edge of the guide grid.
2. In Properties, set the *Guide Spacing*, as shown in Figure A–16.

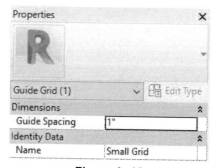

Figure A–16

A.5 Importing and Exporting Schedules

Schedules are views and can be copied into your project from other projects. Only the formatting information is copied; the information about individually scheduled items is not included. That information is automatically added by the project the schedule is copied into. You can also export the schedule information to be used in spreadsheets.

How To: Import Schedules

1. In the *Insert* tab>Load from Library panel, expand ⬜ (Insert from File) and click ⬜ (Insert Views from File).
2. In the Open dialog box, locate the project file containing the schedule you want to use.
3. Select the schedules you want to import, as shown in Figure A–17.

*If the referenced project contains many types of views, change Views: to **Show schedules and reports only**.*

Figure A–17

4. Click **OK**.

How To: Export Schedule Information

1. Switch to the schedule view that you want to export.

2. In the File tab, click 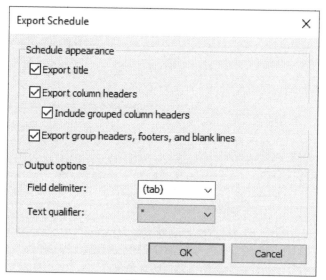 (Export)> (Reports)> (Schedule).

3. Select a location and name for the text file in the Export Schedule dialog box and click **Save**.

4. In the Export Schedule dialog box, set the options in the *Schedule appearance* and *Output options* areas that best suit your spreadsheet software, as shown in Figure A–18.

Figure A–18

5. Click **OK**. A new text file is created that you can open in a spreadsheet, as shown in Figure A–19.

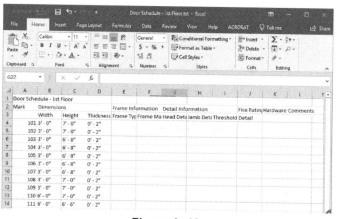

Figure A–19

A.6 Creating Building Component Schedules

A Building Component schedule is a table view of the type and instance parameters of a specific element. You can specify the parameters (fields) you want to include in the schedule. All of the parameters found in the type of element you are scheduling are available to use. For example, a door schedule (as shown in Figure A–20) can include instance parameters that are automatically filled in (such as the **Height** and **Width**) and type parameters that might need to have the information assigned in the schedule or element type (such as the **Fire Rating** and **Frame**).

\<Door Schedule\>

A	B	C	D	E	F	G	H
	Dimensions			Frame Information			Fire
Mark	Width	Height	Thickness	Frame Type	Frame Material	Finish	Rating
	8' - 3 1/2"	9' - 4 1/4"					
101	3' - 0"	7' - 0"	0' - 2"	A	Steel	Brushed	A
102	3' - 0"	7' - 0"	0' - 2"	A	Steel	Brushed	A
103	3' - 0"	6' - 8"	0' - 2"		Wood	Painted	B
104	3' - 0"	6' - 8"	0' - 2"		Wood	Painted	B
105	3' - 0"	6' - 8"	0' - 2"	B	Wood	Painted	B
106	3' - 0"	6' - 8"	0' - 2"	B	Wood	Painted	B
107	3' - 0"	6' - 8"	0' - 2"	B	Wood	Painted	B
108	3' - 0"	7' - 0"	0' - 2"		Wood	Painted	A
109	3' - 0"	7' - 0"	0' - 2"		Wood	Painted	A
110	6' - 0"	7' - 0"	0' - 2"		Wood	Painted	
111	6' - 0"	6' - 10"	0' - 2"	C	Aluminum	Brushed	

Figure A–20

How To: Create a Building Component Schedule

1. In the *View* tab>Create panel, expand ▦ (Schedules) and click ▦ (Schedule/Quantities) or in the Project Browser, right-click on the Schedule/Quantities node and select **New Schedule/Quantities**.

2. In the New Schedule dialog box, select the type of schedule you want to create from the *Category* list, as shown in Figure A–21.

In the Filter list drop-down list, you can specify the discipline(s) to show only the categories that you want to display.

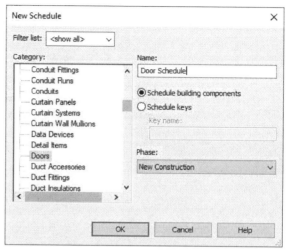

Figure A–21

3. Type a new *Name*, if the default does not suit.
4. Select **Schedule building components.**
5. Specify the *Phase* as needed.
6. Click **OK**.
7. Fill out the information in the Schedule Properties dialog box. This includes the information in the *Fields*, *Filter*, *Sorting/Grouping*, *Formatting*, and *Appearance* tabs.
8. Once you have entering the schedule properties, click **OK**. A schedule report is created in its own view.

Schedule Properties – Fields Tab

In the *Fields* tab, you can select from a list of available fields and organize them in the order in which you want them to display in the schedule, as shown in Figure A–22.

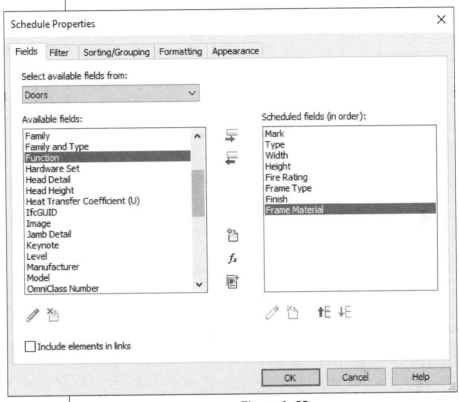

Figure A–22

How To: Fill Out the Fields Tab

You can also double-click on a field to move it from the Available fields area to the Scheduled fields area or double-click on a field to remove it from the Scheduled Fields area.

1. In the *Available fields* area, select one or more fields you want to add to the schedule and click ⇒ (Add parameter(s)). The field(s) are placed in the *Scheduled fields (in order)* area.

2. Continue adding fields, as needed.

   - Click ⇐ (Remove parameter(s)) to move a field from the *Scheduled fields* area back to the *Available fields* area.

   - Use ↑E (Move parameter up) and ↓E (Move parameter down) to change the order of the scheduled fields.

Other Fields Tab Options

Select available fields from	Enables you to select additional category fields for the specified schedule. The available list of fields depends on the original category of the schedule. Typically, they include room information.
Include elements in links	Includes elements that are in files linked to the current project, so that their elements can be included in the schedule.
(New parameter)	Adds a new field according to your specification. New fields can be placed by instance or by type.
f_x **(Add Calculated parameter)**	Enables you to create a field that uses a formula based on other fields.
(Combine parameters)	Enables you to combine two or more parameters in one column. You can put any fields together even if they are used in another column.
(Edit parameter)	Enables you to edit custom fields. This is grayed out if you select a standard field.
(Delete parameter)	Deletes selected custom fields. This is grayed out if you select a standard field.

Schedule Properties – Filter Tab

In the *Filter* tab, you can set up filters so that only elements meeting specific criteria are included in the schedule. For example, you might only want to show information for one level, as shown in Figure A–23. You can create filters for up to eight values. All values must be satisfied for the elements to display.

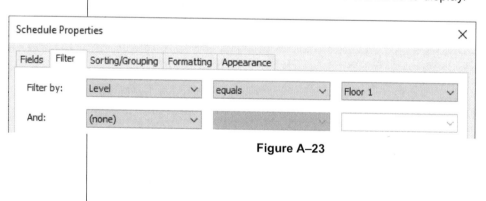

Figure A–23

- The parameter you want to use as a filter must be included in the schedule. You can hide the parameter once you have completed the schedule, if needed.

Filter by	Specifies the field to filter. Not all fields are available to be filtered.
Condition	Specifies the condition that must be met. This includes options such as **equal**, **not equal**, **greater than**, and **less than**.
Value	Specifies the value of the element to be filtered. You can select from a drop-down list of appropriate values. For example, if you set *Filter By* to **Level**, it displays the list of levels in the project.

Schedule Properties – Sorting/Grouping Tab

In the *Sorting/Grouping* tab, you can set how you want the information to be sorted, as shown in Figure A–24. For example, you can sort by **Mark** (number) and then **Type**.

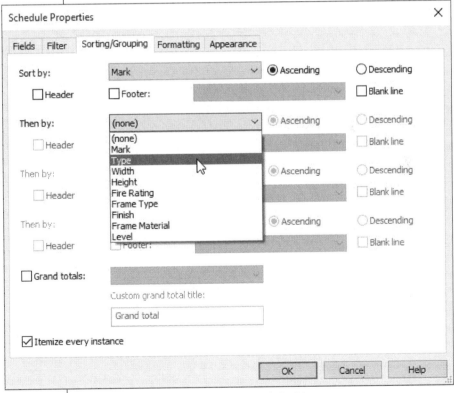

Figure A–24

Sort by	Enables you to select the field(s) you want to sort by. You can select up to four levels of sorting.
Ascending/ Descending	Sorts fields in **Ascending** or **Descending** order.
Header/ Footer	Enables you to group similar information and separate it by a **Header** with a title and/or a **Footer** with quantity information.
Blank line	Adds a blank line between groups.
Grand totals	Selects which totals to display for the entire schedule. You can specify a name to display in the schedule for the Grand total.
Itemize every instance	If selected, displays each instance of the element in the schedule. If not selected, displays only one instance of each type, as shown below.

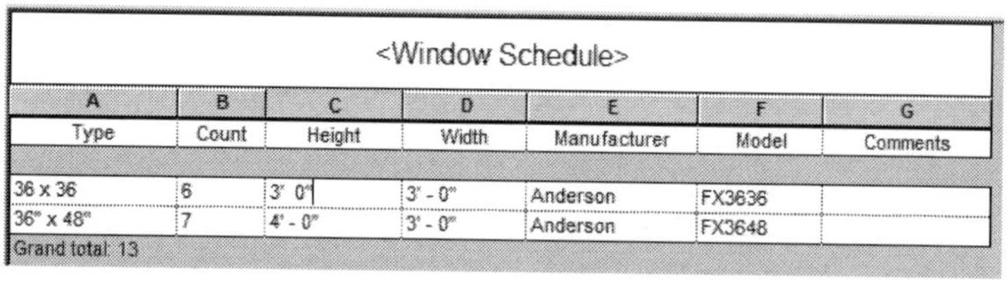

<Window Schedule>						
A	B	C	D	E	F	G
Type	Count	Height	Width	Manufacturer	Model	Comments
36 x 36	6	3' 0"	3' - 0"	Anderson	FX3636	
36" x 48"	7	4' - 0"	3' - 0"	Anderson	FX3648	
Grand total: 13						

Schedule Properties – Formatting Tab

In the *Formatting* tab, you can control how the headers of each field display, as shown in Figure A–25.

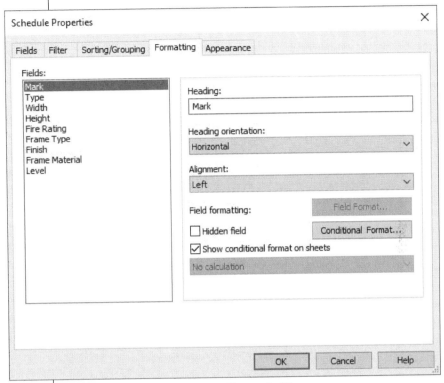

Figure A–25

Fields	Enables you to select the field for which you want to modify the formatting.
Heading	Enables you to change the heading of the field if you want it to be different from the field name. For example, you might want to replace **Mark** (a generic name) with the more specific **Door Number** in a door schedule.
Heading orientation	Enables you to set the heading on sheets to **Horizontal** or **Vertical**. This does not impact the schedule view.
Alignment	Aligns the text in rows under the heading to be **Left**, **Right**, or **Center**.
Field Format...	Sets the units format for the length, area, volume, angle, or number field. By default, this is set to use the project settings.
Conditional Format...	Sets up the schedule to display visual feedback based on the conditions listed.
Hidden field	Enables you to hide a field. For example, you might want to use a field for sorting purposes, but not have it display in the schedule. You can also modify this option in the schedule view later.
Show conditional format on sheets	Select if you want the color code set up in the Conditional Format dialog box to display on sheets.
Calculation options	Select the type of calculation you want to use. All values in a field are: • **Standard** - Calculated separately. • **Calculate totals** - Added together. • **Calculate minimum** - Reviewed and only the smallest amount is displayed. • **Calculate maximum** - Reviewed and only the largest amount is displayed. • **Calculate minimum and maximum** - Reviewed and both the smallest and largest amounts are displayed. • This is often used with rebar sets.

Schedule Properties – Appearance Tab

In the *Appearance* tab, you can set the text style and grid options for a schedule, as shown in Figure A–26.

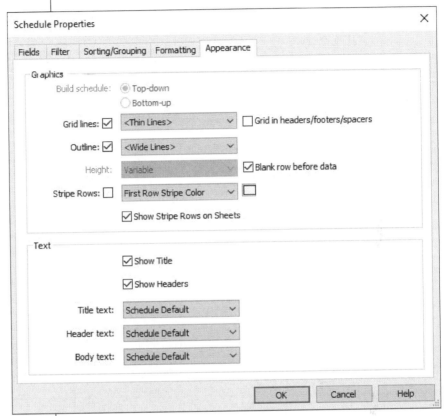

Figure A–26

Grid lines	Displays lines between each instance listed and around the outside of the schedule. Select the style of lines from the drop-down list; this controls all lines for the schedule, unless modified.
Grid in headers/ footers/spacers	Extends the vertical grid lines between the columns.
Outline	Specify a different line type for the outline of the schedule.
Blank row before data	Select this option if you want a blank row to be displayed before the data begins in the schedule.
Stripe rows	Select this option if you want to highlight alternating rows within the schedule to help differentiate the rows in large schedules.

Show Title/Show Headers	Select these options to include the text in the schedule.
Title text/Header text/Body text	Select the text style for the title, header, and body text.

Schedule Properties

Schedule views have properties including the *View Name*, *Phases* and methods of returning to the Schedule Properties dialog box, as shown in Figure A–27. In the *Other* area, select the button next to the tab that you want to open in the Schedule Properties dialog box. In the dialog box, you can switch from tab to tab and make any required changes to the overall schedule.

Figure A–27

A.7 Creating a Repeating Detail

Repeating detail components are very useful when working on complex details, such as those that include a brick wall. You can also create a repeating detail using any detail component, such as the glass block shown in Figure A–28.

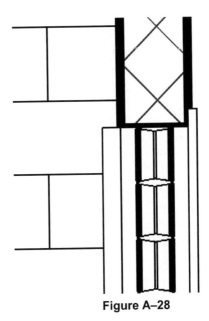

Figure A–28

How To: Create a Repeating Detail

1. Load the detail component you want to use.

2. In the *Annotate* tab>Detail panel, expand (Component) and click (Repeating Detail Component).

3. In Properties, click (Edit Type).

4. In the Type Properties dialog box, click **Duplicate...**. Enter a name.

5. Set the *Detail* parameter. This is the component name.

6. Fill out the rest of the parameters, as shown in Figure A–29.

Figure A–29

7. Set the *Layout* to **Fill Available Space**, **Fixed Distance**, **Fixed Number**, or **Maximum Spacing**. Select **Inside** if you want all components to be within the specified distance or line. Leaving this option clear causes the first component to start before the first point.

8. Set the *Spacing* between components if you are using **Fixed Distance** or **Maximum Spacing**.

9. Set the *Detail Rotation* as needed, and close the dialog box.

A.8 Revision Tracking

When a set of working drawings has been put into production, you need to show where changes are made. Typically, these are shown on sheets using revision clouds and tags along with a revision schedule in the title block, as shown in Figure A–30. The revision information is set up in the Sheet Issues/Revisions dialog box.

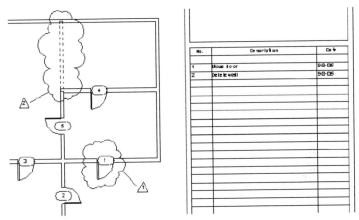

Figure A–30

- More than one revision cloud can be associated with a revision number.

- The title blocks that come with the Autodesk Revit software already have a revision schedule inserted into the title area. It is recommended that you also add a revision schedule to your company title block.

How To: Add Revision Information to the Project

1. In the *View* tab>Sheet Composition panel, click (Sheet Issues/Revisions).
2. In the Sheet Issues/Revisions dialog box, set the type of *Numbering* you want to use.
3. Click **Add** to add a new revision.

4. Specify the *Date* and *Description* for the revision, as shown in Figure A–31.

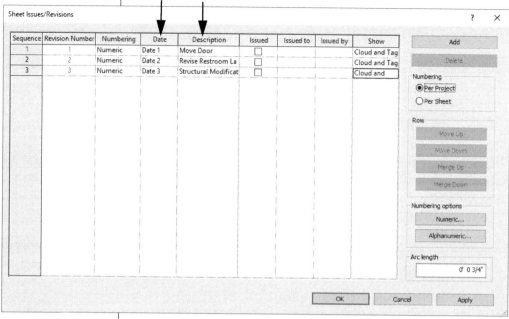

Figure A–31

- Do not modify the *Issued*, *Issued by*, or *Issued to* columns. You should wait to issue revisions until you are ready to print the sheets.

5. Click **OK** when you have finished adding revisions.

- To remove a revision, select its *Sequence* number and click **Delete**.

Revision Options

- *Numbering:* Specify **Per Project** (the numbering sequence is used throughout the project) or **Per Sheet** (the number sequence is per sheet).

- *Row*: To reorganize the revisions, select a row and click **Move Up** and **Move Down**, or use **Merge Up** and **Merge Down** to combine the revisions into one.

- *Numbering Options:* Click **Numeric...** or **Alphanumeric...** to bring up the Customize Numbering Options dialog box where you can specify the numbers or letters used in the sequence as well as any prefix or suffix, as shown for the *Alphanumeric* tab in Figure A–32.

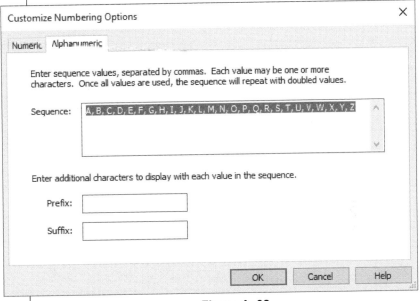

Figure A–32

- *Arc length:* Specify the length of the arcs that form the revision cloud. It is an annotation element and is scaled according to the view scale.

How To: Add Revision Clouds and Tag

1. In the *Annotate* tab>Detail panel, click (Revision Cloud).
2. In the *Modify | Create Revision Cloud Sketch* tab>Draw panel, use the draw tools to create the cloud.

3. From Properties, select which *Revision* type to use, as shown in Figure A–33.

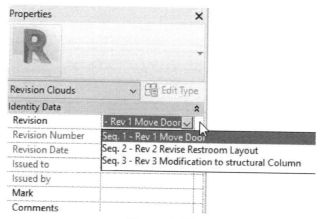

Figure A–33

4. Click ✓ (Finish Edit Mode).

•   To modify a revision cloud, select on a revision cloud, then from the Options Bar or Properties, expand the Revision drop-down list and select the revision, as shown in Figure A–34.

If the revision table has not be set up, you can do this at a later date.

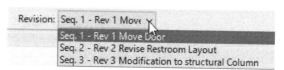

Figure A–34

5. In the *Annotate* tab>Tag panel, click (Tag By Category).

6. Select the revision cloud to tag. A tooltip containing the revision number and revision from the cloud properties displays when you hover the cursor over the revision cloud, as shown in Figure A–35.

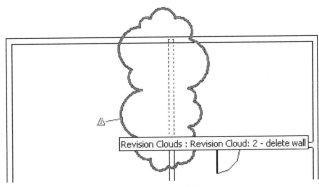

Figure A–35

- If the revision cloud tag is not loaded, load **Revision Tag.rfa** from the *Annotations* folder in the Revit Library.

- The *Revision Number* and *Date* are automatically assigned according to the specifications in the revision table.

- Double-click on the edge of revision cloud to switch to the Edit Sketch mode and modify the size or location of the revision cloud arcs.

- You can create an open cloud (e.g., as a tree line), as shown in Figure A–36.

Figure A–36

Issuing Revisions

When you have completed the revisions and are ready to submit new documents to the field, you should first lock the revision for the record. This is called issuing the revision. An issued revision is noted in the tooltip of a revision cloud, as shown in Figure A–37.

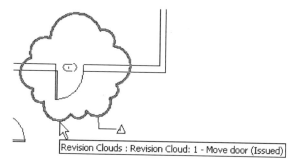

Revision Clouds : Revision Cloud: 1 - Move door (Issued)

Figure A–37

How To: Issue Revisions

1. In the *View* tab>Sheet Composition panel, click (Sheet Issues/Revisions).
2. In the Sheet Issues/Revisions dialog box, in the row for the revision that you are issuing, type a name in the *Issued to* and *Issued by* fields, as needed.
3. In the same row, select **Issued**.
4. Continue issuing any other revisions, as needed.
5. Click **OK** to finish.

- Once **Issued** is selected, you cannot modify that revision in the Revisions dialog box or by moving the revision cloud(s). The tooltip on the cloud(s) note that it is **Issued**.

- You can unlock the revision by clearing the **Issued** option. Unlocking enables you to modify the revision after it has been locked.

A.9 Keynoting and Keynote Legends

Keynotes are a special kind of tag that apply specific numbers to various elements in a detail. They can be used on all model and detail elements, as well as materials. Using keynotes requires less room on a view than standard text notes, as shown in Figure A–38. The full explanation of the note is shown in a corresponding *keynote legend* placed elsewhere in the sheet or sheet set.

By default, the Autodesk Revit software uses the CSI master format system of keynote designations.

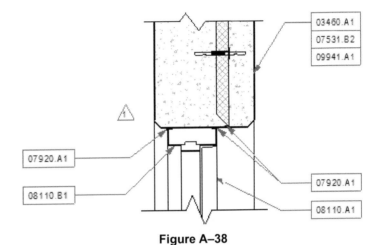

Figure A–38

- Keynote tags are found in the Revit Library in the *Annotations* folder and should be loaded into a project before you can apply them.

There are three types of keynote tags:

- **Element:** Used to tag elements, such as a door, wall, or detail components.

- **Material:** Used for the material assigned to a component or applied onto a surface.

- **User:** A keynote that must first be developed in a keynote table.

How To: Place a Keynote

1. In the *Annotate* tab>Tag panel, expand (Keynote) and click (Element Keynote), (Material Keynote), or (User Keynote).
2. Move the cursor over the element you want to keynote and select it.
3. If an element has keynote information assigned to it, the keynote is automatically applied. If it is not assigned, the Keynotes dialog box opens, as shown in Figure A–39.

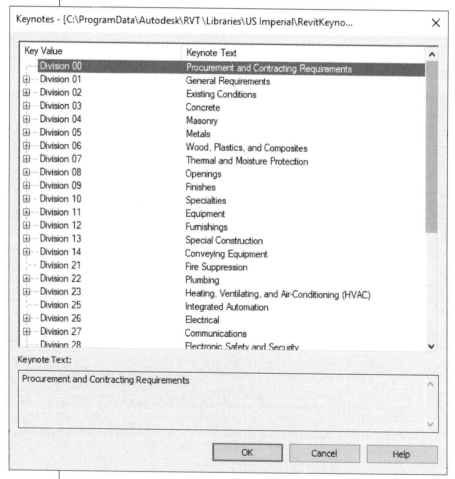

Figure A–39

4. Select the keynote you need from the list of divisions and click **OK**.

The keynote remembers the leader settings from the last time it was used.

- The options for keynotes are the same as for other tags, including orientation and leaders, as shown in Figure A–40.

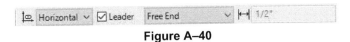

Figure A–40

Hint: Setting the Keynote Numbering Method

Keynotes can be listed by the full keynote number or by sheet, as shown in Figure A–41. Only one method can be used at a time in a project, but you can change between the two methods at any time in the project.

1. In the *Annotate* tab>Tag panel, expand (Keynote) and click (Keynoting Settings).

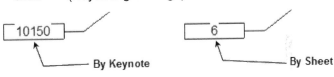

Figure A–41

2. In the Keynoting Settings dialog box, specify the *Keynote Table* information and the *Numbering Method*, as shown in Figure A–42.

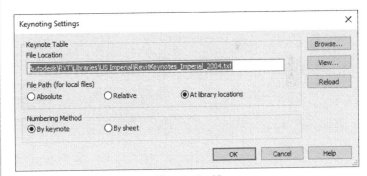

Figure A–42

- If you are using keynoting by sheet, create the Keynote Legend and in the Keynote Legend Properties, in the *Filter* tab, select **Filter by Sheet.**

- Keynotes are stored in a keynote table (a text file), as shown in Figure A–43. Any updates made to the keynote table are reflected in the project after it is closed and then re-opened.

Figure A–43

Keynote Legends

A keynote legend is different from a standard legend.

A keynote legend is a table containing the information stored in the keynote that is placed on a sheet, as shown in Figure A–44. In the Autodesk Revit software, it is created in a similar way to schedules.

Figure A–44

How To: Create a Keynote Legend

1. In the *View* tab>Create panel, expand [icon] (Legends) and click [icon] (Keynote Legend).
2. Type a name in the New Keynote Legend dialog box and click **OK**.

3. The Keynote Legend Properties dialog box typically only displays two scheduled fields, which are already set up for you, as shown in Figure A–45.

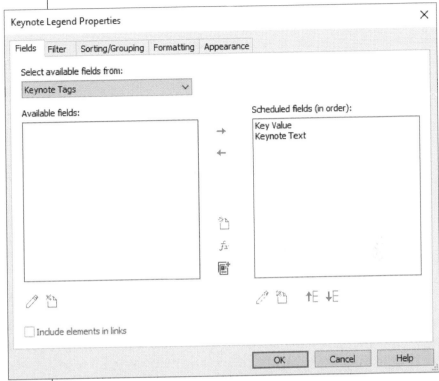

Figure A–45

4. In the other tabs, set up the format of the table as needed.
5. Click **OK** to create the keynote legend.
6. When you are ready to place a keynote legend, drag it from the Project Browser onto the sheet. You can manipulate it in the same way, similar to modifying other schedules.

• As you add keynotes to the project, they are added to the keynote legend.

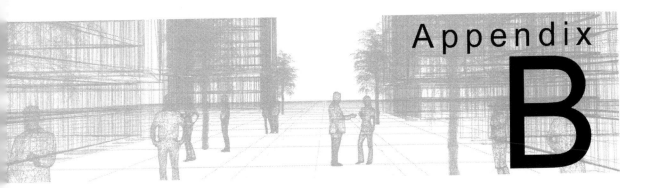

Appendix
B

Introduction to Worksets

Autodesk® Revit® worksharing gives multiple team members connected on the same network the ability to co-author a single project model (one .RVT file). The appropriate team member creates a central model and worksets. Team members open and work in a local copy of the model that is linked back to the central model through saving and synchronizing.

For more information about establishing and using worksets, refer to the ASCENT guide *Autodesk Revit: Collaboration Tools*.

Learning Objectives in This Appendix

- Review worksharing terminology and workflow.
- Learn about opening a local file to make changes to your part of a project.
- Review how to synchronize your local file with the central model, which contains changes from all the local files.

B.1 Introduction to Worksets

When a project becomes too big for one person, it needs to be subdivided so that a team of people working on the same network can work on it. Since Autodesk Revit projects include the entire building model in one file, the file needs to be separated into logical components, as shown in Figure B–1, without losing the connection to the whole. This process is called *worksharing* and the main components are worksets.

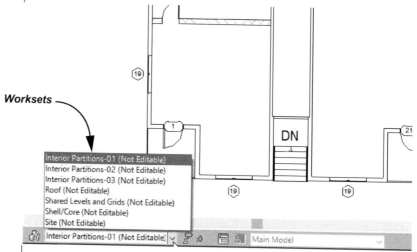

Figure B–1

When worksets are established in a project, there is one **central model** and as many **local files** as needed for each person on the team to have a file, as shown in Figure B–2.

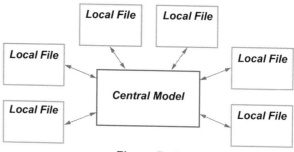

Figure B–2

- The **central model** is created by the BIM manager, project manager, or project lead and is stored on a server, enabling multiple users to access it.

- A **local file** is a copy of the central model that is stored on your computer.

- All local files are saved back to the central model, and updates to the central model are sent out to the local files. This way, all changes remain in one file, while the project, model, views, and sheets are automatically updated.

Workset Terminology

Workset: A collection of related elements in a project. Each user-created workset matches a part of the project that an individual team member would work on (such as specific sections of the building or the exterior shell, site, or interior partitions). There are also worksets created automatically for Families, Project Standards (such as materials and line styles), and Views. Worksets can be checked out so that others cannot modify them without permission.

Workshared file: A Revit project model that worksets have been enabled in that everyone can access and work on simultaneously.

Active workset: The active workset is the workset that all new elements are added to. It is important to verify which workset you are in before adding new elements.

Central model: Also called the central file. The master project model that stores all of the worksets. This is the file to which everyone saves their changes. You should never edit this model directly.

Local file: A copy of the central model that is saved to your local computer. This is the file that you modify. You then save the file locally and synchronize it with the central model.

Element borrowing: Refers to the process of modifying items in the project that are not part of the workset you have checked out. This either happens automatically (if no one else has checked out a workset) or specifically, when you request to have control of the elements (if someone else has a workset checked out).

General Process of Using Worksets

1. Create a local file from the central model that is set up by the appropriate team member.
2. Open the local file and select the workset on which you need to work to make it active. This is the workset on which any new elements are placed.
3. Add, delete, and modify elements, as needed.
   - You may need to request access to elements in worksets that are currently checked out by other team members.

4. Save the local file as frequently as you would save any other project.

5. Synchronize the local file with the central model several times a day or as needed by company policy or project status.

- This reloads any changes from the central model to your local file and vice versa.

- If the option to **Save Local File before and after synchronizing with central** is checked, your local file will be saved. It is always recommended to save the local file every time you synchronize to the central model.

How To: Create a Local File

1. In the *File* tab or Quick Access Toolbar, click 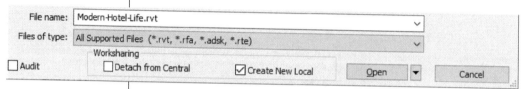 (Open). In the Open dialog box, navigate to the central model server location and select the central model. Do not work in this file. Select **Create New Local**, as shown in Figure B–3, and click **Open**.

File name:	Modern-Hotel-Life.rvt			
Files of type:	All Supported Files (*.rvt, *.rfa, *.adsk, *.rte)			

Worksharing

☐ Audit   ☐ Detach from Central   ☑ Create New Local   Open ▼   Cancel

Figure B–3

2. A copy of the project is created. It is named the same as the central model, but with your *User Name* added to the end.

- If you are working with a recently used central model, it may display in the Home Screen with the icon shown in Figure B–4. Clicking this file automatically creates a local copy of the model. The first time you use this option, a warning displays, as shown in Figure B–5.

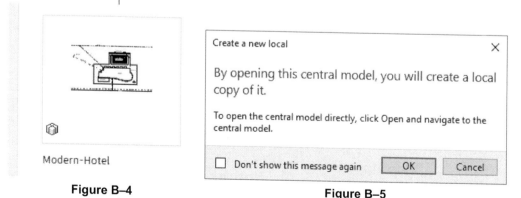

Modern-Hotel

Figure B–4

Create a new local   ✕

By opening this central model, you will create a local copy of it.

To open the central model directly, click Open and navigate to the central model.

☐ Don't show this message again   OK   Cancel

Figure B–5

3. You can save the file using the default name, or use

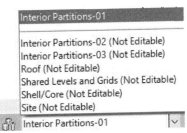 (Save As) and name the file according to your office's standard. It should include *Local* in the name to indicate that it is saved on your local computer, or that you are the only one working with that version of the file.

- Delete any old local files to ensure that you are working on.

How To: Work in a Workset-Related File

1. Open your local file.
2. In the Status Bar, expand the Active Workset drop-down list and select a workset, as shown in Figure B–6. By setting the active workset, other people can work in the project but cannot edit elements that you add to the workset.

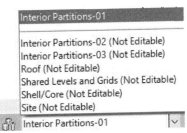

Figure B–6

3. Work on the project as needed.

Saving Workset-Related Files

When you are using a workset-related file, you need to save the file locally and centrally.

- Save the local file frequently (every 15-30 minutes). In the Quick Access Toolbar, click (Save) to save the local file just as you would any other project.

- Synchronize the local file with the central model periodically (every hour or two) or after you have made major changes to the project.

Hint: Set Up Notifications to Save and Synchronize

You can set up reminders to save and synchronize files to the central model in the Options dialog box, on the *General* pane, as shown in Figure B–7.

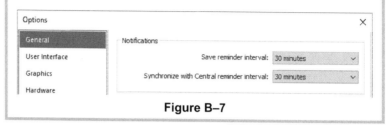

Figure B–7

Synchronizing to the Central Model

There are two methods for synchronizing to the central model. They are located in the Quick Access Toolbar or the *Collaborate* tab>Synchronize panel.

Click (Synchronize Now) to update the central model and then the local file with any changes to the central model since the last synchronization. This does not prompt you for anything. It automatically relinquishes elements borrowed from a workset used by another person, but retains worksets used by the current person.

Click (Synchronize and Modify Settings) to open the Synchronize with Central dialog box, as shown in Figure B–8, where you can set the location of the central model, add comments, save the file locally before and after synchronization, and set the options for relinquishing worksets and elements.

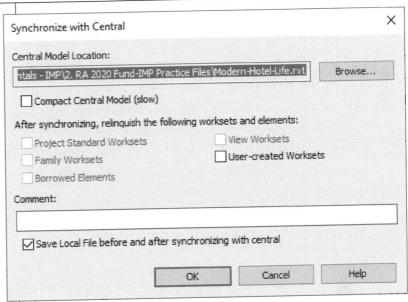

Figure B–8

- Ensure that **Save Local file before and after synchronizing with central** is checked before clicking **OK**. Changes from the central model might have been copied into your file.

- When you close a local file without saving to the central model, you are prompted with the options shown in Figure B–9.

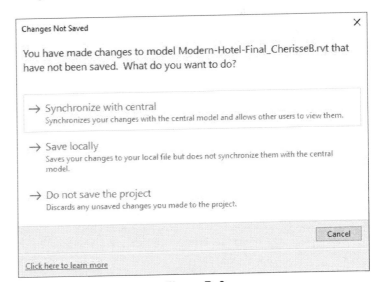

Figure B–9

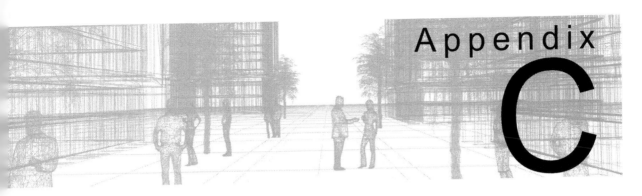

Appendix C

Working with Curtain Walls

Curtain walls are often used to create complex windows and storefronts. Curtain walls are created based on a curtain wall type to which additional grids and mullions can be added and individual panels swapped out to create the needed pattern.

Learning Objectives in This Appendix

- Create basic curtain walls and storefronts using curtain wall types.
- Modify the curtain grid pattern.
- Switch out curtain wall panels with other panel types, doors, or windows.
- Add mullions to curtain wall grids.

C.1 Creating Curtain Walls

Curtain walls are non-bearing walls consisting of panels laid out in a grid pattern. They can encase an entire building like a membrane or, as shown in Figure C–1, fill a cutout in a standard wall, often called a storefront.

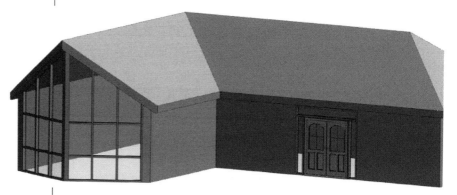

Figure C–1

How To: Create a Curtain Wall

Panels can be a specific material (such as glass or stone) or can incorporate doors, windows, or other wall types.

1. In a plan view, model a wall using a curtain wall type.
2. In an elevation or 3D view, add grids to the curtain wall.
3. Modify the panels of the curtain wall.
4. Add mullions to separate the panels.

The components of a curtain wall are shown in Figure C–2.

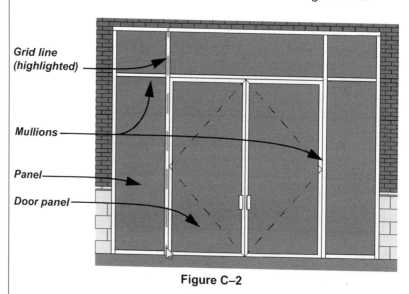

Grid line (highlighted)

Mullions

Panel

Door panel

Figure C–2

- The simplest way to create a curtain wall is to use a curtain wall type with a preset uniform grid already applied to it, such as the three types that come with the software, as shown in Figure C–3.

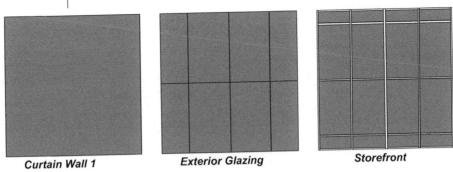

Curtain Wall 1   **Exterior Glazing**   **Storefront**

Figure C–3

- Many curtain walls do not have a uniform pattern of exact distances between grids, as shown in Figure C–4. Therefore, you need to create these designs directly on the curtain wall. You can start with a curtain wall type that has a basic uniform grid, if applicable.

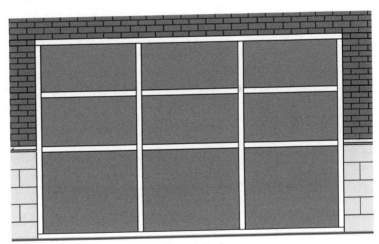

Figure C–4

Creating Storefronts

Storefront wall types are not included in the default Residential template and must be transferred from another project.

Some curtain walls are embedded into other walls, as shown in Figure C–5. They can also be used to create what looks like a complex set of windows. The **Storefront** curtain wall type is designed to be embedded in another wall.

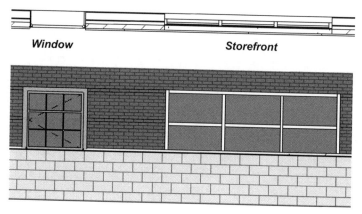

Window   **Storefront**

Figure C–5

How To: Add a Storefront Wall in an Existing Wall

1. In the *Architecture* tab>Build panel, click 🛢 (Wall).
2. In the Type Selector, select **Curtain Wall: Storefront**. In Properties, set the *Base Constraint, Top Constraint*, and *Offsets* as needed. The height can be less than the height of the wall in which you are embedding.
3. Select a point on the existing wall, as shown in Figure C–6.

Figure C–6

4. Select the second point along the wall. (Hint: Press <Tab> to cycle from the default Horizontal and Nearest snap to the dynamic dimension and then type the distance for the embedded curtain wall.) The wall displays, as shown in Figure C–7.

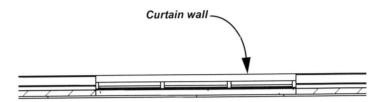

Curtain wall

Figure C–7

5. Open the appropriate elevation view. Select the outside edge of the curtain wall and use the shape handles and dynamic dimensions to modify the size of the storefront, as shown in Figure C–8.

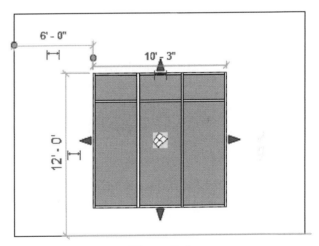

Figure C–8

C.2 Adding Curtain Grids

Once you have a curtain wall in place with at least one panel, you need to separate it into multiple panels for the design. Each grid line divides a panel into two or more smaller panels, as shown in Figure C–9.

Panels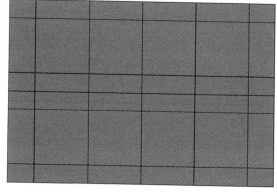

Figure C–9

How To: Create a Curtain Grid

1. After you have drawn the base curtain wall in a plan view, switch to an elevation or 3D view.

2. In the *Architecture* tab>Build panel, click (Curtain Grid).

3. In the *Modify | Place Curtain Grid* tab>Placement panel, select an insertion method, as described below.

╪ **(All Segments)**	Creates a grid line through the entire curtain wall height or width.
╪ **(One Segment)**	Creates a grid line between only the selection point and the next line. The entire grid line is established, but only one segment displays. You can add other segments later.
╪ **(All Except Picked)**	Creates a grid line through the entire grid and permits you to go back and remove segments of the grid line. The removed segment displays as a dashed line until you add another grid line or start another command.

4. Move the cursor over an edge of the curtain wall or an existing curtain grid line. Dynamic dimensions are displayed, as shown in Figure C–10. The new grid line is perpendicular to the edge at the point you select. Click at the required location.

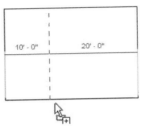 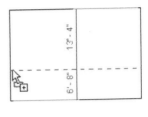

Figure C–10

- Curtain grids automatically snap to the midpoint or 1/3 point of the panel. They also snap to levels, column grids, and reference planes.

- You can ⊙ (Copy) and ⊞ (Array) curtain grid lines. This method can be the fastest way of creating grids across the length of a wall.

Modifying Curtain Grids

Once you have placed the grid lines, they might not be exactly where you want them or overlap other lines where you do not want them to overlap. You can modify the location of lines in the grid and add or remove segments from the lines, as shown in Figure C–11.

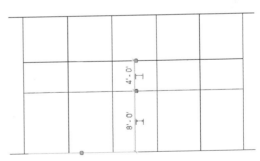

Figure C–11

- To modify the grid, you must select a grid line, not a wall or the mullion. Hover your cursor over the area and press <Tab> to cycle through elements.

- To move a grid line, select it and use dynamic dimensions or 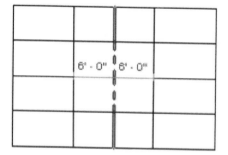 (Move).

- If you select a grid line that was created using the Curtain Wall style, (Prevent or allow change of element position) is displayed, indicating that the element is constrained to a host element. Click the icon to enable you to move the line.

How To: Add or Remove Segments of Curtain Grids

1. Select a grid line to modify.
2. In the *Modify | Curtain Wall Grids* tab>Curtain Grid panel, click (Add/Remove Segments).
3. Click on the part of the grid that you want to add or remove. The line displays as dashed when you click to remove a segment, as shown in Figure C–12. You must select grid lines, one at a time, with this command.

6' - 0"   6' - 0"

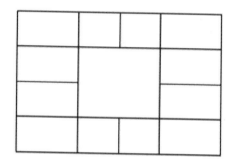

Figure C–12

4. Click in an empty space in the drawing area to finish the command.

- You can create non-rectangular panels by removing individual grid segments.

Hint: Aligning and Locking

When you use the **Align** command, you can also lock the lines together so if one moves, the other does as well. However, locking also causes the software to slow down. Therefore, be careful how much you use the **Lock** option and apply it only when you expect to make a lot of modifications.

C.3 Working with Curtain Wall Panels

The default panel for a curtain wall is typically a glazed panel. As you create the curtain grid and refine the wall design, you might want to use other materials for some of the panels, including wall types to insert doors, as shown in Figure C–13. You can select the existing panels and in the Type Selector, select a panel type with the material you want to use.

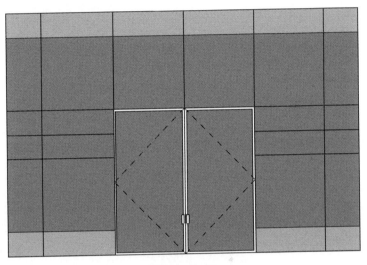

Figure C–13

- Additionally, the panel type controls the thickness and can define a door or window for the panel.

- To select a panel, hover the cursor over its edge, press <Tab> until it highlights, and then click to select it.

- To select all of the panels, select the edge of the curtain wall, right-click, and select **Select Panels on Host.**

- If ⚲ (Prevent or allow change of element position) displays (as shown in Figure C–14), it indicates that the panel is locked and that changes to the element are not permitted. Click the icon to toggle off the lock and modify the panel.

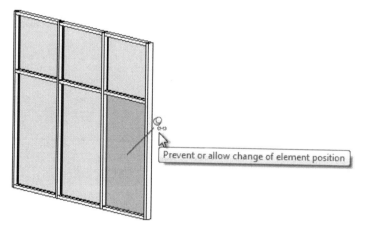

Prevent or allow change of element position

Figure C–14

- To unpin multiple panels, select them and type **UP** (for **Unpin**).

Default Panel Types

Three panel types come with the default project template:

Empty Panel	You cannot delete a panel in a curtain wall, but you can change the panel type to an empty panel.
Glazed Panel	A typical panel type with glass as its material.
Solid Panel	A panel type using a solid material. You can create variations of this type with other materials.

- You can use any other wall type (including other curtain wall types) to fill in a panel.

- Door and window panels are available through the Revit Library. Similar to other panel types, door and window panels fill the size of the panel to which they are applied. Adjust the curtain grid for the correct sizes, as shown in Figure C–15.

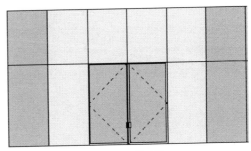

Figure C–15

How To: Place Doors and Windows in Curtain Wall Panels

1. Load the door or window type that can be used as a curtain wall panel, such as the **Door-Curtain-Wall-Double-Glass.rfa** shown in Figure C–16.

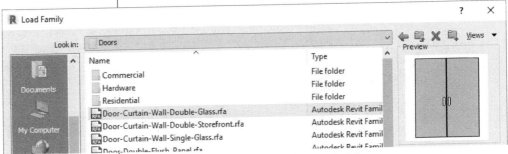

Figure C–16

2. Modify the curtain grid layout to ensure that the size of the opening in the curtain wall matches the size of the door you want to use.
3. Select the curtain wall panel.

4. In the Type Selector, select the type that you want to use as the panel, as shown in Figure C–17.

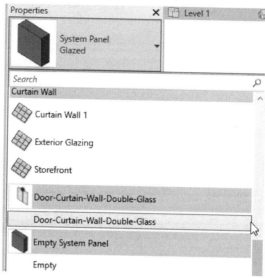

Figure C–17

5. The door or window fills the panel area.

Creating a Curtain Wall Panel

While you can create curtain wall panels in many complex ways, a basic technique is to specify a material for a flat system panel, as shown in Figure C–18.

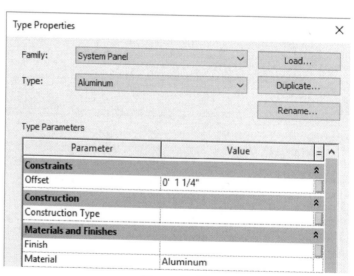

Figure C–18

How To: Create a Curtain Wall Panel

1. Select a panel and use <Tab> to select the entire panel (i.e., select a solid panel to create a new solid panel type). If it is locked, unlock it by clicking 🔓 (Prevent or allow change of element position).

2. In Properties, click ⊞ (Edit Type), or, in the *Modify | Curtain Panels* tab>Properties panel, click ⊞ (Type Properties).

3. In the Type Properties dialog box, click **Duplicate** to create a copy of the existing family type.

4. Give the panel a new name that describes its purpose (e.g., **Brick** or **Aluminum**). The new name automatically includes the family name, such as **System Panel**.

5. Set the *Thickness*, *Offset*, *Material,* and any other parameters as needed. Many materials are available in the Material Browser that opens when you click ⬚ (Browse) in the Materials list.

6. Click **OK** to close the dialog box and finish the panel. It is automatically applied to the panel you selected for modification.

- The *Thickness* of the material is centered on the grid if you did not specify an *Offset.* If you want the panel to be recessed in the wall, use a negative offset. If you want the panel to stand out from the wall, use a positive offset.

- Materials with patterns, such as the brick shown in Figure C–19, do not display the pattern when the view is zoomed out far. Zoom in to view the material.

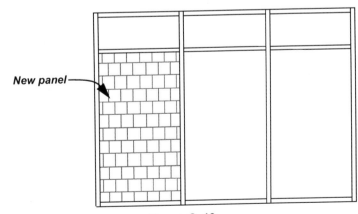

Figure C–19

C.4 Attaching Mullions to Curtain Grids

Mullions are the frameworks for curtain wall panels, as shown in Figure C–20. They can be many sizes, shapes, and materials. Add them as the final step in your curtain wall design after you have placed the grid lines.

Mullions

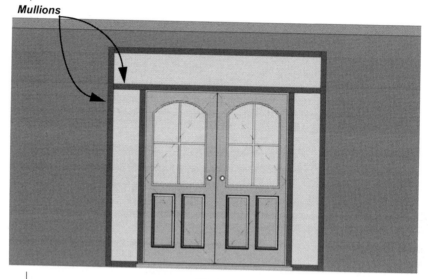

Figure C–20

How To: Add Mullions

1. In the *Architecture* tab>Build panel, click ▦ (Mullion).
2. In the Type Selector, select the mullion style. There are no modifiable properties when you insert a mullion.
3. In the *Modify | Place Mullion* tab>Placement panel, select a *Create Mullion on* method: ▦ (Grid Line), ▦ (Grid Line Segment), or ▦ (All Grid Lines), as shown in Figure C–21.

Mullions must be placed individually; they cannot be copied or arrayed.

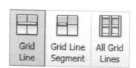

Figure C–21

4. Select the grid line on which you want to place the mullion. If the grid line is inside a grid, the mullion is placed on the grid's center line. If it is on the edge of the wall, the mullion is placed so that its exterior is flush with the outside of the wall.

- Hold <Shift> to place a mullion only on the selected segment.
- Hold <Ctrl> to place the mullion on all empty grid segments (i.e., all without mullions).

- Corner mullion types are designed for the intersection of two curtain walls. They adjust to fit the angle of the intersection.

Modifying Mullions

To quickly select mullions, hover your cursor over a curtain wall or mullion, right-click and select **Select Mullions**. The mullion options include **On Vertical Grid** or **On Horizontal Grid**, **Inner Mullions**, **Border Mullions**, or **Mullions on Host**, as shown in Figure C–22.

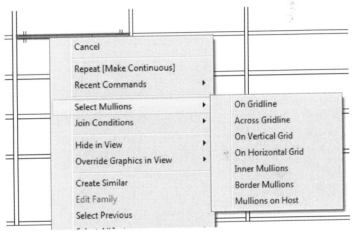

Figure C–22

- Modify mullion styles by changing their type in the Type Selector.

- To move mullions, you need to hover your cursor over the mullion and use <Tab> to select the curtain grid, then move the grid line and the mullions will move with it.

- If you delete a grid line, the mullion is also deleted. However, if you delete a mullion, the grid line is not deleted.

- You can change the way mullions intersect. Select the mullion and in the *Modify | Curtain Wall Mullions* tab>Mullion panel, click ⊞ (Make Continuous) or ⊩ (Break at Join). Alternatively, select the mullion and click the **Toggle Mullion Join** control, as shown in Figure C–23.

Before   *After*

Figure C–23

C.5 Creating Curtain Wall Types with Automatic Grids

If you have a curtain wall with a fixed distance or a fixed number of grids in the vertical or horizontal direction, you can create a curtain wall type containing this information, as shown in Figure C–24. The automatic grid lines can also be set to an angle.

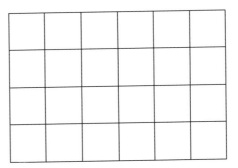

Figure C–24

How To: Create a Curtain Wall with Automatic Grids

1. In the *Architecture* tab>Build panel, click (Wall).
2. In the Type Selector, select a curtain wall similar to the one you want to create.
3. In Properties, click (Edit Type).
4. In the Type Properties dialog box, click **Duplicate...** to create a copy of the existing family type.
5. In the Name dialog box, give the curtain wall a name that describes its purpose, as shown in Figure C–25.
6. The new name automatically includes the family name, such as **Curtain Wall**. Therefore, you do not have to include the family name.

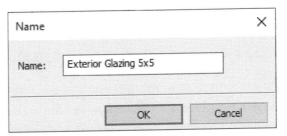

Figure C–25

Type Parameters apply to all instances of that type inserted into the Autodesk Revit software. This is true for all families (e.g., walls, doors, windows, etc.). Changing a Type Parameter changes all instances of that type in the project.

7. In the Type Properties dialog box, enter information for the *Construction*, *Vertical* and *Horizontal Grid Pattern*, and *Vertical* and *Horizontal Mullions* parameters, as shown in Figure C–26.

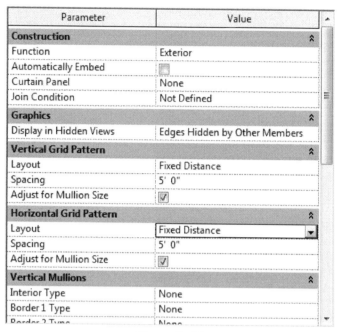

Parameter	Value
Construction	⌄
Function	Exterior
Automatically Embed	☐
Curtain Panel	None
Join Condition	Not Defined
Graphics	⌄
Display in Hidden Views	Edges Hidden by Other Members
Vertical Grid Pattern	⌄
Layout	Fixed Distance
Spacing	5' 0"
Adjust for Mullion Size	☑
Horizontal Grid Pattern	⌄
Layout	Fixed Distance
Spacing	5' 0"
Adjust for Mullion Size	☑
Vertical Mullions	⌄
Interior Type	None
Border 1 Type	None
Border 2 Type	None

Figure C–26

- Enable the *Automatically Embed* parameter if you want to use the curtain wall as a storefront.
- Set the *Curtain Panel* to the primary type you plan to use. You can modify the panels once they are in the project.
- The Grid Patterns can be set to the following:

Fixed Distance	Grids are placed a specified distance apart. Specify the size in the **Spacing** option.
Fixed Number	Grids are divided across a wall based on a specified number. The *Number* of grid lines is specified in the Instance Parameters.
Maximum Spacing	Grids are spaced evenly with the greatest distance between them specified in the **Spacing** option.
None	No grids are specified.

- The **Adjust for Mullion Size** parameter ensures that panels inserted between grid lines are equal in size. This is very important if you use a different size of mullion on the borders from the ones on the interior separations.

- Mullions can be specified in the Type Parameters for Interior and Border mullions. The vertical **Border 1** type is applied to the left of the curtain wall and **Border 2** is applied to the right. The horizontal **Border 1** type is at the bottom and **Border 2** is at the top.

- You can pre-apply the mullions to the grid in the type or add them later. If you are planning to use the curtain wall type as a base to create a more complex curtain wall, do not add mullions in the type because doing so makes it difficult to select the grid lines to modify them.

8. Click **OK** to close the Type Properties dialog box.

9. In Properties, set the *Vertical* and *Horizontal Grid Pattern* (including *Number* for Fixed Number, *Justification*, *Angle*, and *Offset*), as shown in Figure C–27.

The options in Properties are Instance Parameters applied to the selected instance of the type inserted into the Autodesk Revit software.

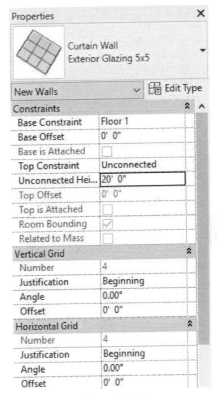

Figure C–27

Index

Made in the USA
Monee, IL
16 August 2021